ELECTRICAL ENGINEERING SERIES
Editor: F. T. Chapman, C.B.E., D.Sc.(Eng.), M.I.E.E.

ELECTRICAL
MACHINES

ELECTRICAL MACHINES

By

A. DRAPER

B.Sc.(Eng.), M.I.E.E.

Vice-Principal
Rugby College of Engineering Technology

LONGMANS, GREEN AND CO
LONDON : NEW YORK : TORONTO

LONGMANS, GREEN AND CO LTD
6 & 7 CLIFFORD STREET LONDON W I
THIBAULT HOUSE THIBAULT SQUARE CAPE TOWN
605–611 LONSDALE STREET MELBOURNE C I

LONGMANS, GREEN AND CO INC
55 FIFTH AVENUE NEW YORK 3

LONGMANS, GREEN AND CO
20 CRANFIELD ROAD TORONTO 16

ORIENT LONGMANS PRIVATE LTD
CALCUTTA BOMBAY MADRAS
DELHI HYDERABAD DACCA

First published 1956
Second Impression 1958

Made and printed in Great Britain by
William Clowes and Sons, Limited, London and Beccles

FOREWORD

THE subject of Electrical Machines can be treated from the point of view of the designer and manufacturer, *or* of the industrial user, *or* of the supply engineer who deals with machines as elements in a power supply system, *or* of the student whose interest is to extend his knowledge of fundamental principles and to confirm that knowledge by experience in applying it in as many fields as possible. Comparatively few of the students who take up the subject of electrical machines become designers and this minority require special training in design office methods which will be obtained in the design office itself. The majority will be concerned with applications of electrical technology which may involve electrical machines as important features. For both groups a broad knowledge of the fundamental principles underlying the theory and operation of electrical machines, with some appreciation of designers' problems, is desirable. It is this aspect of the subject which Mr. Draper has had in mind in writing this book.

Although much of the theory of electrical machines is reduced to electric circuit theory which is not greatly different from other circuit theory, and assumes linear parameters, the most instructive part of the study of these machines is connected with their magnetic circuits. The non-linear magnetic properties of iron and the magnetomotive forces of distributed windings combine to provide some very interesting and instructive problems which give the study of electrical machines a special value that can be followed up very profitably in the laboratory.

Mr. Draper has not attempted to deal with the more intricate magnetic problems which concern only the designer who needs, amongst other things, to be able to estimate iron losses in order to predict efficiency and temperature rise. These matters and those connected with heat transfer are appropriate to more specialised books for those actually engaged on or preparing for design.

The treatment which Mr. Draper gives is the result of many years' experience in teaching the subject to student apprentices engaged in a large works manufacturing a wide range of machines while he, himself, has been in close contact with many members of the engineering staff of the firm. He is therefore well aware of students' difficulties and of the relative importance of the principles on which he has written.

F. T. CHAPMAN

PREFACE

THIS book has been written as a text-book for students and not as a treatise for electrical machine designers. It is intended primarily for students taking heavy current subjects in Higher National Certificate, Engineering Degree and Diploma Courses.

It covers the greater part of the syllabuses relating to the subject of Electrical Machines up to the Part III standard of the Institution Examination of the Institution of Electrical Engineers and of the final degree examinations of London University. Typical examination questions from these courses are given as worked examples in the text and additional questions have been collected in an appendix.

It is assumed that the student will already be familiar with the elementary aspects of the subject and have attained a standard corresponding to the Ordinary National Certificate in Electrical Engineering; and it is also expected that he will be using a general text-book in Electrical Engineering such as the companion volume in this series *Electrical Engineering* (*General*), by Dover and Chapman. Some knowledge of vector representation by complex numbers is expected of the reader.

Although separate chapters have been devoted to a detailed account of individual machines, induction motor, d.c. machines, polyphase commutator machines, etc., those matters which are common to all machines, namely windings, magnetic circuits and leakage fluxes have been treated collectively. With this background it is hoped that the student will be able to proceed, at a later stage, to advanced matrix methods of Electrical Machine Analysis.

The M.K.S. system of units (for both mechanical and electrical quantities) and the symbols of B.S. 1991:1954 have been used throughout.

Some slight departure from traditional methods has been made which it is hoped the reader will not find confusing.

The transformer is treated as a four-terminal network, which, together with careful attention to circuit diagram conventions leads to a simplification of the relevant vector diagrams.

Vector diagrams for the induction motor have been drawn where possible with the voltage vectors horizontal in order to line up with circuit theory where the real axis is commonly used for power and the imaginary axis for reactive volt-amperes.

After consultation with numerous design engineers it was decided to employ p as the symbol for the number of poles of a machine and not for pole pairs.

Not much space has been devoted to the mechanical construction of machines with which the student is expected to become sufficiently familiar in the laboratory and the drawing office.

The author wishes to thank all those friends and colleagues who have contributed.

First and foremost Dr. F. T. Chapman editor of this series of text-books, not only for his guidance and helpful criticism of the manuscript but for his example and inspiration to the author and to so many other engineering teachers and students over many years.

Also thanks are due to Dr. W. J. Gibbs, Mr. C. H. Chaplain, Mr. B. Pringle, Mr. K. W. McBain and other engineers of the B.T.H. Co. Ltd. for assistance with drawings; to the British Standards Institution for permission to reproduce parts of British Standards, to the Examination Boards of London University, the Institution of Electrical Engineers and the City and Guilds of London Institute for the use of questions from past examination papers, to the author's colleagues Mr. R. W. G. Ward, Mr. W. K. Low and especially to Mr. H. L. Hoyce for proof-reading and mathematical criticism.

A. DRAPER.

Rugby, 1956.

CONTENTS

CHAPTER 1. Principles and Conventions

CHAPTER 2. The Transformer—I

CHAPTER 3.   The Transformer—II

CHAPTER 4.   Windings

CHAPTER 11. D.C. Machines

CHAPTER 1

PRINCIPLES AND CONVENTIONS

1.1. Introduction

By definition, a machine is an apparatus or contrivance which accepts energy in some form and at some place, and transfers this energy—possibly in alternative form—to a point where it is directly of use. The various mechanical machines —pulleys, wheel and axle, spur gearing, hydraulic jacks, are all well-known examples.

Electrical machines also conform to this definition, but here we are principally concerned with the conversion of energy from one form to another. A generator converts mechanical energy into electrical energy, and the duty of a motor is the reverse.

The transfer of energy by electrical means involves the co-existence of electric and magnetic fields, and for this reason a study of the geometry and properties of both types of field, as they exist in machines, is of the greatest importance.

When attempting to apply the laws of electrotechnology to electrical plant and machinery, the engineer is always confronted with the need for making simplifying assumptions. The first step in reducing the complexity of a practical machine usually consists of assuming that effects which are actually distributed over a large area can be supposed to be concentrated in one place without involving serious error. Thus, as far as voltage-drop is concerned, the resistance R of the whole armature conductors of a d.c. machine, might be considered to be concentrated in one of the leads between terminal box and brush-gear, leaving the remainder of the circuit to be represented by a perfect conductor. In a similar manner, the distributed inductances and capacitances of a winding are separated as though they were due to individual inductors and capacitors connected externally. The result of this concentration or "lumping", as it is termed, finally enables the machine to be represented by an electrical network known as the equivalent circuit.

A considerable portion of the following chapters will be devoted to developing equivalent circuits for various types of machine. It is important, however, to bear in mind from the outset the degree of approximation that is involved in lumping parameters which are in fact distributed, and that although these equivalent circuits enable the performance of the machine to be predicted—and can thus reasonably be said to represent the machine—the individual elements comprising the circuit have not a separate existence. Furthermore, in many cases they are given values which are assumed constant over a range of operation though in point of fact considerable variation actually takes place.

It is also important to realise that many factors—pole face losses, harmonics, etc.—cannot be represented in simple equivalent circuits, and also that circuits based on steady-state conditions often require modification if a study of the transient behaviour of the machine is to be made.

1.2. Circuit Conventions

It is as well to review and to restate some of the conventions relating to electrical circuits that have been discussed at greater length in the companion volumes I and II of this series.

1.2.1. Double Subscript Notation

The simplest electrical circuit shown in fig. 1.1 consists of a d.c. source of energy on the left connected to a load on the right by resistanceless leads **ab–cd**.

Fig. 1.1

If a current of I amperes flows around the circuit in the direction **a–b–c–d**, this current is designated

$$I_{abcd}$$

but it is sufficient to specify the current in one lead as I_{ab}, where I_{ab} is a positive number, the order of the subscripts indicating the direction of flow.

The statement that $I_{ab} = -5$ A means that a current of -5 A is flowing from **a** to **b**, which is equivalent to a current of $+5$ A flowing from **b** to **a**.

Thus

$$I_{ab} \equiv -I_{ba} \quad . \quad . \quad . \quad . \quad . \quad . \quad (1.1)$$

Now again referring to fig. 1.1. we wish to express the fact that a potential difference of 100 V exists between the lines with the line **ab** positive to **cd**.

This is expressed in the statement

$$V_{bc} = +100 \text{ V}$$

which tells us that the voltage drop across the load from **b** to **c** is 100 V.

Again

$$V_{bc} \equiv -V_{cb} \quad . \quad . \quad . \quad . \quad . \quad . \quad (1.2)$$

1.2.2. Electromotive Force

There is of course only one voltage in the circuit of fig. 1.1, namely the p.d. between the lines. Looking at this from the point of view of the load it is a voltage drop V_{bc} across the load. But it is sometimes advisable to think in terms of the source. It is insufficient, however, merely to state that the source provides an e.m.f. equal to the p.d. To avoid ambiguity it is necessary to apply double subscripts to the symbol E for e.m.f. Thus

$$E_{da} = V_{bc} \quad . \quad . \quad . \quad . \quad . \quad . \quad (1.3)$$

which reads: "The e.m.f. E acting in the direction from **d** to **a** within the source is equal to the voltage drop across the load from **b** to **c**."

Again

$$E_{da} \equiv -E_{ad} \quad . \quad . \quad . \quad . \quad . \quad . \quad (1.4)$$

emphasising the fact that the positive or negative sign must be interpreted together with the order of the subscripts.

1.2.3. Power

Still referring to fig. 1.1 the power expended in the load

$$P_{\text{load}} = V_{\text{bc}}I_{\text{bc}} \quad \cdots \cdots \cdots \quad (1.5)$$

and with V_{bc} and I_{bc} both positive quantities, P will be positive, indicating power supplied via the circuit to the load, that is, power converted from electrical energy to some other form in the load.

Again, at the source,

$$P_{\text{source}} = E_{\text{da}}I_{\text{da}} \quad \cdots \cdots \cdots \quad (1.6)$$

where a positive value of P now means that power is being supplied by the source to the circuit.

In consequence it follows that when negative values of power emerge, the source developing negative power is not a source at all but is really a load, and in the same way a load where P_{load} is negative is in effect returning energy to the circuit and is thus really a source.

1.2.4. A.C. Steady-state Conditions

It is particularly important to adopt a clear notation when dealing with a.c. problems, and we shall therefore employ a double subscript nomenclature similar to that already described.

Fig. 1.2 shows a single-phase alternator connected to a load.

The expression for the instantaneous e.m.f. of the alternator

$$e_{\text{da}} = \sqrt{2} . E_{\text{da}} \sin \omega t \quad \cdots \cdots \cdots \quad (1.7)$$

states clearly the magnitude of e_{da} at the instant t where $\omega = 2\pi \times$ frequency and E_{da} is the r.m.s. value of the voltage.

If e_{da} at a given instant is a positive number, then at that instant terminal **a** will be positive with respect to terminal **d**.

Fig. 1.2

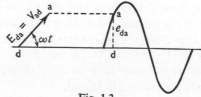

Fig. 1.3

It is customary to represent this voltage by a rotating vector, rotating anti-clockwise with velocity ω, the projection of which on the vertical yields the value of e_{da} to a suitable scale (fig. 1.3).

At the instant chosen in the diagram angle ωt is in the first quadrant and $\sin \omega t$ is positive.

The vector however must be correctly labelled to show that this corresponds to the fact that **a** is now positive to **d**, and this may be done in three ways.

The symbols E_{da} or V_{ad} may be written on the side of the vector and the arrow-head arranged as shown, or better still the ends of the vector may be labelled **d** and **a** respectively with **a** at the arrow-headed end. The fact that **a** is above **d** in the diagram makes it clear that at this instant the point **a** is positive with respect to **d**.

Now it will be seen that since (equation 1.4)

$$E_{da} \equiv -E_{ad}$$

the vectors E_{ad} and E_{da} will differ in phase by 180° (fig. 1.4).

This is not another voltage but indicates exactly the same conditions as before —**a** above **d** in potential at that instant. Either vector may be used as required for the circuit analysis, but correct labelling is essential.

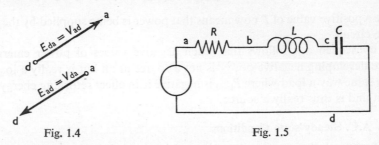

Fig. 1.4   Fig. 1.5

1.2.5. The Circuit Elements R, L and C

In the circuit of fig. 1.5 the three circuit elements R, L and C are shown connected in series with each other to a voltage source. Suppose that at a given instant the voltage source has such a value that a current i is flowing and that this current is increasing at a rate di/dt.

Each circuit element under these circumstances will be receiving energy. The resistance R is converting energy into heat at a rate $i^2 R$.

Since the current is increasing, the magnetic field of the inductor is increasing and energy is in the process of being stored in this element and at this moment the total energy in the store amounts to $\frac{1}{2}Li^2$. Increase of this energy involves a drain from the source, but, unlike the energy dissipated in the resistor, the energy of the magnetic field may at a later time be returned to the circuit.

The capacitance C also represents an energy store—this time in the form of electric field energy. As current flows into the capacitor the charge on the plates increases and so does the voltage. When the p.d. across the plates is v_{cd} the energy stored is $\frac{1}{2}Cv_{cd}^2$.

To return to the circuit of fig. 1.5, the instantaneous voltage

$$e_{da} = v_{ad} = v_{ab} + v_{bc} + v_{cd} \quad . \quad . \quad . \quad . \quad . \quad (1.8)$$

and each one of these terms will be positive.

Multiplying by i, where $i = i_{abcd}$,

$$e_{da}i = v_{ab}i + v_{bc}i + v_{cd}i \quad . \quad . \quad . \quad . \quad . \quad (1.9)$$

where

     $e_{da}i$ is the power supplied by the source;

     $v_{ab}i$ is the power dissipated by the resistance;

     $v_{bc}i$ is the rate at which energy is being stored in the magnetic field of L;

     $v_{cd}i$ is the rate at which energy is being stored in the electric field of C.

Now the definitions of R, L and C show that

$$v_{ab} = iR$$
$$v_{bc} = L \cdot di/dt$$
and
$$v_{cd} = q/C = (1/C)\int i \cdot dt.$$

Thus equation (1.8) becomes

$$v_{ad} = Ri + L \cdot di/dt + (1/C)\int i \cdot dt \quad . \quad . \quad . \quad . \quad (1.10)$$

Now on occasion energy may be in the process of removal from a store and returning to the circuit; for example when current is falling in an inductance

$$v_{bc} = L \cdot di/dt \quad . \quad . \quad . \quad . \quad . \quad (1.11)$$

becomes negative (di/dt being negative), and since $e_{bc} = -v_{bc}$, e_{bc} will then be positive, that is, the element can now be regarded as a source with

$$e_{bc} = -L \cdot di/dt \quad . \quad . \quad . \quad . \quad . \quad (1.12)$$

This alternative conception has its uses. It is often suggested that when current changes in an inductance a back e.m.f. (negative sign) is set up.

But in general in this book this alternative view point will be avoided and equation (1.11) will be used in preference to the alternative (1.12).

Inductances will invariably be regarded as "loads", a positive value of $v_{bc}i_{bc}$ indicating energy transfer from the circuit to the magnetic field.

1.3. Per-unit Values

The relative size of two quantities of the same kind is best expressed as the ratio of two numbers.

For example, if we are told that the current taken by a motor is 75 A this statement does not give any indication as to whether the machine is a large one on a comparatively light load or a smaller one overloaded. On the other hand, if we know that the full-load current of the machine is 50 A, then we can compare the two numbers 75 and 50. The ratio

$$75/50 = 1.5/1$$

and we can say that the motor is taking a current 1·5 times full-load or, alternatively, that the current *has a per-unit value of* 1·5.

It could also be stated that the current is 150% of the full-load value or that the machine is taking a 50% overload. Both these expressions are in common use, but the statement "the per-unit value is 1·5" is simpler and more direct.

Another example of the use of per-unit values is in the calculation of efficiency.

A motor whose efficiency is 0·9 has an output of 0·9 *per-unit of input power*.

Although percentage values are familiar means of comparison they have always to be converted to per-unit values before they are of use in an equation, e.g. if efficiency is 50%,

$$\text{output} = 50/100 \times \text{input}$$
$$= 0.5 \times \text{input}.$$

Power factor is a further example of a per-unit figure, this being seldom quoted as a percentage though there is no special reason to the contrary.

In machine problems it is often convenient to compare quantities with their equivalent values corresponding to full-load conditions. Operating values of current, voltage and power can be usefully expressed as per-unit values by dividing the actual values in amperes, volts or kilowatts by the corresponding values at full load according to the nameplate rating of the machine.

It must be remembered that a per-unit value is a ratio, and has no dimensions.

Resistance can also be expressed with advantage as a per-unit value in the following way.

For example, in the statement "the armature resistance of a 50-kW 500-V generator is $0 \cdot 1 \, \Omega$" it is not immediately apparent (without further calculation) whether the value quoted is sensible or not and a decimal-point error can easily be made.

The full-load armature current of this machine is 100 A, and therefore the resistance drop

$$IR_a = 100 \times 0 \cdot 1 = 10 \text{ V},$$

so if this voltage is compared with the rated voltage of the machine, then the

$$\text{per-unit resistance} = R_{p.u.} = 10/500 = 0 \cdot 02.$$

More strictly this should be termed the *per-unit resistance drop at full-load* but this is condensed in the more concise expression "per-unit resistance".

This figure is now available for direct comparison with other machines of different voltages and different ratings. Per-unit values can be used in formulae in the normal way. To find the actual voltage drop due to resistance when the per-unit value of current is $I_{p.u.}$ and the resistance $R_{p.u.}$

$$V_{p.u.} = I_{p.u.} R_{p.u.} \quad \cdot \quad \cdot \quad \cdot \quad \cdot \quad \cdot \quad (1.13)$$

and hence

$$\text{volt-drop due to resistance} = I_{p.u.} R_{p.u.} \times \text{rated voltage} \quad . \quad (1.14)$$

Reactance and impedance can be treated similarly.

In the following sections per-unit values will be used in preference to percentages, and where possible graphs depicting the characteristics of machines will have their axes scaled in per-unit values.

CHAPTER 2

THE TRANSFORMER—I

2.1. Types of Transformer

A TRANSFORMER is a piece of electrical apparatus which consists of two or more electrical circuits interlinked by a common magnetic circuit for the purpose of transferring electrical energy between them. They range in size from some of the largest single units of electrical equipment manufactured—large power transformers for converting the energy of whole power stations to voltages suitable for transmission over large distances—to very small items, such as intervalve transformers used in portable radio sets, which are scarcely larger than postage stamps.

They may be classified according to frequency into groups:

(a) power frequency, 50—60 c/s;
(b) audio frequency, 50 c/s—20 kc/s;
(c) radio frequency, 20 kc/s and above;
(d) pulse transformers.

Again, according to the mode of operation, we have a classification: (i) voltage transformers, in which the voltage applied to one winding is approximately constant under normal operating conditions and the transformer maintains a nearly constant voltage-ratio irrespective of load changes; and (ii) current transformers, in which one winding is in series with a current source and the purpose of the transformer is to maintain a nearly constant ratio of the currents in its windings.

CLASSIFICATION OF METHODS OF COOLING

Method of cooling	Type	Abbreviation
Natural cooling	Air natural cooling Oil-immersed natural cooling Oil-immersed forced-oil-circulation with natural cooling	AN ON OFN
Artificial cooling (air)	Oil-immersed forced-oil-circulation with air-blast cooling Oil-immersed air-blast cooling Air-blast cooling	OFB OB AB
Artificial cooling (water)	Oil-immersed water cooling Oil-immersed forced-oil-circulation with water cooling	OW OFW

Alternatively the classification may be made according to purpose where we have:

(a) power transformers;
(b) distribution transformers;
(c) testing transformers;
(d) instrument transformers;
      (i) voltage transformers; (ii) current transformers.

Transformers of the power and distribution types are constructed in accordance with British Standard 171: 1936, "Electrical Performance of Transformers for Power and Lighting".

In this specification the above types are further classified according to methods of cooling as shown in the table above.

2.1.1 Rating and Losses

In common with all other items of electrical equipment the continuous rating of a transformer is determined by the value of its voltage and the current that can flow in it continuously without exceeding the maximum safe temperature for the class of insulation used. Small transformers rely on the dissipation of their losses to the surrounding air by simple radiation and convection, and the rating is thus that for which the losses can adequately be dissipated without exceeding a certain temperature rise. The limit is specified as a rise of 55°C above ambient temperature, as measured by the increase of resistance, for insulation of Class A type (paper, cotton, etc.).

Now since the losses in a transformer are roughly proportional to its weight, that is, to (length)^3, and the surface area through which the dissipation of the losses takes place depends on (length)^2, it follows that the larger the transformer the more difficult is the problem of heat dissipation unless material is to be used in uneconomic proportions.*

Oil-immersed transformers up to about 25 kVA may thus have plain tanks, the surface area of the sides being quite adequate to dispose of the losses, but larger ratings up to 5000 kVA need to have the surface area increased by the

---

* In the following table two transformers having the same proportions are compared. The linear dimensions of A are k times the corresponding dimensions of B. Flux density and current density are the same in the two transformers.

Quantity	Relative size A:B
Core area	k^2
Flux	k^2
Voltage	k^2
Conductor area	k^2
Current	k^2
kVA rating	k^4
Weight	k^3
Losses	k^3
Surface area	k^2
Losses/surface area	k
Losses/output $= (1-\eta)$	k^{-1}

The larger unit has an improved efficiency but the loss/surface area is also increased.

addition of rows of pipes—in some cases as many as four rows being used. Over 5000 kVA detachable radiators are usually fitted.

For still larger transformers separate radiators are required and oil is pumped from the tank through the radiators.   In the largest sizes of all, water-cooling coils are added or air-blast cooling is arranged on the surface of the radiators.

2.2. Construction
2.2.1. Core and Shell Types

Two general types of construction are used by manufacturers which though similar in performance give different appearances to the product.   They are known as (a) core-type, (b) shell-type construction.

In the core type the magnetic core is built of laminations to form a rectangular frame and the windings are arranged concentrically with each other on cylinders around the side members known as the legs or limbs of the core.   The top and bottom members are referred to as the yokes.   With the shell type, the windings are flat circular or rectangular coils interleaved with each other.   The core is usually divided and built around the coils on either side.   Shell- and core-type

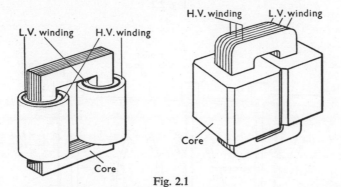

Fig. 2.1

construction are compared in the simple sketch of fig. 2.1.   In the core type the impression is created that the coils have been wound around the core, whereas with the shell type that the core has been built around the coils.   This impression is particularly marked in recent American practice with distribution transformers of the shell type in which the core on either side is formed by coiling a long steel strip wound around like a clock spring.   This construction enables the best use to be made of grain-oriented cold-rolled steel having a minimum loss factor.

Most of the larger transformers built in this country are of the core type.

2.2.2. Cores

The cores are constructed of high-grade silicon steel, the silicon content reducing losses and preventing ageing, in laminations about 0·014 in. thick, cut in rectangular strips, punched and then annealed to recondition the material. Each lamination is coated with a tough flash enamel insulation resistant to hot transformer oil.

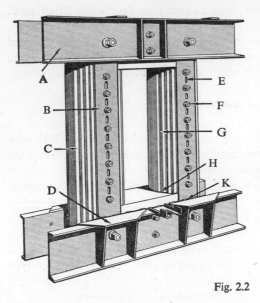

A. Structural steel yoke clamps shot-blasted and enamelled before building into transformer.

B. Extra heavy outer retaining sheet of special low loss steel.

C. Sheet asbestos sectional insulation.

D. Bracket for supporting end insulation and winding.

E. Patented form of transverse ventilating duct.

F. Core clamping bolts insulated with heat resisting impregnated asbestos, moulded on under high pressure.

G. Silicon steel laminations annealed after cutting to shape and piercing.

H. All magnetic joints interleaved.

K. Yoke clamping structure thoroughly insulated and suitably spaced from yoke.

Fig. 2.2

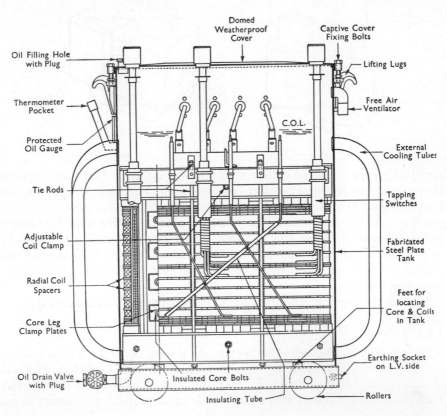

Fig. 2.3 (a)

The laminations are assembled in the required shape, the corners being inter-leaved to add to rigidity and to reduce the reluctance of the magnetic circuit. In some cases slots are arranged to improve heat transfer from the core to the oil.

The core is clamped by a heavy clamping structure insulated and spaced from the core.　Core bolts passing through the core are also carefully insulated with sheet asbestos and synthetic resin moulded directly on the bolts.

The greatest importance is attached to rigidity and mechanical strength.

2.2.3. Windings

Apart from electrical and thermal considerations the windings must have great mechanical strength.　The high mechanical stresses set up under short-circuit conditions of modern power systems may otherwise lead to a complete mechanical collapse of the windings.

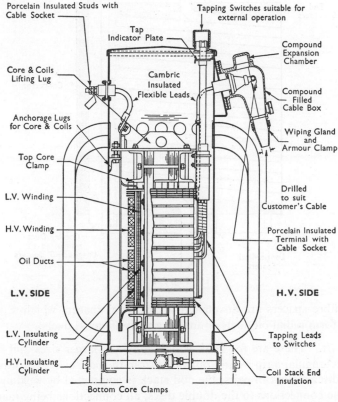

Fig. 2.3 (b)

With the core-type transformer the coils are wound on insulating cylinders of cemented pressboard or bakelised paper which form a strong foundation.　The conductors are of copper, usually of rectangular section in the larger sizes, and are paper insulated.

The details of construction of a particular winding vary with current and voltage rating. Heavy current windings employ two or more conductors in parallel and with these the conductors are transposed at frequent intervals to avoid circulating currents between the strands (fig. 2.4). The following are the types of coil used.

Section Coils. Round enamelled or paper-covered wire or strip conductors are employed in this type and wound in layers about an inch to two inches wide on paper tapes, having either end flanges of fibre, or a reinforcement produced by folding the paper tape (fig. 2.5 (a)).

Helical Coils. For heavy-current low-voltage windings these usually consist of a number of strands in parallel wound in the form of a continuous helix over axial spacers attached to the base cylinder (fig. 2.4).

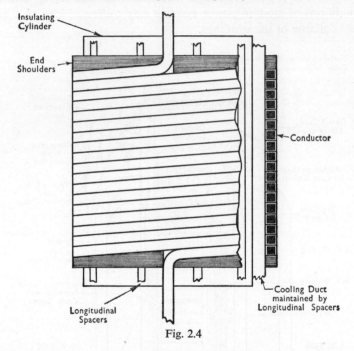

Fig. 2.4

Radial fibre spacers are dovetailed to the axial spacers which separate the turns and form radial oil ducts connecting with the axial ducts.

Disc Coils. These are for H.V. windings of the larger sizes and consist of turns of rectangular strip wound outwards from the base cylinder forming discs. With the discs wound in pairs, the coil stack is completed by welding together in series the connections to the double discs, all connections being made on the outside (fig. 2.5 (b)).

Continuous Disc Coils. A special winding technique enables the discs to be wound without joints from continuous strip producing a winding consisting of alternate coils, the one wound outwards from the cylinder and the next inwards to the cylinder and so on. Axial and radial spacers again maintain oil ducts in both directions (fig. 2.6).

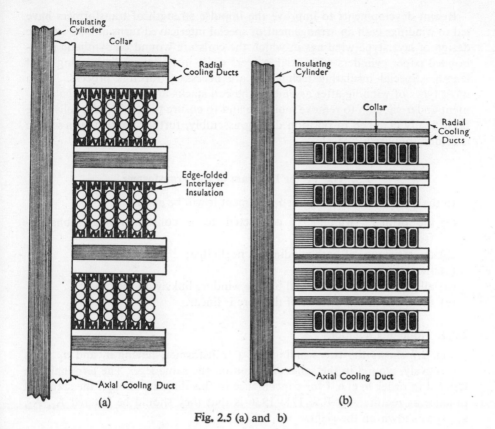

Fig. 2.5 (a) and b)

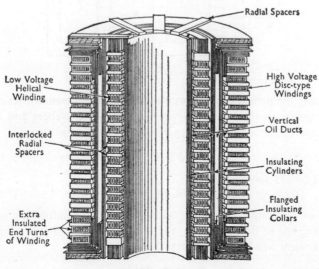

Fig. 2.6.

Recent developments to improve the impulse strength of transformers have led to windings with an arrangement of special interleaved turns and also to the design of layer-type windings in which the coils are wound on synthetic resin-bonded paper cylinders with axial spacers only, in layers of diminishing axial length. Special insulating techniques are necessary for this process. With most types of winding after assembly, the coil stacks are given shrinkage treatment under vacuum to remove moisture and to ensure that, when the coils have been finally clamped in position during assembly, further tightening in service is seldom required.

2.3. The Vector Diagram of the Transformer

In the first place for a simplified treatment it will be assumed:

(a) the primary winding is connected to a constant-voltage, constant-frequency source;

(b) the resistance of both windings is negligible;

(c) the core losses are zero;

(d) all magnetic flux generated by one winding links with the other;

(e) the magnetisation curve of the core is linear.

2.3.1. No-load Conditions

Fig. 2.7 shows the two windings of a transformer, having n_1 and n_2 turns respectively, wound in the same direction on the same leg. The terminals are lettered in order **b, c, e, f** for convenience in this diagram though the standard practice as required by B.S. 171: 1936 is that they should be lettered A_1, A_2, a_1, a_2 as shown on the right.

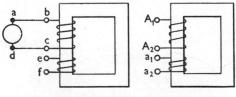

Fig. 2.7

Winding **bc** is the primary and it is connected to the alternator terminals **a, d**.

Now let the flux in the leg at a given instant t be ϕ webers and the instantaneous voltage of the alternator be given by

$$e_{da} = \sqrt{2} . E_{da} \cos \omega t \quad . \quad . \quad . \quad . \quad (2.1)$$

Thus in the primary circuit

$$e_{da} = v_{bc} = n_1 . d\phi/dt \quad . \quad . \quad . \quad . \quad (2.2)$$

There being no resistance, the voltage drop across the winding can only be due to a rate of change of flux within it, and since the secondary winding encircles the same flux there will be a secondary voltage drop

$$v_{ef} = n_2 . d\phi/dt \quad . \quad . \quad . \quad . \quad (2.3)$$

Now since
$$e_{da} = \sqrt{2}.E_{da} \cos \omega t$$
$$n_1.d\phi/dt = \sqrt{2}.E_{da} \cos \omega t$$
$$d\phi/dt = (\sqrt{2}.E_{da}/n_1) \cos \omega t$$

and integrating

$$\phi = (\sqrt{2}.E_{da}/\omega n_1) \sin \omega t \quad . \quad . \quad . \quad . \quad (2.4)$$

The flux must therefore vary with time in a sinusoidal manner; its maximum value will be

$$\Phi = \sqrt{2}.E_{da}/\omega n_1 = \sqrt{2}.E_{da}/2\pi f n_1$$

Thus
$$E_{da} = V_{bc} = \sqrt{2}.\pi f \Phi n_1 . \quad . \quad . \quad . \quad . \quad (2.5)$$

and similarly
$$V_{ef} = \sqrt{2}.\pi f \Phi n_2 . \quad . \quad . \quad . \quad . \quad (2.6)$$

These equations establish the voltages of the windings and by division

$$V_{ef}/V_{bc} = n_2/n_1 \quad \text{or} \quad V_{ef} = V_{bc}.n_2/n_1 . \quad . \quad . \quad . \quad (2.7)$$

The secondary voltage is thus a multiple of the primary voltage in accordance with the ratio of the number of turns. The prime function of a transformer is of course to increase or decrease voltage in this manner.

Now these voltages V_{bc} and V_{ef} together with the flux φ are shown in the vector diagram, fig. 2.8, the cosine waves leading the sine waves by 90°. Since ultimately the secondary winding is to be regarded as a source, it is as well to remember that

$$V_{ef} = E_{fe} \quad . \quad . \quad . \quad . \quad (2.8)$$

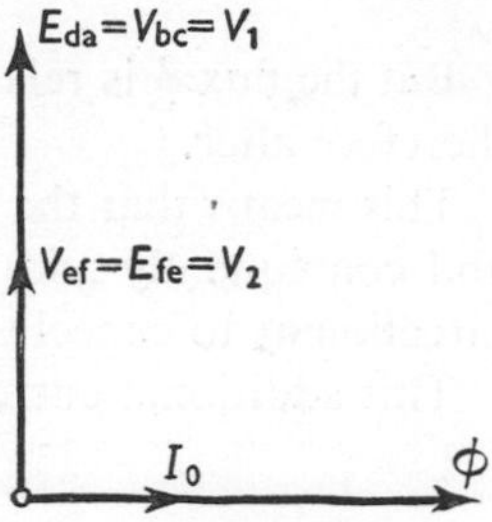

Fig. 2.8

V_{ef} and V_{bc} will in future be referred to as V_2 and V_1.

We have assumed a flux ϕ in the transformer leg.

In order to produce flux in any magnetic circuit, magnetising ampere-turns are needed, and the number of ampere-turns required to produce a given flux depends on the dimensions and material of the core. The reluctance of the magnetic circuit is kept low in order to reduce the number of ampere-turns required.

Assuming the magnetisation curve to be linear, it will be seen from fig. 2.9 that the ampere-turns required instant by instant will be represented by another sine wave in phase with the flux.

Now current can readily circulate in the primary as we have assumed this circuit to be resistanceless. The current here can theoretically be of any magnitude without incurring any voltage drop.

The value of this current, referred to as the magnetising current, is I_0 and $I_0 n_1$ is the r.m.s. value of the magnetising ampere-turns in phase with the flux. This vector has been added to fig. 2.8.

2.3.2. The Transformer on Load

Since a p.d. V_{ef} is established between the terminals **e** and **f**, we now consider the winding as having an internal e.m.f. E_{fe} and utilise this e.m.f. as a source in a secondary circuit.

Connecting a load impedance

$$Z = Z \exp j\psi$$

across these terminals a current I_{fegh} will flow (fig. 2.10), where

$$I_{fegh} = V_{gh}/Z = E_{fe}/Z \quad . \quad . \quad . \quad . \quad . \quad (2.9)$$

provided, of course, E_{fe} is maintained. This current I_{fe} (later to be designated I_2) flowing in the turns n_2 of the secondary winding is the cause of ampere-turns $I_{fe}n_2$ which tend to modify the flux ϕ.

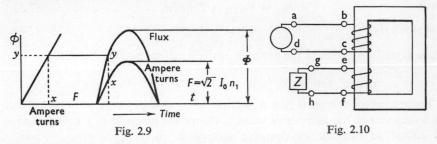

Fig. 2.9   Fig. 2.10

But the flux ϕ is related to the alternator voltage (equation (2.4)) and cannot therefore alter.

This means that the *total* magnetising ampere-turns must remain unchanged and consequently additional current is set up in the primary circuit in such a direction as to cancel the effect of $I_{fe}n_2$.

This additional current I'_{bc} is such that

$$I'_{bc}n_1 = I_{fe}n_2 \quad . \quad . \quad . \quad . \quad . \quad . \quad (2.10)$$

or

$$I'_{bc} = I_{fe} \cdot n_2/n_1 \quad . \quad . \quad . \quad . \quad . \quad (2.11)$$

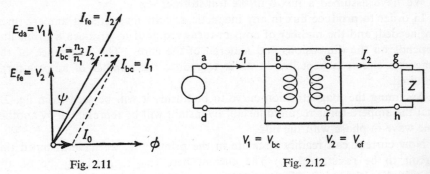

Fig. 2.11   Fig. 2.12

The total primary current is then the vector sum of I_0 and I'_{bc} which will be known as I_1. Fig. 2.11 shows these currents and is the vector diagram of the ideal transformer.

The magnetising current I_0 is relatively small compared with the full-load currents I_1 and I_2 (about 5% of I_1). In general, therefore,

$$I_2 \simeq I_1 \cdot n_1/n_2 \quad . \quad . \quad . \quad . \quad . \quad (2.12)$$

whence it is seen that the ratio of the two currents is approximately the inverse ratio of the turns. Comparing this with the voltage equation (2.7) we see that when a transformer has a larger number of secondary turns than primary turns voltage is stepped up and current is correspondingly reduced in the secondary winding.

It is usual for the circuit diagram of a transformer to be represented as shown in fig. 2.12, in which the transformer is depicted as a four-terminal network.

It should be noted that the currents I_1 and I_2 are practically in phase but that directions of their m.m.f.s within the transformer windings are in opposition.

2.4. The Real Transformer

The performance of a real transformer departs from that of the ideal in a number of ways, and the idealised equivalent circuit must be modified if account is to be taken of the power losses, magnetic leakage and the non-linearity of the magnetisation curve. Tests on an actual transformer show these deviations.

2.4.1. No-load Test

A transformer is tested on no load by applying full-rated voltage to its primary winding with the secondary terminals open circuited. The no-load current I_0 can thus be measured.

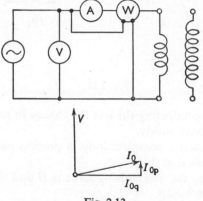

Fig. 2.13

It is preferable to choose the L.V. winding as the primary for this test, as a supply at this voltage and suitable instruments are usually more readily available. Voltmeter, ammeter and wattmeter are connected as shown in fig. 2.13.

It is found that:

(a) the current I_0 is small as expected but not entirely wattless, the power factor usually being in the region 0·1–0·2;

(b) the wave-form of I_0 is not sinusoidal but has a characteristic shape (*see* fig. 2.19), indicating the presence of harmonics in addition to the fundamental.

I_0 is therefore represented as the sum of two components $I_{0,p}$ and $I_{0,q}$ in phase and in quadrature with the voltage. A third component representing the harmonics is present also, but this cannot be drawn on a fundamental frequency vector diagram.

2—E.M.

2.4.2. Core Loss

The power measured in this test is dissipated as heat in the core and is known as core loss.   The losses in iron undergoing cyclical magnetisation have already been discussed (Volume II), where they are seen to depend on two distinct causes: (a) hysteresis, (b) eddy currents.

2.4.3. Hysteresis Loss

In an experiment on the magnetisation of a specimen of iron in the form of a ring, if flux density B is plotted against the magnetising force H (ampere-turns per metre), as the latter is increased from zero to maximum, reduced to zero again, increased to negative maximum and reduced again to zero, two values of B are observed for each value of H; one as the ampere-turns are increasing and the other when decreasing.   The graph when plotted forms a loop known as the B/H loop.

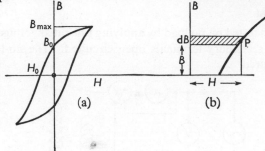

Fig. 2.14

It is assumed that in conducting the test the change in magnetisation is made step by step comparatively slowly.

Fig. 2.14 (a) shows such a complete loop, a portion only of the rising part of the curve being repeated at (b).

Now at point P, when the magnetising force is H and the flux density B, let H increase by dH and B by dB.

Let i = current corresponding to P,
     n = turns on the magnetising coil,
    A = area of cross-section of the specimen
and l = magnetic length of the specimen.

$$\text{Total flux } \phi = BA.$$

$$\text{Rate of change of flux} = d\phi/dt = A \cdot dB/dt.$$

Applied voltage required to cause the change at this rate,

$$v = An \cdot dB/dt.$$

Energy used in time dt,

$$
\begin{aligned}
dw &= vi \cdot dt = Ani \cdot dB \\
&= Al(in/l)dB \text{ joules} \\
&= HdB \text{ joules per cubic metre} \quad . \quad . \quad . \quad . \quad . \quad . \quad (2.13) \\
&= \text{area of the shaded strip in fig. 2.14 (b).}
\end{aligned}
$$

In fig. 2.15 (a) we see the energy required as the current increases from zero to I_{max} to be the summation of the areas of the elemental strips. When the current is reduced to zero the energy returned to the circuit is again shown as a shaded area (fig. 2.15 (b)), and finally the difference between the two is observed to be the loss of energy in the process (fig. 2.15 (c)).

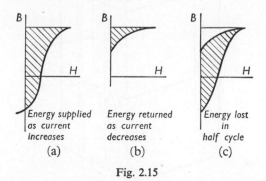

Fig. 2.15

The energy loss in joules per cubic metre per cycle is thus the area of the complete B/H loop.

When iron undergoes a.c. magnetisation at f cycles per second the power loss in watts due to hysteresis is thus

$$P_h = (\text{area of loop}) . fv \quad . \quad . \quad . \quad . \quad . \quad (2.14)$$

(f = frequency, v = volume).

Now the area of the loop depends on the maximum value of B achieved during the cycle, but the relation is by no means a simple one. For some purposes where an approximate value is required it is assumed that the area is proportional to B^x where x varies from 1·6 to 2·0 with different grades of iron. Thus

$$P_h = K_h B^x fv \quad . \quad . \quad . \quad . \quad . \quad . \quad (2.15)$$

It will be obvious that the loop area for the type of iron used in transformer cores should be as small as can be obtained economically.

2.4.4. Eddy-current Loss

This is due to the presence of circulating currents set up in the iron. Fig. 2.16 shows a single lamination of a transformer core of thickness t. A portion is taken 1 m wide 1 m deep.

Let there be two elementary sections of thickness dx spaced a distance x on either side of the centre line. Current will be set up in these elements in the directions shown due to the rate of change of such flux as exists between them. (It will be seen that they form a loop around this flux. They are continued in the sections above and below and extend to the edge of the sheet where the end connections have negligible length.) On the assumption that there is a uniform flux density B (which is reasonably true at power frequencies if the sheets are sufficiently thin as in the case of transformer laminations),

flux linking with the elements $= B(2x \times 1)$.

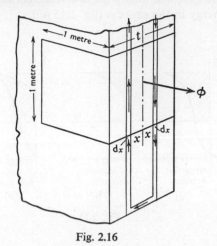

Fig. 2.16

From equation (2.5), the e.m.f. acting around the loop is given by

$$e = 4 \cdot 44 fB(2x \times 1).$$

The resistance of the elements $(\rho l/a)$

$$= \rho 2/(dx \times 1).$$

Power dissipated (e^2/R)

$$= (e^2 dx)/2\rho.$$

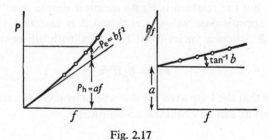

Fig. 2.17

Power dissipated in whole width

$$= \int_0^{t/2} (e^2/2\rho) dx$$

$$= 4 \cdot 44^2 f^2 B^2 (4/2\rho) \int_0^{t/2} x^2 dx$$

$$= 4 \cdot 44^2 f^2 B^2 (2/\rho)(t^3/24)$$

This loss occurs in a volume $1 \times 1 \times t$, and the

loss per unit volume $= (4 \cdot 44^2/12\rho) f^2 B^2 t^2.$.   .   .   . (2.16)

Thus in a transformer with a core of given volume and lamination thickness

$$\text{eddy current loss } P_e = K_e f^2 B^2 \quad . \quad . \quad . \quad . \quad (2.17)$$

It is worthy of note that since P_e depends on the square of the lamination thickness it is always possible to reduce this factor by choosing thinner laminations.

An economic compromise results in laminations about 0·014 inches thick.

2.4.5. A Test to Separate the Components of Core Loss

It is useful to be able to determine the proportion of the components hysteresis and eddy-current loss in the total core loss.

Since

$$P_e \propto f^2 \quad \text{and} \quad P_h \propto f$$

(equations (2.15) and (2.17)), a variable frequency test may be used for their separation. The transformer is energised from variable voltage and frequency mains with meters connected as in fig. 2.13, the secondary being open-circuited.

Since from equation (2.5)

$$V_1 = \sqrt{2} . \pi f \Phi n_1,$$

the maximum flux Φ will remain constant if the test is conducted so that the ratio V_1/f is held constant.

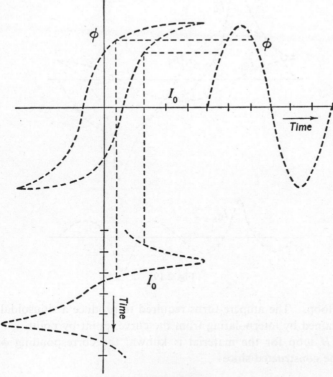

Fig. 2.18

Equations (2.15) and (2.17) will then reduce to:

$$P_h = af$$
$$P_e = bf^2$$

and the total loss

$$P = P_h + P_e = af + bf^2 \quad . \quad . \quad . \quad . \quad . \quad (2.18)$$

Thus by varying frequency, and at the same time adjusting V_1 so that V_1/f is constant, a series of power-loss values are obtained, which can be plotted to a base of frequency giving a curve as shown in fig. 2.17 (a).

The equation to this curve is evidently that of (2.18).

Dividing by f,

$$P/f = a + bf \quad . \quad . \quad . \quad . \quad . \quad . \quad (2.19)$$

Thus plotting P/f to base of f (fig. 2.17 (b)) the curve is reduced to a straight line from which a and b are easily found.

The original loss curve can then be subdivided as shown.

2.4.6. Wave-form of Magnetising Current

The relationship between the magnetising current and the flux produced in a magnetic core is not linear as has been suggested in the simple treatment, but

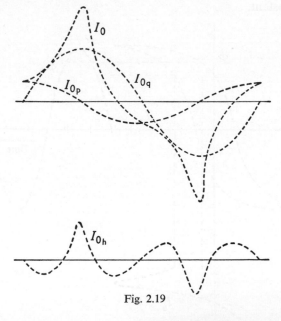

Fig. 2.19

is in fact a loop. The ampere-turns required to produce a sinusoidal flux can only be obtained by interpolating from the curve, point by point.

If the B/H loop for the material is known, the corresponding ϕ/amperes graph can be constructed since

$$\phi = B \times \text{area} \quad \text{and} \quad i_0 = H \times \text{length}/n_1.$$

The true loss loop is strictly somewhat larger than this due to the effect of eddy-current loss.

The sinusoidal flux wave is drawn on the right of the loop to a time axis. Point by point the flux values are projected to the loop and the corresponding current values also plotted to the time-base. This can be conveniently arranged as shown in fig. 2.18 by making the time-base for the current graph vertical.

The current wave-form is replotted in fig. 2.19 where it is seen to contain:

(a) a fundamental frequency component in phase with the flux;

(b) a fundamental frequency component in quadrature with the flux;

(c) the remainder, obtained by subtraction from the diagrams.

The first component is recognised as the magnetising component already designated $I_{0,q}$. The second is the loss component, $I_{0,p}$, in phase with the voltage and dependent on the breadth of the loop. The third is introduced by the non-linearity of the flux-current relationship. It is seen to consist mainly of current at three times normal frequency though higher harmonics are also present. It will be designated $I_{0,h}$. This component cannot be represented on a vector diagram of fundamental frequency and its presence is often unimportant. In three-phase transformers, however, certain special problems frequently arise.

Demonstration of Loss Loop by Cathode-ray Oscilloscope. The total loss loop of a transformer can only be determined by oscillographic methods if readings are to be taken under actual working frequency conditions. The transformer

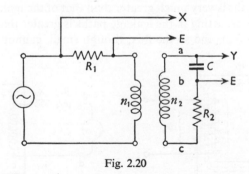

Fig. 2.20

on open circuit is connected across normal voltage mains ensuring a sinusoidal supply and hence also a sinusoidal flux wave. A small resistor R_1 is connected in series, the p.d. across this being used to measure current (fig. 2.20). It is important that the p.d. across this is small compared with the total voltage or the p.d. applied to the transformer will not be sinusoidal.

An integrating circuit is used across the secondary to measure flux. This consists of a capacitor C and a high resistance R_2 in series with it. It is important that the reactance of C is small compared with R_2.

The p.d. across C is taken to the Y plates of the oscilloscope and that across R_1 to the X plates. If amplifiers are used in conjunction with the C.R.O. it is important that no phase shift should be incurred.

Theory of the integrating circuit :

In fig. 2.20

$$v_{ac} = n_2 . d\phi/dt$$
$$i_{ac} = v_{ac}/Z \simeq v_{ac}/R_2 \quad \text{since } R_2 \gg 1/\omega C$$
$$= (n_2/R_2)d\phi/dt.$$

Integrating, $\int i . dt = \int (n_2/R_2)d\phi$

and the capacitor's charge

$$q = \phi n_2/R_2.$$

Thus $v_{ab}C = \phi n_2/R_2$
$$\phi = (R_2 C/n_2)v_{ab} \quad . \quad . \quad . \quad . \quad . \quad . \quad . \quad (2.20)$$

That is, the capacitor voltage is a measure of flux.

2.4.7. Effect of Winding Resistance and Leakage Flux

It is convenient to remove the resistance from the windings of the transformer and to think of it as concentrated in one of the connecting leads. There, when the transformer is on load, a voltage drop will be set up proportional to and in phase with the current. The copper losses I^2R can be considered to be taking place in these resistances and the actual winding to be loss-free.

Now, when the transformer is on load, the flux linking with the primary turns n_1 differs somewhat from that linking with n_2 if leakage lines exist. Such lines are shown in fig. 2.21 as ϕ_a and ϕ_b. The amount of such flux is small compared with the main flux ϕ since they take paths through the air, and the reluctance offered by such paths is very much greater than that of the main magnetic circuit. The m.m.f., however, acting in the leakage paths is greater than that in the main flux path (Section 5.2), and so the flux, though small, cannot be neglected.

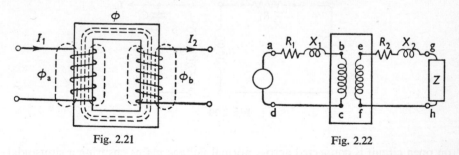

Fig. 2.21   Fig. 2.22

These flux linkages, like the resistances, can also be considered to be removed from the transformer and concentrated in the leads where they become series reactors. The transformer is thus said to have *leakage reactance* and reactance drop will be set up across these series elements.

Labelling these reactors X_1 and X_2 and the resistors R_1 and R_2 the transformer can be represented by the circuit of fig. 2.22. The following simultaneous equations must be satisfied.

In the primary circuit:

$$V_{ad} = E_{da} = V_{ab} + V_{bc} = I_{ab}(R_1 + jX_1) + V_{bc} \quad . \quad . \quad (2.21)$$

In the secondary circuit:

$$V_{ef} = E_{fe} = V_{eg} + V_{gh} = I_{eg}(R_2 + jX_2) + V_{gh} \quad . \quad . \quad (2.22)$$

where
$$V_{gh} = I_{gh}Z.$$

Also

$$V_{bc} = n_1 . d\phi/dt \quad \text{and} \quad V_{ef} = n_2 . d\phi/dt \quad . \quad . \quad . \quad (2.23)$$

both leading the flux by 90°, and the total ampere-turns produced by both windings, magnetising the core, is given by

$$I_{bc}n_1 - I_{fe}n_2 = I_0 n_1 \quad . \quad . \quad . \quad . \quad . \quad . \quad (2.24)$$

where $I_0 n_1$ are the primary ampere-turns on no load. $I_0 n_1$ will lead the flux by a small angle due to core loss.

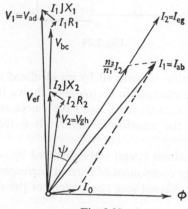

Fig. 2.23

The simple vector diagram of fig. 2.11 must therefore be modified to that of fig. 2.23 which refers to a transformer feeding a lagging-power-factor load.

Commencing with the secondary terminal voltage $V_2 = V_{gh}$ the current $I_2 = V_2/Z$ and lags behind V_2 by ψ the phase angle of the load. It is required to find the primary voltage and current.

Equation (2.22) can be illustrated by adding $I_2(R_2 + jX_2)$ to V_2 with $I_2 R_2$ parallel to I_2. Thus the axis of V_{ef} is established and the flux axis can be drawn at right angles to it.

From equation (2.23)

$$V_{bc} = (n_1/n_2)V_{ef}$$

and this vector can now be drawn.

I_0 is next added in correct relation to ϕ and I_1 obtained by adding the vector I_0 to $(n_2/n_1)I_2$ according to equation (2.24).

Having found I_1 the vector $I_1(R_1 + jX_1)$ can be added in correct relation to I_1 at the extremity of the vector V_{bc}, thus arriving at the primary terminal voltage $V_{ad} = V_1$.

2.5. The Equivalent Circuit of the Transformer

In fig. 2.22 the transformer has been reduced almost to a simple network of circuit elements with the exception that within the portion **bcef** the following changes take place:

$$V_{ef} = (n_2/n_1)V_{bc} \quad \cdots \cdots \quad (2.25)$$

and

$$I_1 = I_0 + (n_2/n_1)I_2 \quad \cdots \cdots \quad (2.26)$$

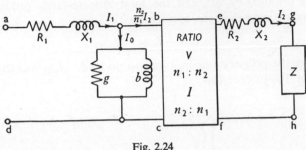

Fig. 2.24

If the transformer portion is replaced by an idealised ratio change in which currents and voltages are changed in the manner shown in fig. 2.24, and also a shunt circuit is added to account for I_0, we have a network which produces the same vector diagram as the transformer itself. It is therefore known as the equivalent circuit.

It is preferable for the shunt circuit to be depicted by two parallel elements g and b, g taking the energy component of current corresponding to core loss and b the strictly quadrature magnetising component of the no-load current.

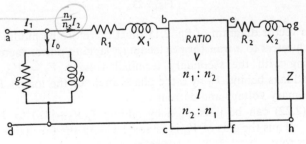

Fig. 2.25

2.5.1. The Approximate Equivalent Circuit

Since the no-load current I_0 is relatively small, as also are the relative voltage drops in R_1 and X_1, that part of the voltage drop in R_1 and X_1 due to the current I_0 is negligible. The circuit may therefore be modified to that of fig. 2.25 by transferring the magnetising admittance to the input terminals, without appreciable inaccuracy.

2.5.2. Equivalent Values of R and X

With the above simplification the primary voltage is given by the equation

$$V_1 = (n_2/n_1)I_2(R_1+jX_1)+(n_1/n_2)[I_2(R_2+jX_2)+V_2]$$
$$= (n_1/n_2)[I_2\{R_2+(n_2^2/n_1^2)R_1+jX_2+j(n_2^2/n_1^2)X_1\}+V_2] \quad . \quad . \quad (2.27)$$

the latter equation corresponding to the circuit of fig. 2.26.

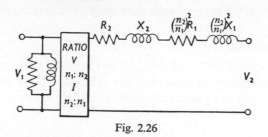

Fig. 2.26

It is thus customary to suggest that reactance and resistance in one winding can be replaced in effect by added reactance and resistance to the other winding, the value of the element to be added being the original value multiplied by the square of the turns ratio.

The total resistance and reactance in that winding—the opposite winding being considered impedanceless—is then known as *the equivalent resistance and reactance referred to that winding*.

Thus in fig. 2.26 the equivalent secondary resistance

$$R_2' = R_2+(n_2/n_1)^2R_1 \quad . \quad . \quad . \quad . \quad . \quad (2.28)$$

and the equivalent reactance referred to the secondary

$$X_2' = X_2+(n_2/n_1)^2X_1 \quad . \quad . \quad . \quad . \quad . \quad (2.29)$$

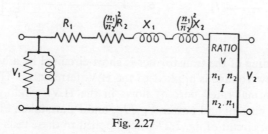

Fig. 2.27

Equally well, the reactance and resistance of the secondary can be referred to the primary, corresponding to fig. 2.27, when the equivalent values of primary resistance and reactance become:

$$R_1' = R_1+(n_1/n_2)^2R_2 \quad . \quad . \quad . \quad . \quad . \quad (2.30)$$
$$X_1' = X_1+(n_1/n_2)^2X_2 \quad . \quad . \quad . \quad . \quad . \quad (2.31)$$

The vector diagram of the transformer is now reduced to the much more simple one of fig. 2.28 corresponding to the circuit diagram of fig. 2.27.

Drawing first the vectors of the output voltage and current, V_2 and I_2, it is only necessary to add $I_2 R_2'$ and $I_2 j X_2'$ and the resultant vector is $(n_2/n_1)V_1$ from which V_1 is easily found.   The primary current is given by the vector summation

$$I_1 = I_0 + (n_2/n_1)I_2 \quad . \quad . \quad . \quad . \quad . \quad . \quad (2.26)$$

If V_1 is maintained and the load is removed, the terminal voltage V_2 will rise to the value $(n_2/n_1)V_1$ as the vectors $I_2 R_2'$ and $I_2 X_2'$ disappear.

The vector $(n_2/n_1)V_1$ is thus $V_{2,0}$ the secondary voltage on open circuit.

2.5.3. The Short-circuit Test

To draw the vector diagram of fig. 2.28 corresponding to a particular transformer it is first necessary to determine the values of the equivalent resistance and reactance referred to a particular winding.   These values are obtained from a short-circuit test.

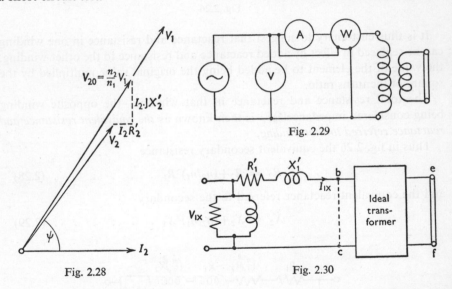

Fig. 2.29

Fig. 2.28   Fig. 2.30

The L.V. winding of the transformer is short-circuited by a heavy-gauge conductor, and a low voltage is applied to the H.V. terminals.   This voltage is increased until normal rated current flows in the H.V. winding.   Readings of applied voltage, current and power $V_{1,x}$, $I_{1,x}$ and P_x are taken (fig. 2.29).

The equivalent circuit of fig. 2.27 when applied to these tests becomes that of fig. 2.30.   It will be seen that the short circuit across the terminals **e, f** is effectively transferred to the points **b, c**.

Since the voltage is very small, the parallel magnetising circuit takes negligible current and can be omitted (this means the flux and core loss are negligible), and the transformer is reduced to a simple circuit with R_1' and X_1' in series.

The applied voltage $V_{1,x}$ is thus the impedance voltage of the transformer.

The power

$$P_x = I_{1,x}^2 R' \quad . \quad . \quad . \quad . \quad . \quad . \quad . \quad (2.32)$$

the copper loss in both windings.

$$V_{1,x} = I_{1,x}Z_1' \quad . \quad . \quad . \quad . \quad . \quad . \quad . \quad (2.33)$$

the impedance voltage referred to the H.V. winding.
Thus

$$R_1' = P_x/I_{1,x}^2 \quad . \quad . \quad . \quad . \quad . \quad . \quad . \quad (2.34)$$

$$Z_1' = V_{1,x}/I_{1,x} \quad . \quad . \quad . \quad . \quad . \quad . \quad . \quad (2.35)$$

$$X_1' = \sqrt{(Z_1'^2 - R_1'^2)} \quad . \quad . \quad . \quad . \quad . \quad (2.36)$$

If the referred L.V. values are required

$$R_2' = (n_2^2/n_1^2)R_1' \quad . \quad . \quad . \quad . \quad . \quad (2.37)$$
$$X_2' = (n_2^2/n_1^2)X_1' \quad . \quad . \quad . \quad . \quad . \quad (2.38)$$

It is advantageous to make this test on the H.V. side rather than on the L.V. side, values usually lending themselves to more suitable meter ranges.

SUMMARY

Core loss is measured by the open-circuit test.   Copper loss is measured by the short-circuit test.   The two tests give all the data required to determine the constants of the approximate equivalent circuit from which efficiency and regulation of the transformer can be determined under load conditions.

EXAMPLE

A 12-kVA, 230/400-V, 50-c/s single-phase transformer gave the following test results:

No-load test . . . . 230 V   2 A   120 W   on L.V. side
Short-circuit test . . . 25 V   25 A   80 W   on H.V. side.

Draw the approximate equivalent circuit diagram and find the values of the circuit elements.

In fig. 2.26 the magnetising admittance

$$Y = 2/230 = 0.0087.$$
$$g = 120/230^2 = 0.002\ 27.$$
$$b = \sqrt{(0.0087^2 - 0.002\ 27^2)} = 0.0084.$$

$$Y = 0.002\ 27 + j0.0084.$$

The secondary (H.V.) referred impedance

$$Z' = 25/25 = 1.00.$$
$$R' = 80/25^2 = 0.128.$$
$$X' = \sqrt{(1.00^2 - 0.128^2)} = 0.99.$$
$$Z_2' = 0.128 + j0.99.$$

2.6. Calculation of Transformer Efficiency

$$\text{Efficiency} = (\text{output power})/(\text{input power}) \quad . \quad . \quad (2.39)$$

Although it would be a simple matter to insert wattmeters to measure the input and output powers of a loaded transformer, the readings of each of the wattmeters are normally liable to a 1% error resulting in a possible 2% error in the value of efficiency obtained by substitution in the above equation.

As the efficiency of a transformer is of the order of 96–99% such a result would be completely valueless.

$$\text{Efficiency} = \text{output/input}$$
$$= (\text{input}-\text{losses})/\text{input}$$
$$= 1-\text{losses/input}$$
$$= 1-\text{losses/(output}+\text{losses})$$

and dividing numerator and denominator of the fraction by output,

$$\text{efficiency} = 1-(\text{per-unit loss})/(1+\text{per-unit loss}) \quad . \quad . \quad (2.40)$$

It thus follows that if the losses are determined corresponding to a given output (from open-circuit and short-circuit tests) the efficiency can be calculated with adequate precision, the effect of meter errors being confined to the calculation of the losses.

This method has also the great advantage that it is not necessary for the transformer to be loaded to its full-load rating during the tests, and the kW rating of the test plant need only be equal to the value of the individual transformer losses.*

2.6.1. Variation of Efficiency with Load

Since

$$\text{efficiency } \eta = \text{output/(output}+\text{losses})$$
$$= V_2 I_2 \cos \phi/(V_2 I_2 \cos \phi+I_2^2 R_2'+W_i) \quad . \quad . \quad (2.41)$$

where W_i is the core loss and R_2' is the referred resistance of the secondary winding. Efficiency thus is seen to depend on the current I_2 and the power factor $\cos \phi$.

First considering power factor constant, plotting η against I gives a curve similar to fig. 2.31 indicating that at some current value the efficiency is a maximum.

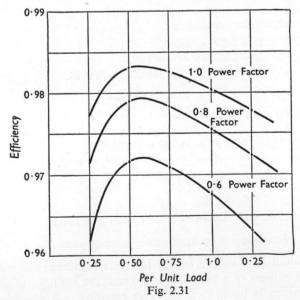

Fig. 2.31

* The kVA ratings are $V_1 I_0$ for the open-circuit test and $I_1^2 Z_1'$ for the short circuit test.

Differentiating equation (2.41) and equating to zero for a maximum

$$0 = \frac{d\eta}{dI_2} = \frac{(V_2I_2\cos\phi+I_2{}^2R_2'+W_i)V_2\cos\phi-V_2I_2\cos\phi(V_2\cos\phi+2I_2R_2')}{(V_2I_2\cos\phi+I_2{}^2R_2'+W_i)^2}$$

$$0 = V_2I_2\cos\phi+I_2{}^2R_2'+W_i-V_2I_2\cos\phi-2I_2{}^2R_2'$$

$$I_2{}^2R_2' = W_i \quad . \quad . \quad . \quad . \quad . \quad . \quad . \quad . \quad . \quad . \quad . \quad . \quad . \quad . \quad (2.42)$$

Maximum efficiency thus occurs at the particular value of load which makes copper loss equal to core loss. The relative value of these losses is in the control of the designer of the transformer according to the relative amounts of copper and iron he uses.

A transformer which is to operate continuously on full load would therefore be designed to have maximum efficiency at full load, but in the case of distribution transformers which operate for long periods on light load the point of maximum efficiency is usually arranged to be between three-quarter and half load.

It is important to appreciate that, since the copper loss depends on current and the iron loss depends on voltage, the total loss in the transformer depends on the volt-ampere product only, and not on the phase angle between voltage and current, i.e. is independent of the load power factor. The rating of the transformer is therefore in kilovolt-amperes and not kilowatts.

2.6.2. Variation of Efficiency with Power Factor

For a given volt-ampere output of a transformer the losses will be constant. Let the ratio

$$\text{losses}/V_2I_2 = x \quad . \quad . \quad . \quad . \quad . \quad . \quad (2.43)$$

Efficiency
$$\eta = 1-\text{losses}/(V_2I_2\cos\phi+\text{losses})$$
$$= 1-(\text{losses}/V_2I_2)/(\cos\phi+\text{losses}/V_2I_2)$$
$$= 1-x/(\cos\phi+x) \quad . \quad . \quad . \quad . \quad . \quad . \quad (2.44)$$
$$= 1-(x/\cos\phi)/(1+x/\cos\phi) \quad . \quad . \quad . \quad . \quad (2.45)$$

Thus in fig. 2.31 where the efficiency curve for a transformer has been drawn for the unity power factor case, the corresponding ordinates at other power factors have been found from the above equation.

EXAMPLE

A 100-kVA transformer has a copper loss at full load of 1·5 kW and a core loss of 0·5 kW. Plot efficiency/load curves for power factors of unity, 0·8 and 0·6.

At unity power factor:

Per-unit load	Per-unit copper loss	Per-unit core loss	Total per-unit loss = x	x/(1+x)	η
0·25	0·003 75	0·02	0·023 75	0·0232	0·9768
0·5	0·007 50	0·01	0·0175	0·0172	0·9828
0·75	0·011 25	0·006 67	0·017 92	0·0176	0·9824
1·00	0·015 00	0·005	0·02	0·0196	0·9804
1·25	0·018 75	0·004	0·022 75	0·0223	0·9777

At 0·8 power factor:

Per-unit load	$x/\cos\phi$	$\dfrac{x/\cos\phi}{1+x/\cos\phi}$	η
0·25	0·0296	0·0288	0·9712
0·5	0·0219	0·0213	0·9787
0·75	0·0224	0·0218	0·9782
1·00	0·0250	0·0244	0·9756
1·25	0·0283	0·0275	0·9725

At 0·6 power factor:

Per-unit load	$x/\cos\phi$	$\dfrac{x/\cos\phi}{1+x/\cos\phi}$	η
0·25	0·0395	0·0381	0·9619
0·5	0·0292	0·0284	0·9716
0·75	0·0299	0·0291	0·9709
1·00	0·0333	0·0322	0·9678
1·25	0·0380	0·0367	0·9633

2.7. Transformer Regulation

The rated voltage of a transformer winding is the value assigned to the no-load voltage between its terminals. Thus a 1000/400-V transformer will be expected to give 400 V across the L.V. terminals on an open-circuit test, when the applied voltage to the H.V. winding is 1000 V.

The vector diagram of fig. 2.28 shows the difference that will take place in the output voltage of a transformer as load is applied, assuming that the primary voltage remains constant. It falls from a value $V_{2,0}$ at no load to V_2. The numerical value of this reduction is of importance to the user and is known as the *inherent voltage regulation* of the transformer. It obviously varies with the value of the load and its power factor.

$$\text{Inherent voltage regulation} = V_{2,0} - V_2 \quad . \quad . \quad . \quad (2.46)$$

2.7.1. Per-unit Values

The values of the various voltage drops, corresponding to full load, are often most conveniently expressed as a fraction of the rated voltage of the transformer. For example, if the resistance voltage of a transformer is 10 V, the significance of this cannot be appreciated unless it is compared with the rated voltage of say 1000 V.

The ratio 10/1000 or 0·01 is called the "per-unit" drop and indicates directly the relative importance of the quantity.

The per-unit resistance voltage at full load

$$r_{\text{p.u.}} = I_2 R_2'/V_{2,0} \quad . \quad . \quad . \quad . \quad . \quad (2.47)$$

The per-unit reactance voltage at full load

$$x_{\text{p.u.}} = I_2 X_2'/V_{2,0} \quad . \quad . \quad . \quad . \quad . \quad (2.48)$$

The per-unit impedance voltage at full load

$$z_{p.u.} = \sqrt{(r_{p.u.}^2 + x_{p.u.}^2)}$$
$$= I_2 Z_2'/V_{2,0} \quad \cdot \quad \cdot \quad \cdot \quad \cdot \quad \cdot \quad \cdot \quad \cdot \quad (2.49)$$

and, similarly, the per-unit voltage regulation

$$D = (V_{2,0} - V_2)/V_{2,0} \quad \cdot \quad \cdot \quad \cdot \quad \cdot \quad \cdot \quad (2.50)$$

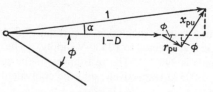

Fig. 2.32

Dividing all the quantities shown in fig. 2.28 by $V_{2,0}$, the original $V_{2,0}$ becomes a unit vector in fig. 2.32; the resistance and reactance voltages are replaced by their per-unit values and from equation (2.50),

$$V_2/V_{2,0} = 1 - D \quad \cdot \quad \cdot \quad \cdot \quad \cdot \quad \cdot \quad \cdot \quad (2.51)$$

Considering the geometry of fig. 2.32,

$$1 - D = \cos \alpha - r_{p.u.} \cos \phi - x_{p.u.} \sin \phi$$

$$= 1 - 2 \sin^2 \frac{\alpha}{2} - r_{p.u.} \cos \phi - x_{p.u.} \sin \phi$$

also $$\sin \alpha = x_{p.u.} \cos \phi - r_{p.u.} \sin \phi$$

and therefore since α is small,

$$\sin \frac{\alpha}{2} \simeq \tfrac{1}{2}(x_{p.u.} \cos \phi - r_{p.u.} \sin \phi)$$

and $$\sin^2 \frac{\alpha}{2} \simeq \tfrac{1}{4}(x_{p.u.} \cos \phi - r_{p.u.} \sin \phi)^2$$

Hence

$$1 - D \simeq 1 - \tfrac{1}{2}(x_{p.u.} \cos \phi - r_{p.u.} \sin \phi)^2 - r_{p.u.} \cos \phi - x_{p.u.} \sin \phi.$$

Thus the per-unit regulation

$$D \simeq r_{p.u.} \cos \phi + x_{p.u.} \sin \phi + \tfrac{1}{2}(x_{p.u.} \cos \phi - r_{p.u.} \sin \phi)^2 \quad . \quad (2.52)$$

This is sufficiently accurate for all transformer specifications having per-unit impedances up to 0·2 and covering power and distribution transformers in normal use.

For many simple calculations an even simpler expression may be used since the final term is often small enough to be omitted so that

$$D \simeq r_{p.u.} \cos \phi + x_{p.u.} \sin \phi \quad \cdot \quad \cdot \quad \cdot \quad \cdot \quad (2.53)$$

Values of D can thus be calculated corresponding to various load power factors.

3—E.M.

At unity power factor $D \simeq r_{\text{p.u.}}$ and increases to $x_{\text{p.u.}}$ at zero power factor, the maximum value being $z_{\text{p.u.}}$ and occurring at a power factor equal to $r_{\text{p.u.}}/z_{\text{p.u.}}$.

At leading power factors it will be seen that $x \sin \phi$ is negative and that D is reduced to zero at a leading power factor $x_{\text{p.u.}}/z_{\text{p.u.}}$, after which it has a negative value indicating that under these circumstances the output voltage rises as load is applied.

EXAMPLE

A 150-kVA single-phase transformer takes a current of 2 A at 0·4 power factor when the primary winding is connected to a 3300-V supply. The corresponding voltage at the secondary terminals is 240 V. The resistances of the primary and secondary windings are 1·1 Ω and 0·005 Ω respectively, and the equivalent reactance referred to the secondary side is 0·02 Ω.

Determine the efficiency and secondary terminal voltage when the input to the primary is 150 kVA at 3300 V, 0·8 power factor lagging.   [L.U.]

$$I_1 = 150\,000/3300 = 46\cdot5 \text{ A}.$$
$$R_1' = 1\cdot1 + (3300/240)^2 0\cdot005 = 1\cdot1 + 0\cdot95 = 2\cdot05.$$
$$X_1' = 0\cdot02(3300/240)^2 = 3\cdot8.$$

Copper loss = $46\cdot5^2 \times 2\cdot05/1000$ =   4·45 kW
Core loss = $3300 - 2 \times 0\cdot4/1000$ =   2·64
                                                      ————
                                                      7·1 kW
                                                      ————

Efficiency = $1 - 7\cdot1/150.0\cdot8 = 0\cdot941$.

Regulation drop on secondary side
$$= 46\cdot5(2\cdot05.0\cdot8 + 3\cdot8.0\cdot6)240/3300$$
$$= 46\cdot5.3\cdot92.240/3300 = 13\cdot3 \text{ V}.$$

$$V_2 = 240 - 13\cdot3 = 226\cdot7 \text{ V}.$$

CHAPTER 3

THE TRANSFORMER—II

3.1. The Auto-transformer

A NORMAL two-circuit transformer becomes an auto-transformer when the primary and secondary windings have a common part or parts.

The difference will be seen in fig. 3.1 in which a comparison is made between a two-circuit transformer on the left and an auto-transformer arranged for the same duty on the right. The two-circuit transformer has an H.V. winding **ab** and an L.V. winding **cd** with a turns ratio 3:1. Magnetising current and impedance drops will be neglected. The voltage ratio shows

$$V_{ab} = 3V_{cd}$$

and the current ratio

$$I_{dc} = 3I_{ab}.$$

Let

$$I_{ab} = 100 \text{ A} \quad \text{and} \quad I_{dc} = 300 \text{ A}.$$

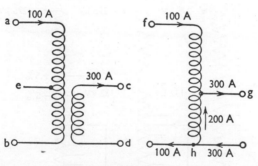

Fig. 3.1

Choosing a tapping point **e** one-third of the way along the H.V. winding it will be appreciated that $V_{eb} = V_{cd}$, and if the terminals **b** and **d** are joined together, then points **e** and **c** will be at the same potential. The winding **cd** will have just the same number of turns as the section **eb** and will in fact be concentric with it.

If the two windings are merged into one, we have the auto-transformer on the right.

The two currents I_{eb} and I_{dc} will be superimposed, and the winding section **gh** will only carry $300 - 100 = 200$ A.

A considerable saving in copper can now be made since windings carrying 400 A in all have been reduced to one with the same number of turns carrying 200 A.

35

Alternatively, the transformer **fgh** can be thought of as a transformer with two sections **fh** and **hg** having a turns ratio 2:1. The winding voltage ratio is 2:1 and the winding current ratio is 1:2. The output current at the point **h** becomes the sum of the two winding currents. It is evident therefore that the whole of the output power is greater than the power transferred between the windings by electromagnetic action, and it will be appreciated that the physical size of an auto-transformer will be less than the corresponding two-circuit transformer.

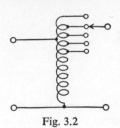

Fig. 3.2

The series connection of the windings, however, involves the necessity for insulating a winding to a higher value than that of the voltage generated in it.

Auto-transformers find their greatest sphere of application where many tappings are required for providing a variable voltage for a load from a constant-voltage source (fig. 3.2).

The most favourable case arises when V_1 and V_2 are nearly equal, e.g. 240/200 V to enable 200-V equipment to be supplied from a 240-V circuit.

One particular application in this class is the auto-transformer starter for induction and synchronous motors; whereby a reduced voltage is applied to the machine during starting.

The largest auto-transformers to be constructed are likely to be the transformers to be used to interconnect the proposed 275-kV British Grid system to

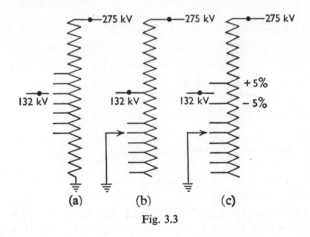

Fig. 3.3

the existing 132-kV grid. Three sizes have been proposed in the preliminary plans: 120 MVA, 180 MVA and 240 MVA, though it is possible that the largest size will be too large to permit haulage by road under existing regulations.

The windings will be star connected with neutral solidly earthed.

The tappings will be arranged in three separate forms to provide:

(a) a full range 15% on-load ratio variation at the 132-kV tapping point;
(b) a full range 15% on-load variation at the neutral end;
(c) on-load variation of $\pm 10\%$ at the neutral end combined with off-load tappings of $\pm 5\%$ at the 132-kV connection point (fig. 3.3).

For small outputs, auto-transformers with a sliding tapping find a large field of application where completely variable voltage over a range is required (fig. 3.4).

These voltage regulators can be made up to 20 kVA for 110 V or 230 V as a toroidal winding on a circular core. The conductors are of enamelled wire, the covering of which has been removed over a small width to enable a narrow carbon brush to make contact and to slide over the turns.

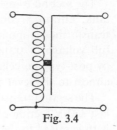

Fig. 3.4

The voltage per turn does not exceed one volt on this type of transformer and as the brush continuously short-circuits one turn in sliding along, it must be narrow and its resistance must be high so as to reduce the circulating current set up.

The brush tends to run hot, and the heat is carried away by a heavy copper brush holder.

3.1.1. Chain-connected Auto-transformers

A particularly interesting application of the auto-transformer is in the production of small units generating H.V. for testing work.

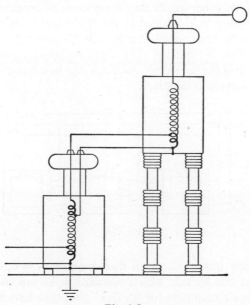

Fig. 3.5

Two auto-transformers, each designed to produce 250 kV, can be connected so as to produce 500 kV without introducing additional stress on the insulation of either transformer in the following way (fig. 3.5).

The first transformer is energised from a 400-V L.V. winding, one terminal of which is earthed and connected to the transformer tank. The main H.V.

250-kV winding is connected in series with it and also with a second 400-V section at the H.V. end.

Both the main H.V. terminal and the lower tapping are brought out by a concentric conductor through the H.V. bushing.

The second transformer is identical in construction with the exception that its tank, although connected to the L.V. terminal, is not earthed. The whole transformer is mounted on an insulated platform capable of withstanding the full voltage of transformer number one. This platform is usually supported by post-type porcelain insulator legs raising the height of the second transformer almost to the level of the bushing of the first.

The second transformer is energised by connecting its L.V. winding across the last 400-V section of the first transformer. The tank of the second transformer is thus raised to the H.V. potential of the first and its voltage is added in series, with the result that its H.V. terminal will be at a potential of 500 kV to earth.

Three or even four transformers may be connected in this way, the insulating platforms becoming increasingly higher.

3.2. Three-phase Transformers

In fig. 3.6 three identical single-phase transformers have been shown with their primary windings connected to a three-phase supply, one winding across each pair of lines. In other words they form a mesh-connected system.

The fluxes ϕ_1, ϕ_2 and ϕ_3 produced in the individual units will all be equal in magnitude but will be phase displaced by 120° to each other. The secondary voltages will therefore be similar. The three transformers are spoken of as a three-phase bank, and the secondary windings can be connected in either star or mesh to form a three-phase supply.

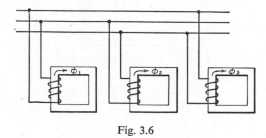

Fig. 3.6

Now, since at any instant the total flux $\phi_1+\phi_2+\phi_3 = 0$, if the three transformers are placed side by side with a common yoke top and bottom there is no need to provide a return path for the flux. We thus have a three-limb transformer of the core type shown in fig. 3.7 which is the usual form of three-phase transformers produced by manufacturers in this country.

The lengths of the magnetic circuits of the three phases are not quite equal since the outer limbs include a portion of the yoke, consequently the magnetising currents are never exactly in balance.

Some of the largest transformers made in this country have five-limb cores, the winding being confined to the middle three limbs. This device is adopted to reduce the height of the yoke and hence the overall height of the transformer, a procedure which is necessary in the largest outputs to conform with the British Railway loading gauge.

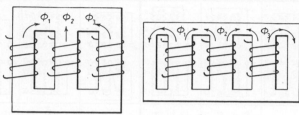

Fig. 3.7

3.2.1. Winding Connections

The method of marking and identifying the terminals of a three-phase transformer is given by British Standard 171: 1936, "Electrical Performance of Transformers for Power and Lighting".

The standard lettering for the phases is A, B, C. Capital letters A, B, C are used for the H.V. winding and lower-case letters **a**, **b**, **c** for the L.V. winding with (A), (B), (C) for a tertiary if used.

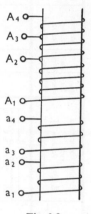

In general the two ends of a winding will be given suffixes and marked A_1, A_2, but if tappings are brought out or there are sections of the same winding the marking will be in sequence as shown in fig. 3.8.

It is important that the direction of the winding shall be the same for both primary and secondary winding, so as to ensure that the p.d. $V_{A_2A_1}$ is in phase with $V_{a_2a_1}$.

To test if a transformer has been correctly marked, it is suggested in the Standard that the two windings in question should be connected in series with the terminal A_2 connected to a_1, and an alternating voltage applied

Fig. 3.8

between A_1 and a_2. If the transformer has been correctly marked, the voltage measured between A_1 and A_2 will be less than the applied voltage.

3.2.2. Line Connections

The interconnection of the phase windings to produce a three-phase, three- or four-wire supply introduces three alternative modes of connection, (a) mesh or delta, (b) star, (c) zigzag, and each of these can be achieved in two ways. For example a star connection may be made by joining together A_1, B_1 and C_1 to form the neutral and using A_2, B_2 and C_2 as the line terminals.

The alternative is to make A_2, B_2 and C_2 the neutral and to use A_1, B_1 and C_1 for the lines.

Now, since primary and secondary can be treated in either of these ways, at least twelve methods of connection are possible.

The twelve standard methods are shown in fig. 3.9 (from B.S. 171: 1936).

These are arranged in four main groups, according to the phase displacement
which exists between the line voltages on the two sides of the transformer.   This
will be appreciated when the vector diagrams have been explained.

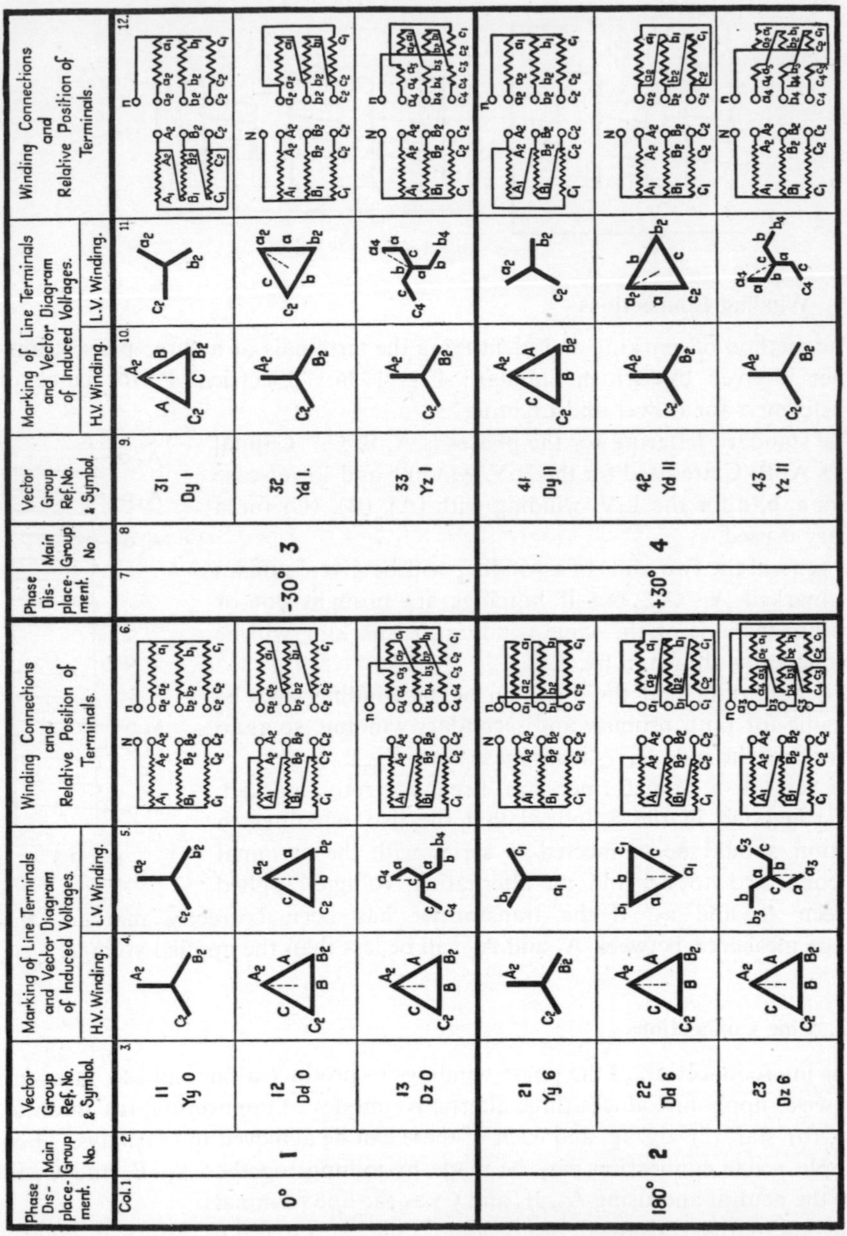

Fig. 3.9

First of all the winding connections of the various schemes should be examined
and the corresponding vector diagrams studied.

For example the most popular mode of connection of transformers is the
delta/star connection 41 Dy 11.

The connection diagram shows the relative position of the terminals in the terminal box and the internal connections that are made. The H.V. winding is connected to a three-wire supply, of phase sequence A-B-C, and at the instant chosen the potential of A is at its maximum positive value. Thus the line voltages on the H.V. side will form an equilateral triangle, as shown, with A as its apex and standing on the base CB. The line terminals are A_2, B_2 and C_2 and the corners of the triangle are so marked. Note that the phase A of the transformer lies between A_2 and B_2, phase B between B_2 and C_2, and phase C between C_2 and A_2, because of the internal connections used.

Now we examine the L.V. winding. Since $V_{a_2a_1}$ is in phase with $V_{A_2A_1}$ the line na_2 must be drawn parallel to B_2A_2 thus establishing the direction of this phase-voltage vector. Similarly nb_2 and nc_2 depend on C_2B_2 and A_2C_2 respectively, and the L.V. vector diagram shows the voltages of the terminals a_2, b_2 and c_2 with respect to n.

It is thus to be observed that although the voltage of the H.V. line A_2 is at its maximum value, the L.V. line a_2 has been advanced 30°, in fact the transformer connections have produced this displacement for all lines.

All the other modes of connection in the same main group No. 4 show a similar 30° advance which is the basis of the classification.

With group 1 there is no phase displacement, but with group 2 the displacement is 180°. It is recommended that the use of the connections of group 2 should be discouraged. All transformers of group 3 cause the L.V. line voltage to lag by 30°.

When transformers are to operate in parallel, that is, between the same H.V. and L.V. bus-bars, it is obvious that an essential requirement is that the transformer connections shall belong to the same main group.

3.3. Parallel Operation

Transformers are said to be connected in parallel if their windings are connected to H.V. and L.V. bus-bars common to both. The two single-phase transformers A and B of fig. 3.10 are connected in this way. Obviously care

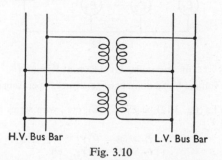

H.V. Bus Bar   L.V. Bus Bar

Fig. 3.10

must be taken that the correct terminals are joined together and that the voltage ratios of the transformers are approximately equal.

Representing each transformer secondary by a source with an e.m.f. equal to its open-circuit voltage in series with the referred impedance of the transformer, the circuits are reduced to those of fig. 3.11, $V_{A,0}$ and $V_{B,0}$ being the open-circuit voltages, Z_A and Z_B being the referred impedances and Z the common load impedance.

Since Z_A and Z_B are small, unless $V_{A,0}$ and $V_{B,0}$ are nearly alike, a large circulating current will be set up even if Z is disconnected.

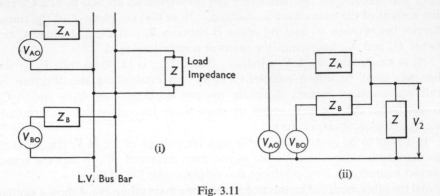

(i)

L.V. Bus Bar

(ii)

Fig. 3.11

To find the value of the currents in each transformer and the common terminal voltage, the "Parallel Generator Theorem"* can be used, from which it is seen that

$$V_2 = \frac{V_{A,0}/Z_A + V_{B,0}/Z_B}{1/Z_A + 1/Z_B + 1/Z} \quad . \quad . \quad . \quad . \quad (3.1)$$

and the currents

$$I_A = (V_{A,0} - V_2)/Z_A \quad . \quad . \quad . \quad . \quad (3.2)$$

$$I_B = (V_{B,0} - V_2)/Z_B \quad . \quad . \quad . \quad . \quad (3.3)$$

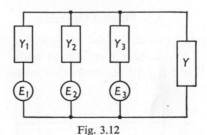

Fig. 3.12

* THE PARALLEL GENERATOR THEOREM

The common terminal voltage V of a number of generators operating in parallel is determined in the following way.

Let the generator e.m.f.s (fig. 3.12) be E_1, E_2, E_3, etc., with series admittances Y_1, Y_2, Y_3 and the load admittance Y.

Then

$$I_1 = (E_1 - V)Y_1 \quad . \quad . \quad . \quad . \quad . \quad . \quad (3.4)$$
$$I_2 = (E_2 - V)Y_2, \quad \text{etc.}$$

and

$$I = VY = I_1 + I_2 + I_3 + \ldots$$

Thus

$$VY = (E_1 - V)Y_1 + (E_2 - V)Y_2 + \ldots$$

$$V(Y + Y_1 + Y_2 + \ldots) = E_1Y_1 + E_2Y_2 + \ldots$$

and

$$V = \frac{E_1Y_1 + E_2Y_2 + \ldots}{Y + Y_1 + Y_2 + \ldots} \quad . \quad . \quad . \quad . \quad . \quad (3.5)$$

The individual currents can then be found by substitution in equation (3.4).

3.3.1. Equal Voltage Ratios

Usually the open-circuit voltages of transformers selected for parallel operation are equal and the equivalent circuit therefore reduces to that of fig. 3.13, from which it is seen that Z_A and Z_B are effectively in parallel.

In this case

$$I_A = I . Z_B/(Z_A+Z_B) \quad . \quad . \quad . \quad . \quad . \quad (3.6)$$

and

$$I_B = I . Z_A/(Z_A+Z_B) \quad . \quad . \quad . \quad . \quad . \quad (3.7)$$

by the usual laws of impedances in parallel. Multiplying by the conjugate $\bar{V}_2$ of the output voltage the individual powers are obtained:

$$P_A+jQ_A = (P+jQ)Z_B/(Z_A+Z_B) \quad . \quad . \quad . \quad . \quad (3.8)$$

and

$$P_B+jQ_B = (P+jQ)Z_A/(Z_A+Z_B) \quad . \quad . \quad . \quad . \quad (3.9)$$

where

$$P+jQ = \bar{V}I \quad . \quad . \quad . \quad . \quad . \quad . \quad (3.10)$$

the total load. These formulae enable the load-sharing properties of the transformers to be observed.

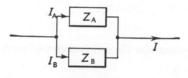

Fig. 3.13

It may be noted that this depends upon the complex ratios $Z_A/(Z_A+Z_B)$ and $Z_B/(Z_A+Z_B)$. If these ratios are real numbers then

$$P_A+jQ_A = k(P_B+jQ_B) \quad . \quad . \quad . \quad . \quad . \quad (3.11)$$

and

$$P_A/P_B = Q_A/Q_B . \quad . \quad . \quad . \quad . \quad . \quad (3.12)$$

The transformers are thus sharing kilowatts and reactive kilovolt-amperes in equal proportion, that is, their power factors are equal. This in turn depends on the ratio Z_A/Z_B being a real number, in which case $R_A/R_B = X_A/X_B$.

This power-factor equality is obviously desirable in order to achieve the most efficient operating conditions and consequently accurate specification of the ratio X/R is therefore demanded of a transformer required to work in parallel with others.

It is also important to appreciate that since load sharing depends on the ratio Z_A/Z_B the complex impedances used in this expression need not necessarily be in ohms.

Per-unit values $r_{p.u}$ and $x_{p.u}$ may be used provided they are based on the same value of load.

This will be seen in the following example.

SUMMARY

In order that transformers should work satisfactorily in parallel the following conditions must be satisfied.

1. The internal connections of both must belong to the same main group in accordance with fig. 3.9.

2. The terminals must be correctly marked and appropriate terminals connected.

3. The line-voltage ratios must be equal.

4. The impedance voltages on full load must be alike. Current will then be shared accordingly to the rating of the transformer. It is not recommended that transformers differing in kilovolt-ampere rating by more than 3 : 1 should operate in parallel.

5. The reactance/resistance ratios of the transformers should be the same, in order that the transformers operate at the same power factor.

EXAMPLE

Two three-phase transformers which have the same turns ratio are connected in parallel and supply a total load of 800 kW at 0·8 power factor lagging.

Their ratings are as follows:

Transformer	Rating	Per-unit resistance	Per-unit reactance
A	400 kVA	0·02	0·04
B	600 kVA	0·01	0·05

Determine the power output and the power factor of each transformer.

On the basis of 1000 kVA

$$r_a = 0·02 \times \frac{1000}{400} = 0·05. \qquad x_a = 0·04 \times \frac{1000}{400} = 0·1.$$

$$r_b = 0·01 \times \frac{1000}{600} = 0·0167. \qquad x_b = 0·05 \times \frac{1000}{600} = 0·0833.$$

$$S = 800 - j600.$$

$$S_B = (800 - j600)\frac{0·05 + j0·1}{0·05 + j0·1 + 0·0167 + j0·0833}$$

$$= (800 - j600)\frac{0·5 + j1·0}{0·667 + j1·833}$$

$$= 414 - j392.$$

$$S_A = S - S_B = 386 - j208.$$

Transformer A	414 kW	570 kVA	0·726 power factor.
„ B	386 kW	440 kVA	0·878 power factor.

3.4. Transformer Insulation—Impulse Phenomena

Much research work has recently been applied to the behaviour of transformer windings when subjected to impulse voltages. The power transformer is of course the major item of equipment at the termination of overhead transmission lines. It is well known that, particularly in areas where lightning disturbances are prevalent, over-voltages are frequently set up in the lines, and these voltages are propagated along the lines in the form of travelling waves of steep wavefront, or surges.

The effect of such a surge arriving at a transformer has an exceedingly complex effect on the transformer winding. The steeper the front and the flatter the tail of the wave, the more severe is its effect, so we will consider the effect of the application of a rectangular wave which is termed a *step function voltage*. Theoretically the incidence of such a wave means that the line terminal is raised in potential at an infinite rate to the crest value and then held there. Such an infinite rate of rise is impossible because of the capacitance of the winding. The

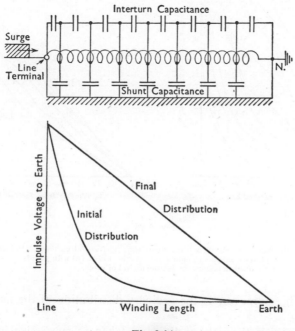

Fig. 3.14

transformer insulation may be considered as a network of capacitance with the interturn insulation acting as a series capacitance chain, each turn having shunt capacitance to earth.

Initially, then, as the line terminal is raised in potential, charging current flows in the capacitors and sets up immediately a potential distribution throughout the winding as shown in fig. 3.14.

By far the greater potential drop occurs across the end turns, since the charging currents of these end capacitors include all the shunt currents. This fact was appreciated many years ago. The insulation of the end turns is likely to be called upon to meet stresses much greater than its normal working values, and in consequence it was considered good practice to reinforce considerably the interturn insulation of the end sections.

However, the curve of fig. 3.14 only represents the initial distribution immediately upon the arrival of the incident wave-front. On the tail of the wave, that is if the over-voltage is maintained at the line terminal, the initial charges causing the initial voltage distribution have the opportunity of redistributing themselves. The effect of winding inductance and resistance has now to be taken into account and the possibility of oscillations taking place becomes apparent. In fact a series of highly complex waves are set up in the winding, before the voltage distribution finally settles down to the straight line that would have been expected if the transformer had had series capacitance

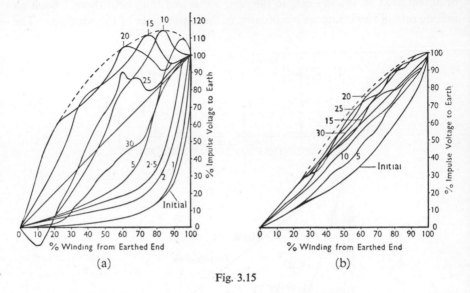

Fig. 3.15

Impulse voltage distribution in shielded transformer winding (neutral earthed). Values obtained from recurrent-surge oscillograph tests on model winding, (a) without shields, (b) with shields.
Figures on curves indicate times in microseconds from arrival of surge.

only and which, moreover, is the ordinary distribution of the normal service voltage.

Fig. 3.15 (a) shows the voltage diagrams taken at successive instants from oscillograph measurements after the arrival of a unit function voltage to a winding undergoing an impulse test. It will be observed that high interturn voltages are produced at the later instants much lower down the winding, and the reinforcement of the end turn insulation is very little assistance, indeed in so far as this reduces the interturn capacitance at the ends, the initial distribution will be still further distorted and the amplitude of the oscillations increased.

3.4.1. Shielded Windings

If the initial voltage distribution were linear, then subsequent oscillations would not arise and the transformer would be "non-resonating".

The application of a line shield, which introduces capacitance between the line terminals and the winding in such diminishing proportion permitting the shunt currents to flow directly from the line, will enable the series-charging currents to have the same value (fig. 3.16 (a)) and linear voltage distribution results.

Such a shield is cumbersome however, and adds considerably to the size, difficulties and cost of manufacture, though completely shielded transformers for 132 kV have been constructed.

A compromise is usually achieved by the introduction of axial shields aiming at improving the initial voltage distribution without going to the full extent of securing linear distribution.

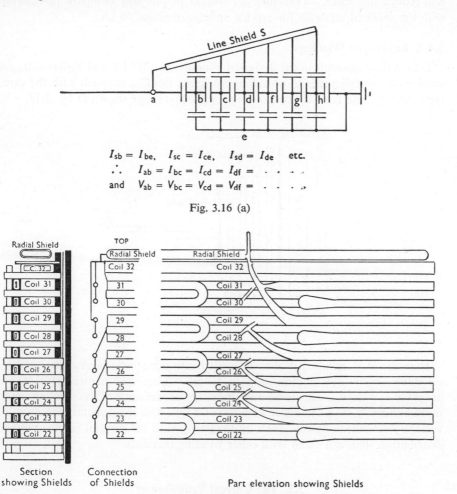

$$I_{sb} = I_{be}, \quad I_{sc} = I_{ce}, \quad I_{sd} = I_{de} \quad \text{etc.}$$
$$\therefore \quad I_{ab} = I_{bc} = I_{cd} = I_{df} = \ldots$$
$$\text{and} \quad V_{ab} = V_{bc} = V_{cd} = V_{df} = \ldots$$

Fig. 3.16 (a)

Fig. 3.16 (b)

Fig. 3.16 (b) shows such shields which take the form of insulated copper conductors somewhat similar to the winding conductors and wound around the outside of its coils. They are suitably proportioned according to the calculation of capacitance required, and connected in groups, not all to the line terminal, but to points of connection higher in the winding.

The improvement due to this form of shielding will be observed in fig. 3.15 (b).

3.4.2. Interleaved Windings

An alternative method of improving the transient behaviour of a transformer is by a process of interleaving the turns of adjacent disc coils, whereby the inter-turn capacitance is considerably increased without causing much increase in the main insulation requirements for the normal service voltage. Now, since the departure from linearity of the initial voltage distribution depends on the ratio (shunt capacitance)/(series capacitance), increasing the interturn capacitance will reduce this ratio. Transformers wound in this way compare favourably with the shielded methods for service voltage of about 66 kV.

3.4.3. Layer-type Windings

Recent developments in the design of windings for 275 kV and higher voltages emphasise the difficulties of obtaining adequate impulse strength with the disc-type winding, and have led to windings of the layer type shown in fig. 3.17.

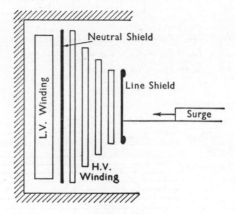

Fig. 3.17

Here the H.V. winding is shown divided into concentric layers separated by oil ducts, each layer diminishing in length. Line and neutral shields are arranged as shown. This form distributes the capacitance of the winding much more uniformly than can occur with the disc type and consequently the impulse voltage distribution agrees much more closely with the normal service voltage distribution than can occur with other winding methods.

3.5. The Current Transformer

Instead of placing an ammeter directly in an H.V. line as shown in fig. 3.18, a transformer might be interposed between the circuit and the instrument.

The latter arrangement has the following advantages:

(a) The instrument has been removed from the line and one terminal has been earthed, with the result that a normal instrument may be used and the observer and the instrument can be remote from any source of danger.

(b) Assuming for the moment an idealised transformer of ratio $1:K$, the current in the meter will be $1/K$ times the line current, and hence a meter with, say, a 5-A movement can be used to measure much larger currents.

It will be seen that the transformer is working under conditions quite different from those of transformers with constant applied voltage. Its secondary winding is virtually short-circuited, or at least closed by a circuit of constant low impedance.

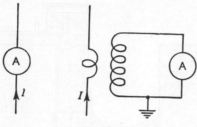

Fig. 3.18

The satisfactory use of the transformer depends upon:

(a) the dependability of the insulation of the primary winding since the first essential is the isolation and the safety of the measuring circuit;
(b) the accuracy of the ratio of the currents in the two windings—any departure from the turns ratio is known as ratio error;
(c) the currents in the two circuits being in phase if wattmeter measurements are to be made, that is, there being no appreciable phase-angle error.

Fig. 3.19

Practical transformers are certain to have some ratio and phase-angle error, and one of the chief problems encountered in design is to keep these errors within prescribed limits for the range of currents to be carried. Apart from current transformers which are used in conjunction with measuring instruments an important field of application is with relay systems of protection of

4—E.M.

transmission lines and machines.   In all cases the accuracy of the system or measurement is directly dependent on the current transformer.

Current transformers may have a primary winding consisting of only one turn, or a bar primary, in which the primary turn consists of a highly insulated conductor passing through a circular core with a toroidal secondary winding. Such transformers are frequently mounted at the base of switchgear or power transformer terminal bushings as shown, for example, in figs. 3.19 and 3.20.

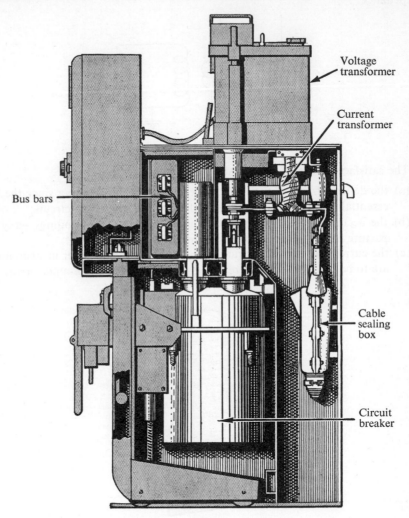

Fig. 3.20

3.5.1. Load on the Current Transformer

Under ideal conditions a current transformer operates with its secondary terminals short-circuited, or at least closed, through a very low impedance load such as an ammeter, but if long secondary leads are used to enable a remote meter to be connected, or if higher impedance relays—usually reactive—are in circuit, then the transformer is said to be connected to a *load* which imposes a volt-ampere *burden* on the transformer. Under these conditions it is much more difficult to minimise the ratio and phase-angle errors as the following vector diagram will show. It is also necessary to know the value of the burden before the transformer can be designed.

3.5.2. Vector Diagram

The vector diagram (fig. 3.21) should be compared with fig. 2.23 which is the corresponding vector diagram of a power transformer.

Commencing with the vector of secondary current $I_2 = I_{fegh}$, since this current flows in the load a voltage drop V_{gh} will be set up across it leading I_2 by the phase angle ψ of the load.

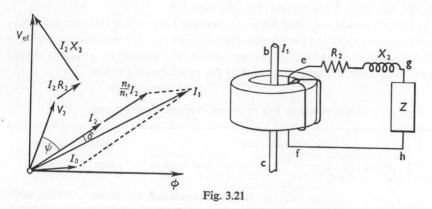

Fig. 3.21

If R_2 is the resistance of the secondary winding and X_2 its leakage reactance, the e.m.f.

$$E_{fe} = V_{ef} = I(R_2 + jX_2) + V_{gh} \quad \cdot \quad \cdot \quad \cdot \quad (3.13)$$

will be required. This establishes the flux ϕ in the core (equation (2.6)).

Although this flux is probably quite small (depending entirely on the value V_{ef}), a magnetising component I_0 of the primary current is required. I_1, the primary current itself, is then obtained from equation (2.24).

The vector diagram has been built up in this sequence in order to show the relationships of the various quantities. In actual fact I_1 is the independent variable and the other quantities adjust themselves to correspond with it.

The fact that I_1 and I_2 are not in phase but differ by the angle δ, and also that their ratio is not exactly equal to the ratio of the turns, will be seen to depend entirely on the relative magnitude and phase of I_0. The use of high-permeability material for the core will do much to minimise this component, but its presence is necessitated by the existence of the flux which in turn depends upon: (a) the impedance of the load and (b) the leakage reactance of the secondary winding. It is these latter quantities which determine phase angle and ratio error.

Effect of an Open Circuit. At this stage it should be noted that if at any time while the primary current is flowing the secondary circuit is broken, the absence of the secondary ampere-turns means that the whole of the primary ampere-turns are available for magnetising the core. A large flux will be produced, and a dangerously high secondary circuit voltage will result, unless the flux is limited by saturation.

At all events this is not to be desired and the greatest care should be taken to avoid its occurrence. It is good practice to short-circuit the secondary terminals of a portable-type current transformer, and switches are often provided for this purpose. It is interesting to compare the short-circuiting of a voltage transformer, which produces abnormal current, with the open-circuiting of a current transformer, producing abnormal voltage.

3.5.3. Specification of Current Transformers

The classes into which current transformers are grouped are given by British Standard 81: 1936, "Instrument Transformers".*

The following tables quoted from the Standard show that these transformers are classified according to permissible limits of error. The conditions of testing in all cases demand that the loads connected to the secondary terminals should be such as to absorb the rated burden at the rated current value.

LIMITS OF ERROR FOR METERING CURRENT TRANSFORMERS

	Absolute error				Variation in error	
Class	From 120% down to 20% of rated current		Below 20% and down to 10% of rated current		From 120% down to 10% of rated current	
	Ratio	Phase diff.	Ratio	Phase diff.	Ratio	Phase diff.
	% + or −	+ or −	% + or −	+ or −	%	
AM	1	30 min	1	30 min	0·5	15 min
BM	1	35 min	1·5	50 min	1	25 min
CM	1	90 min	2	120 min	1·5	60 min

LIMITS OF ERROR FOR TRANSFORMERS USED WITH MEASURING INSTRUMENTS FOR LABORATORY (AL AND BL) OR GENERAL USE (A, B, C AND D)

	Absolute error					
Class	From 120% down to 60% of rated current		Below 60% and down to 20% of rated current		Below 20% and down to 10% of rated current	
	Ratio	Phase diff.	Ratio	Phase diff.	Ratio	Phase diff.
	% + or −	+ or −	% + or −	+ or −	% + or −	+ or −
AL	0·15	3 min	0·15	4 min	0·15	6 min
BL	0·3	10 min	0·4	15 min	0·5	20 min
A	0·5	35 min	0·5	35 min	1·0	50 min
B	1·0	60 min	1·0	60 min	1·5	90 min
C	1·0	120 min	1·0	120 min	2·0	180 min
D	5·0	—	5·0	—	—	—

* Current transformers required for protective gear are covered by B.S. 2046: 1953, "Protective Transformers".

CLASSES OF ACCURACY AND THEIR APPLICATIONS

In view of the intimate connection which exists between the performance of a current transformer and its burden, it is very desirable that the burden or range of burdens at which the transformer is to operate should be stated, at any rate approximately, at the time of ordering. The practice which is sometimes followed of ordering a current transformer for a burden considerably in excess of the actual burden is likely to be detrimental to its performance under operating conditions and is to be deprecated.

It is undesirable that a higher class of accuracy should be called for than is necessary for the function to be fulfilled. To do so is uneconomical and may even involve modifications in the switchgear, without serving any useful purpose.

Application	Class of current transformer	Class of voltage transformer
(i) For precision testing in the laboratory or for use as a sub-standard for the testing of laboratory instrument transformers	AL	AL
(ii) For laboratory and test work in conjunction with (a) sub-standard instruments, (b) the highest grades of integrating meters, (c) indicating "wattmeters for special accuracy" such as those referred to in B.S.S. 89. Also as a sub-standard for the testing of industrial instrument transformers . . .	BL	BL
(iii) For precision industrial metering	AM	A or B
(iv) For industrial metering of sub-standard grade according to B.S.S. 37.	BM	B
(v) For general industrial metering of commercial grade according to B.S.S. 37	CM	B
(vi) For use with sub-standard indicating wattmeters .	A	A
(vii) For use with first-grade indicating and graphic voltmeters and wattmeters	B	B
(viii) For use with first-grade indicating and graphic ammeters	C	C
(ix) For purposes where ratio is of less importance than in the above applications, e.g., ammeters where approximate values only are required . . .	D	D

Terminal Markings. The standard method of marking current-transformer terminals is in accordance with fig. 3.22, where two alternative letterings are shown.

The direction of winding M to L and (M) to (L) is the same. The currents therefore within the winding I_{ML} and $I_{(\text{L})(\text{M})}$ are in phase except for the phase-angle error.

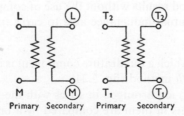

Fig. 3.22

3.5.4. Current Transformer Testing

In order to determine ratio and phase-angle error of a current transformer at various values of current the standard tests employed by the National Physical Laboratory involve comparisons with standard transformers of known errors. The following tests are more suited to college laboratories.

Method A.   Fig. 3.23.   The primary winding is connected in series with a resistance R_1 and supplied from a suitable current source which can be varied over the required range.   The secondary circuit **egh** includes a low resistance R_2 with a slider, the primary of a mutual inductance M which together with the remaining impedance **gh** produces the secondary burden.

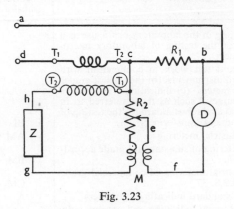

Fig. 3.23

A detector (vibration galvanometer or cathode-ray tube with amplifier) is used to indicate a voltage balance between V_{cb} and V_{cf}.   The values of R_2 and M are adjusted until balance is obtained.   Then

$$I_1 R_1 = I_2(R_2 + j\omega M)$$

and the complex current ratio

$$I_1/I_2 = (R_2 + j\omega M)/R_1 \quad . \quad . \quad . \quad . \quad . \quad . \quad (3.14)$$

In magnitude

$$I_1/I_2 \simeq R_2/R_1 \quad . \quad . \quad . \quad . \quad . \quad . \quad . \quad (3.15)$$

and the phase angle is obtained from

$$\tan \delta \simeq \delta = \omega M/R_2 \quad . \quad . \quad . \quad . \quad . \quad (3.16)$$

in radian measure.

This method gives good results without the use of complicated equipment, but a calibrated variable mutual inductance able to carry full secondary current is needed.

Method B is a test in which a quadrature component is introduced by capacitor and is known as the *Biffi* method (fig. 3.24).

Resistances R_1 and R_2 are arranged in series with the primary and secondary windings and the currents in them are compared by a bridge circuit comprising R_4, R_3 and C.

Current is obtained from a suitable source connected to the terminals **a** and **d**.

R_3 and R_4 are high resistances, R_4 being variable. R_4 is adjusted until balance is obtained, some trimming usually being necessary on the small variable air capacitor C.

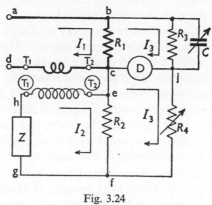

Fig. 3.24

At balance the loop currents I_{bjc} and I_{cjf} are equal and

$$V_{\text{bc}} = V_{\text{bj}}$$

$$(I_1 - I_3)R_1 = I_3 \frac{R_3/j\omega C}{R_3 + 1/j\omega C}.$$

Moreover

$$V_{\text{ef}} = V_{\text{jf}}$$

$$(I_2 - I_3)R_2 = I_3 R_4.$$

$$I_1 = \frac{I_3}{R_1}\left(R_1 + \frac{R_3}{j\omega C R_3 + 1}\right) \quad \cdots \cdots \quad (3.17)$$

$$I_2 = \frac{I_3}{R_2}(R_2 + R_4) \quad \cdots \cdots \quad (3.18)$$

$$\frac{I_1}{I_2} = \frac{R_2}{R_1}\frac{R_1 + j\omega C R_1 R_3 + R_3}{(R_2 + R_4)(1 + j\omega C R_3)}$$

$$= \frac{R_2}{R_1}\frac{(R_1 + R_3 + \omega^2 C^2 R_1 R_3{}^2 - j\omega C R_3{}^2)}{(R_2 + R_4)(1 + \omega^2 C^2 R_3{}^2)} \quad \cdots \cdots \quad (3.19)$$

In this expression C is small, so neglecting C^2

$$\frac{I_1}{I_2} \simeq \frac{R_2}{R_1}\frac{(R_1 + R_3)}{(R_2 + R_4)} \simeq \frac{R_2}{R_1}\frac{R_3}{R_4} \quad \cdots \cdots \quad (3.20)$$

since R_1 and $R_2 \ll R_3$ and R_4

and

$$\tan \delta \simeq \delta = \omega C R_3{}^2/(R_1 + R_3) \simeq \omega C R_3 \quad \cdots \cdots \quad (3.21)$$

in radian measure.

In practice R_1 and R_2 should be in the approximate turns ratio of the transformer with, say, $R_1 = 0\cdot001\ \Omega$, $R_2 = 0\cdot1\ \Omega$, for a 500/5-A transformer.

R_3 and R_4 are 4-decade resistance boxes and C a $0\cdot001$-μF variable air capacitor.

3.6. Saturable Reactors and Magnetic Amplifiers

The control of current in a load fed from constant-voltage mains by means of a variable series resistor is simple and effective, but the system has obvious disadvantages increasing with the rating of the load.

The physical size of the equipment necessary to dissipate the heat increases, and the cost of the energy loss becomes prohibitive. Moreover, a regulator of infinite resistance is required to reduce the current to zero. With a.c. supply a variable reactor might be used in place of the resistance, using a movable iron core to provide the necessary variation. This method almost eliminates the power loss in the regulator and smooth variation is obtained over a wide range. A better way of varying the reactance, however, is to use an additional d.c. winding on the reactor which is arranged to saturate the core and so reduce the flux swing produced by the current in the main winding, in other words to reduce its effective reactance. By varying the direct current in the control or saturating winding, control of the load current is obtained. The introduction of ferromagnetic cores with very marked saturation characteristics has led to many developments in this field, and this, together with the application of feed-back principles such as are used with electronic amplifiers, has enabled high-gain magnetic amplifiers to be constructed capable of controlling large output powers by very small input currents. This type of equipment is a serious competitor of electronic amplifiers for certain applications, its advantages being principally the extreme robustness of the components—coils, ferromagnetic cores, metal rectifiers—together with the possible power-handling capacity and instantaneous availability, no warming-up time being required such as is necessary for comparable mercury-vapour equipment.

3.6.1. Magnetic Material for Saturable Reactors

The ideal material for a saturable reactor is one which has a small-area almost rectangular hysteresis loop with high saturation magnetisation. Three classes of material approximate to this performance:

(a) nickel-iron alloys (77–79% Ni);

(b) grain-oriented silicon irons;

(c) grain-oriented nickel irons (50% Ni).

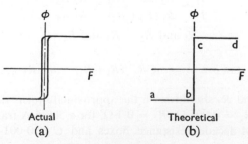

Fig. 3.25

The theoretical magnetisation curve for a perfect core would be as shown in fig. 3.25. It consists of three zones **ab, bc** and **cd**. In zones **ab** and **cd** the reactor is saturated. There can be no change of flux with changing current whilst the magnetisation remains in this zone. In other words the inductance of any winding about the core will be zero and there can be no voltage drop across it. The opposite occurs in zone **bc** where a change of flux occurs without a change of current. This corresponds to infinite inductance. The total m.m.f. must now be zero and the m.m.f. of one winding will be balanced by the effect of current in the others. A reactor of this type whose inductance can change suddenly from infinity to zero must always be connected in series with a load when it acts in the manner of a switch. When saturated the "switch" is closed and in the unsaturated state is "open". The operation of the "switch" is determined by the flux ϕ swinging into and out of saturation, and, since

$$v = n.d\phi/dt \qquad \qquad (2.2)$$

or

$$\phi = (1/n)\int v dt \qquad \qquad (3.22)$$

a change of ϕ demands the application of *volt-seconds* in the correct direction.

3.6.2. Simple Series Reactor Circuit

Consider such a core having two windings with turns n_1 and n_2 (fig. 3.26). n_1 is the main winding or output winding in series with the load (a non-inductive load of resistance R is assumed).

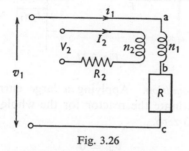

Fig. 3.26

The supply voltage has an instantaneous value

$$v_1 = \sqrt{2}.V_1 \sin \omega t \qquad \qquad (3.23)$$

n_2 is the control winding energised from a d.c. source V_2 with a large series resistance R_2 arranged so that any voltage drop across n_2 is negligible in comparison.

Thus
$$I_2 \simeq V_2/R_2.$$

We will assume that the saturation flux

$$\phi_s \gneq \phi_{max}$$

where

$$\phi_{max} = V_1/4\cdot44 f n_1 \qquad \qquad (3.24)$$

At any instant the core m.m.f. will be

$$F = i_1 n_1 + i_2 n_2 \qquad \qquad (3.25)$$

The operation of the circuit will be considered in three parts:

(i) *The Unsaturated Condition.* Let $V_2 = 0$ when I_2 will be zero and the flux will swing from ϕ_{max} to $-\phi_{max}$ (fig. 3.27).

The m.m.f. $\hspace{4cm} F = 0,$
hence from equation (3.25)
$$i_1 = 0$$
and the voltage drop across the load
$$v_{bc} = i_1 R_1 = 0.$$
Since, in fig. 3.26,
$$v_1 = v_{ac} = v_{ab} + v_{bc} \quad . \quad . \quad . \quad . \quad . \quad . \quad (3.26)$$
in this case
$$v_{ab} = v_1.$$

The load current is thus zero and the whole of the applied voltage appears across the reactor. (In practice the inductance would not be infinite and a very small magnetising current would flow.)

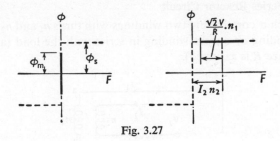

Fig. 3.27

(ii) *The Saturated Condition.* Applying a large current I_2 in the control winding sufficient to saturate the reactor for the whole of the cycle, the flux swing will be reduced to zero.

Thus $\hspace{4cm} v_{ab} = 0$
and from equation (3.26)
$$v_{bc} = v_1$$
and thus $\hspace{4cm} i_1 = v_1/R_1.$

The maximum value of the load current is
$$\sqrt{2}.I_1 = \sqrt{2}.V_1/R_1.$$

The core will remain saturated provided the m.m.f. F never falls to zero.

Therefore $\hspace{3cm} F = i_1 n_1 + I_2 n_2 > 0$

and $\hspace{3.5cm} I_2 n_2 - \sqrt{2}.I_1 n_1 \gtrless 0.$

Thus the control current
$$I_2 \gtrless (\sqrt{2}.V_1/R_1)(n_1/n_2) \quad . \quad . \quad . \quad . \quad (3.27)$$

to maintain this condition.

(iii) *The Intermediate Condition* when

$$0 < I_2 < (\sqrt{2} \cdot V_1/R_1)(n_1/n_2).$$

The reactor will now be saturated for part of the cycle and unsaturated for the remainder. The operation is determined by the equations

$$v_{ac} = v_{ab} + v_{bc} \quad . \quad . \quad . \quad . \quad . \quad . \quad (3.26)$$

$$i_1 = v_{bc}/R_1 \quad . \quad . \quad . \quad . \quad . \quad . \quad (3.28)$$

$$F = i_1 n_1 + I_2 n_2 \quad . \quad . \quad . \quad . \quad . \quad (3.25)$$

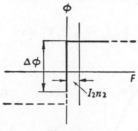

Fig. 3.28

and also since v_{ab}, v_{bc} and i_1 are all alternating quantities they can have no d.c. components. Over the complete cycle then

$$\left. \begin{array}{l} \displaystyle\int_0^{2\pi} v_{ab}\,d\theta = 0 \\[2mm] \displaystyle\int_0^{2\pi} v_{bc}\,d\theta = 0 \\[2mm] \displaystyle\int_0^{2\pi} i_1\,d\theta \ = 0 \end{array} \right\} \quad . \quad . \quad . \quad . \quad (3.29)$$

When the circuit is operating under steady-state condition, d.c. transients having subsided, the wave-forms will be as shown in fig. 3.29.

To understand the cycle we will enter at the instant π when v_{ac} is equal to zero, and in consequence we know i_1 will be zero. The corresponding m.m.f.

$$F_\pi = I_2 n_2 + 0$$

and the core will be saturated. This makes v_{ab} equal to zero, and v_{bc} is equal to v_{ac}.

Now as v_{ac} increases negatively v_{bc} will follow the same wave-form for some time. This is given by:

$$v_{bc}\Big]_\pi^\beta = v_{ac} = \sqrt{2} \cdot V \sin \theta$$

and

$$i_1\Big]_\pi^\beta = \frac{v_{bc}}{R_1} = \frac{\sqrt{2} \cdot V_1}{R_1} \sin \theta.$$

At β the total m.m.f. is reduced to zero, and the core comes out of saturation. Thus

$$F_\beta = 0 = I_2 n_2 + [i_1 n_1]_\beta$$

$$[i_1]_\beta = -I_2(n_2/n_1)$$

$$\sqrt{2}.(V_1/R_1)\sin\beta = -I_2(n_2/n_1) \quad . \quad . \quad . \quad . \quad . \quad (3.30)$$

Thus
$$\sin\beta = -I_2(n_2/n_1)(R_1/\sqrt{2}.V_1) \quad . \quad . \quad . \quad (3.31)$$

The reactor now assumes infinite inductance and this effectively prevents current change, hence i_1 is held constant at this value until saturation again occurs. The load voltage v_{bc} will also remain constant corresponding to i_1.

Thus

$$[v_{bc}]_\beta = \sqrt{2}.V_1 \sin\beta \quad . \quad . \quad . \quad . \quad . \quad (3.32)$$

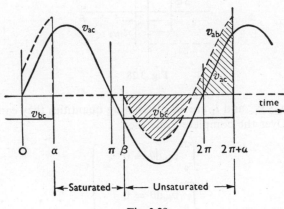

Fig. 3.29

and so the reactor voltage will commence to vary once more and take up the difference between v_{ac} and v_{bc}.

$$v_{ab}\Big]_\beta^{2\pi+\alpha} = (v_{ac} - v_{bc})\Big]_\beta^{2\pi+\alpha}$$

$$= \sqrt{2}.V_1(\sin\theta - \sin\beta)\Big]_\beta^{2\pi+\alpha} \quad . \quad . \quad . \quad . \quad (3.33)$$

The wave-form of v_{ab} consists firstly of a negative half-wave (shown cross-hatched in fig. 3.29) the area of which (volt-seconds) divided by n_1 is the swing of flux $\Delta\phi$. As v_{bc} becomes positive the flux will rise again and ultimately at α the core again saturates. The position of α is determined by the area under the positive half-wave being necessarily equal to the negative half-wave (equation (3.29)) and at this point the voltage v_{ab} falls abruptly to zero. v_{bc} now rises to equal v_{ac} and current i_1 flows for the remainder of the cycle.

The equations to the wave-forms of fig. 3.29 are thus:

$$v_{ac} = \sqrt{2} . V_1 \sin \theta \quad . \quad . \quad . \quad . \quad . \quad . \quad (3.23)$$

$$v_{ab} = \sqrt{2} . V_1 \left(0 \Big]_{\alpha}^{\beta} + (\sin \theta - \sin \beta) \Big]_{\beta}^{2\pi+\alpha} \right) \quad . \quad . \quad . \quad (3.34)$$

$$v_{bc} = \sqrt{2} . V_1 \left(\sin \theta \Big]_{\alpha}^{\beta} + \sin \beta \Big]_{\beta}^{2\pi+\alpha} \right) \quad . \quad . \quad . \quad (3.35)$$

$$i_1 = \frac{\sqrt{2} . V_1}{R_1} \left(\sin \theta \Big]_{\alpha}^{\beta} + \sin \beta \Big]_{\beta}^{2\pi+\alpha} \right) \quad . \quad . \quad . \quad (3.36)$$

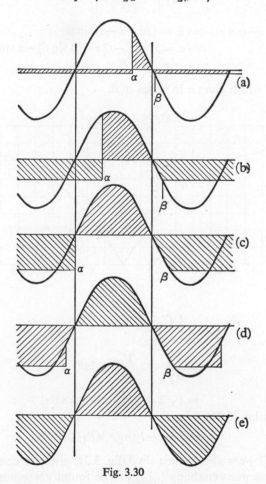

(a)

(b)

(c)

(d)

(e)

Fig. 3.30

Control Characteristics. As the control current I_2 is increased β is retarded from π to its limiting value $3\pi/2$ and α advances correspondingly to ensure that the positive and negative half-cycles of the above wave-form are equal in area and thus comply with equation (3.29).

The mean value of i_1 as would be indicated on a rectifier-type ammeter also increases.

Wave-forms of i_1 are shown in fig. 3.30. The value of $[i_1]_{mean}$ corresponding to $\alpha = \pi/2$ is not exceeded as α advances further to zero, though some alteration of wave-form takes place.

The control characteristic which shows how $[i_1]_{mean}$ depends on I_2 is determined as follows.

From equations (3.29) and (3.36),

$$\int_\alpha^\beta \sin\theta d\theta + \int_\beta^{2\pi+\alpha} \sin\beta d\theta = 0 \quad . \quad . \quad . \quad . \quad (3.37)$$

$$\left[-\cos\theta\right]_\alpha^\beta + \left[\theta\sin\beta\right]_\beta^{2\pi+\alpha} = 0 \quad . \quad . \quad . \quad . \quad (3.38)$$

$$-\cos\alpha + \cos\beta = (2\pi+\alpha-\beta)\sin\beta$$
$$\cos\alpha = \{\cos\beta - (2\pi-\beta)\sin\beta\} - \alpha\sin\beta$$
$$= A\alpha + B$$

the solution of which gives α in terms of β.

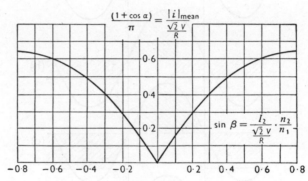

Fig. 3.31

Now

$$[i_1]_{mean} = \frac{1}{\pi}\int_\alpha^\pi i_1 d\theta$$

$$= \frac{1}{\pi}\int_\alpha^\pi \sqrt{2}.\frac{V_1}{R_1}\sin\theta d\theta$$

$$= (\sqrt{2}.V_1/R_1)\{(1+\cos\alpha)/\pi\} . \quad . \quad . \quad . \quad (3.39)$$

and from equation (3.31)

$$\sin\beta = -I_2(n_2/n_1)(R_1/\sqrt{2}.V) \quad . \quad . \quad . \quad (3.40)$$

Thus plotting $(1+\cos\alpha)/\pi$ against $\sin\beta$ (fig. 3.31) gives the control characteristic in dimensionless units enabling $[i_1]_{mean}$ to be found corresponding to I_2 in any specific case.

3.6.3. Parallel-connected Reactors

One of the disadvantages of single reactor operation is the difficulty of de-coupling the control circuit. The voltage across the control winding by transformer action will be $v_{ab}(n_2/n_1)$, and as the turns ratio is invariably much greater than unity (to make $I_2 < I_1$) this voltage will exceed the mains voltage.   Modification of i_2 will occur unless v_2 and R_2 are very large indeed.

If, however, two reactors are used with their main windings connected in parallel (fig. 3.32) the voltage v_{ab} will be common and the induced voltages in the two control windings will be the same.   Now, if these are connected in series opposition, there will be no total induced voltage in the control circuit, R_2 is unnecessary, and a much smaller value of V_2 can be used.

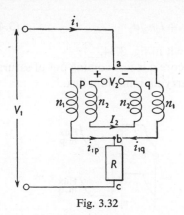

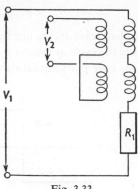

Fig. 3.32   Fig. 3.33

Similar circumstances arise if the main windings are series connected, but the series reactor circuits will not be discussed here though there is an equally wide field of application for them (fig. 3.33).

The cycle of operation of the parallel reactors depends upon the following conditions.   (Suffixes p and q refer to the two cores, respectively.)

(a) Since v_{ab} is common to both reactors

$$v_{ab} = n_1 . d\phi_p/dt = n_1 . d\phi_q/dt \quad . \quad . \quad . \quad . \quad (3.41)$$

thus the rate of change of flux in both cores will always be the same.   When one core is saturated, flux change in the other core will be arrested even though it may be unsaturated.

(b) The control current I_2 flows in opposite directions in the two control windings, hence the m.m.f. in the cores

$$F_p = i_{1,p}n_1 + I_2 n_2 . \quad . \quad . \quad . \quad . \quad . \quad (3.42)$$

$$F_q = i_{2,q}n_2 - I_2 n_2 . \quad . \quad . \quad . \quad . \quad . \quad (3.43)$$

and

$$i_1 = i_{1,p} + i_{1,q} . \quad . \quad . \quad . \quad . \quad . \quad . \quad (3.44)$$

(c) When either core is saturated,

$$d\phi/dt = 0$$

hence

$$v_{ab} = 0$$

$$v_{bc} = v_{ac} = \sqrt{2} . V_1 \sin \omega t$$

and the load current

$$[i_1]_{\text{saturated}} = (\sqrt{2} . V_1/R) \sin \omega t \quad . \quad . \quad . \quad (3.45)$$

(d) When a core is unsaturated

$$F = 0.$$

Thus from equations (3.42) and (3.43)

$$[i_{1,p}]_{unsaturated} = -I_2 n_2/n_1 \quad \ldots \ldots \ (3.46)$$

and $i_{1,p}$ will be held constant at this value until the core saturates again.

Similarly, when core q is unsaturated,

$$[i_{1,q}]_{unsaturated} = +I_2 n_2/n_1 \quad \ldots \ldots \ (3.47)$$

The complete wave-forms are thus as shown in fig. 3.34.

Entering the cycle at instant 0 when the core q is just coming out of saturation we find the core p also unsaturated and carrying minimum flux.

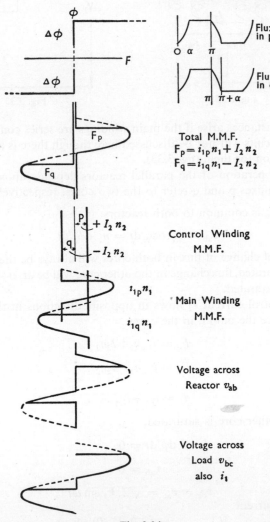

Fig. 3.34

The currents in the main windings $i_{1,p}$ and $i_{1,q}$ will be given by equations (3·46) and (3·47) together with $[i_1]_0 = 0$.

The voltage v_{ab} then follows v_{ac} until instant α when the area under this curve is such that

$$\int_0^{\alpha/\omega} \frac{v_{ab}}{n_1} dt = \Delta\phi$$

and core p saturates. v_{ab} now falls to zero and both fluxes remain constant to the end of the half-cycle. v_{bc} is now following the wave-form of v_{ac} and the total current i_1 is similar.

At instant π,

$$i_1 = 0$$

and

$$i_{1,q}]_\pi = -i_{1,q}]_\pi = I_2 n_2/n_1$$

Thus F_p has returned to zero and the core p comes out of saturation.

The negative half-cycle is similar, flux falling as V_{ab} increases negatively and core q saturates at $\pi+\alpha$.

The equations to the wave-forms are :

$$v_{ab} = \sqrt{2}.\,V\sin\theta \Big]_0^\alpha +0\Big]_\alpha^\pi +\sqrt{2}.\,V\sin\theta \Big]_\pi^{\pi+\alpha} +0\Big]_{\pi+\alpha}^{2\pi} \quad . \quad . \text{ (3.48)}$$

$$v_{bc} = 0\Big]_0^\alpha +\sqrt{2}.\,V\sin\theta \Big]_\alpha^\pi +0\Big]_\pi^{\pi+\alpha} +\sqrt{2}.\,V\sin\theta \Big]_{\pi+\alpha}^{2\pi} \quad . \quad . \text{ (3.49)}$$

$$i_1 = 0\Big]_0^\alpha +\sqrt{2}\frac{V}{R}\sin\theta \Big]_\alpha^\pi +0\Big]_\pi^{\pi+\alpha} +\sqrt{2}\frac{V}{R}\sin\theta \Big]_{\pi+\alpha}^{2\pi} \quad . \quad . \text{ (3.50)}$$

$$i_{1,p} = -I_2\frac{n_2}{n_1}\Big]_0^{2\pi} +0\Big]_0^\alpha +\sqrt{2}.\,V\sin\theta \Big]_\alpha^\pi +0\Big]_\pi^{2\pi} \quad . \quad . \quad . \text{ (3.51)}$$

$$i_{1,q} = I_2\frac{n_2}{n_1}\Big]_0^{2\pi} +0\Big]_0^{\pi+\alpha} +\sqrt{2}.\,V\sin\theta \Big]_{\pi+\alpha}^{2\pi} \quad . \quad . \quad . \text{ (3.52)}$$

$$F_p = 0\Big]_0^\alpha +\sqrt{2}.\,Vn_1\sin\theta \Big]_\alpha^\pi +0\Big]_\pi^{2\pi} \quad . \quad . \quad . \text{ (3.53)}$$

$$F_q = 0\Big]_0^{\pi+\alpha} +\sqrt{2}Vn_1\sin\theta \Big]_{\pi+\alpha}^{2\pi} \quad . \quad . \quad . \text{ (3.54)}$$

Control Characteristics.   Since

$$F_p = i_{1,p}n_1 + I_2 n_2 \quad , \quad . \quad . \quad . \quad . \text{ (3.42)}$$

the average value of F_p over the whole cycle is

$$[F_p]_{mean} = \frac{1}{2\pi}\int_0^{2\pi} F_p d\theta = 0 + I_2 n_2 \quad . \quad . \quad . \text{ (3.55)}$$

$i_{1,p}$ having no d.c. component.

Similarly

$$[F_q]_{mean} = -I_2 n_2 \quad . \quad . \quad . \quad . \quad . \text{ (3.56)}$$

Now from equations (3.50), (3.53) and (3.54)

$$n_1 i_1 = F_p + F_q \quad \cdot \quad \cdot \quad \cdot \quad \cdot \quad \cdot \quad \cdot \quad (3.57)$$

and the value of the rectified average current will be

$$[i]_{mean} = \frac{1}{\pi} \int_0^\pi i_1 d\theta = \frac{2[F_p]_{mean}}{n_1}$$

$$= 2I_2(n_2/n_1) \quad \cdot \quad \cdot \quad \cdot \quad \cdot \quad (3.58)$$

The rectified load current is thus directly proportional to the control current, that is, the control characteristic is linear up to the limit

$$\lim [i_1]_{mean} = (2/\pi)(\sqrt{2} \cdot V/R) \quad \cdot \quad \cdot \quad \cdot \quad \cdot \quad (3.59)$$

when the reactors are saturated for the whole of the cycle.

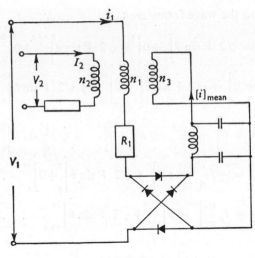

Fig. 3.35

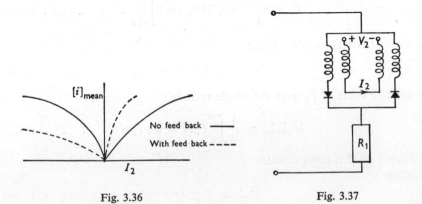

Fig. 3.36   Fig. 3.37

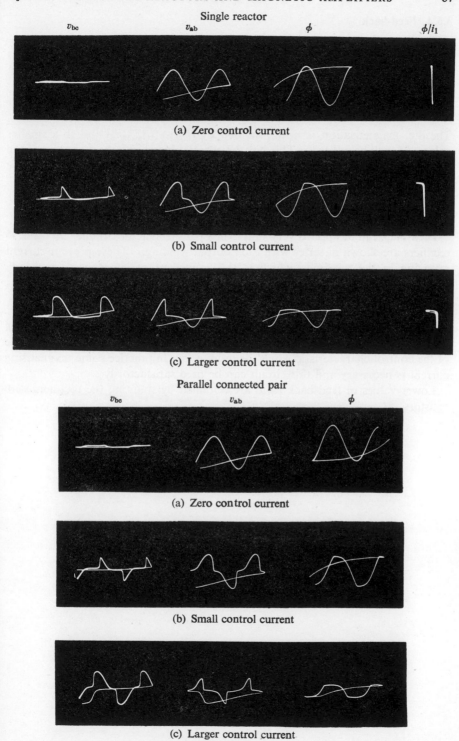

Fig. 3.38.   Oscillograms taken on experimental reactors employing H.C.R. ring cores

3.6.4. Feed-back

The gain of an amplifier can be increased by the application of feed-back. For example, in the simple reactor circuit of fig. 3.35, if the load current is passed through a bridge rectifier and then, after smoothing, to a third coil on the core, equation (3.25) for the m.m.f. becomes

$$F = i_1 n_1 + I_2 n_2 + [i_1]_{mean} n_3 \quad \cdots \quad \cdots \quad (3.60)$$

The d.c. magnetisation is now provided by $[I_2 n_2 + [i_1]_{mean} n_3]$ and so a smaller value of I_2 will be needed. This has the effect of increasing the steepness of the control characteristic (fig. 3.36) for positive values of I_2, but on the negative side the feed-back is in opposition and the slope is reduced.

3.6.5. Auto-excitation

Feed-back can be applied very simply in a parallel reactor circuit. In fig. 3.37 rectifiers are shown in series with each output winding. These prevent current reversing in the windings which is the equivalent of superposing a steady circulating current

$$[i_{1,p}]_{mean} = [i_{1,q}]_{mean} = \tfrac{1}{2}[i_1]_{mean} \quad \cdots \quad \cdots \quad (3.61)$$

The corresponding magnetisation is equivalent to $I_2 n_2$ by equation (3.58), that is, 100% feed-back. Theoretically this would lead to instability as the slope of the control characteristic would be infinite, but in practice some magnetising current is necessary and this circuit can be used satisfactorily.

Lower values of feed-back ratio are obtained by shunting the rectifiers with resistors.

CHAPTER 4

WINDINGS

ELECTRICAL machines usually employ windings distributed in slots over the circumference of the armature core. Each conductor lies at right angles to the magnetic flux and to the direction of its movement so that the induced e.m.f. in the conductor is given by the equation

$$e = Blu \qquad \qquad (4.1)$$

where B = flux density,

$\qquad l$ = length of the conductor

and $\qquad u$ = velocity of relative movement between the conductor and the flux.

These conductors are connected together by means of end connections in what is termed the winding overhang, in such a manner as to form a series-parallel system; conductors being connected in series so as to increase the voltage, and in parallel paths so as to share the current. According to the purpose of the machine, which may have to supply polyphase alternating current, or direct current, or possibly the two superimposed, the winding connections will be found to differ to some extent. In general a d.c. winding is a closed-circuit winding the conductors being connected together in a symmetrical manner forming a closed loop or series of loops.

A.C. windings on the other hand are usually open-circuit windings, suitable conductors being connected in series between the machine terminals.

4.1. Commutator Windings

The field systems of the early two-pole d.c. machines were both heavy and costly and it was soon discovered that a much better use of material could be obtained if the pole area was subdivided and arranged alternately around the armature thus making a multipolar machine. The flux pattern of such a machine is shown in fig. 4.1 the flux crossing the gap under a N pole, entering the armature, dividing, and returning via the S poles on either side.

The direction of the e.m.f. in the armature conductors due to rotation of the armature in this field is shown in the figure (by applying the "Right-hand Rule", *see* Volume I), from which it is observed that the e.m.f.s in conductors separated by a pole pitch are always in opposite directions. Consequently, if coils are made up spanning a pole pitch, the conductor e.m.f.s add together around the loop. Such coils are pre-formed and insulated, and the process of winding the armature consists of placing these coils in position and connecting them together in a special manner. Such coils naturally form a two-layer winding (fig. 4.2) with one side of each coil at the bottom of a slot and the other at the top of a slot a pole pitch away. Successive coils overlap and fit together tidily in the

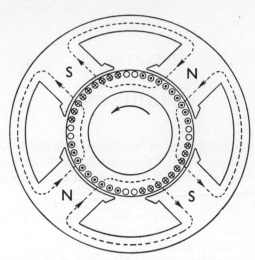

Fig. 4.1

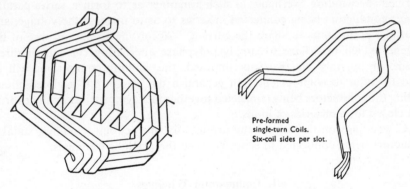

Fig. 4.2

Pre-formed
single-turn Coils.
Six-coil sides per slot.

Fig. 4.3

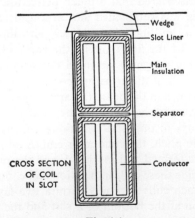

Wedge

Slot Liner

Main
Insulation

Separator

Conductor

CROSS SECTION
OF COIL
IN SLOT

Fig. 4.4

manner shown, each coil being formed to a diamond shape with an evolute bend at the apex.   The ends of the coils are brought out and the connection between the coils is made at the *commutator*.

According to the method of connections we have *lap* or *wave* windings.

In large machines there is only one turn per coil and the conductors are made of rectangular strip on edge (fig. 4.3), but with smaller machines there are several turns usually of round wire.   The turns of a given coil are arranged above each other in the slot and there may be more than two coil sides per slot arranged side by side.   These adjacent coil sides form a *slot layer*.   They are lightly insulated from each other with the main slot insulation embracing them all (fig. 4.4).

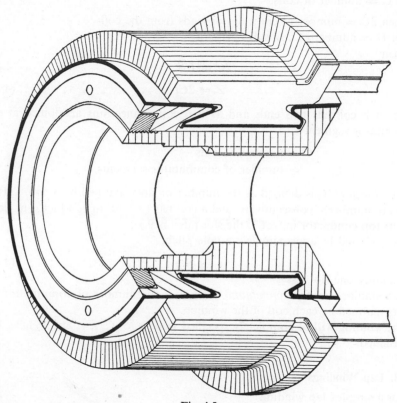

Fig. 4.5

4.1.1. The Commutator

The commutator is a cylinder at one end of the armature formed by a large number of copper segments insulated from each other, and from the shaft, by thin mica or micanite sheets and clamped together by insulated end rings.

For special high-speed operation a dove-tailed method of construction may be used.   Each segment forms the junction between two armature coils, the wires being soldered into milled slots at the end of the segment; or, with large machines, flat strip connectors known as commutator risers are used forming clip connections to the armature conductor bars (fig. 4.5).   Current enters and leaves the armature by means of carbon brushes mounted in insulated brush holders fixed to the frame of the machine, the brushes riding on the surface of the commutator.

4.1.2. Winding Symbols and Rules

Let p = number of poles,
   S = number of slots,
and Z = total number of conductors.

The conductors are first arranged in coils.
Let t = number of turns per coil
and C = number of coils.

Then $2C$ = number of coil sides or leads from the coils.
Let U = number of coil sides per slot.
Then

$$2C = US \qquad . \quad . \quad . \quad . \quad . \quad . \quad . \quad (4.2)$$

and

$$Z = 2Ct \quad . \quad . \quad . \quad . \quad . \quad . \quad . \quad (4.3)$$

Since each coil has two ends and as two coil connections are joined at each commutator segment—

$$C = \text{number of coils}$$
$$= \text{number of commutator segments.}$$

The *slot pitch* y_s is defined as the number of slots spanned by a coil. (If the slots are numbered consecutively, and a coil has its bottom conductor in slot 10 and its top conductor in slot 1, the slot pitch is 9.)

As y_s should be approximately a pole pitch,

$$y_s \simeq S/p \quad . \quad . \quad . \quad . \quad . \quad . \quad (4.4)$$

(commonly one slot less).

In a similar way the *commutator pitch* y_c is the number of commutator segments spanned by each coil of the winding.

The winding will be completely specified when p, S, C, t, y_s and y_c have been determined.

4.1.3. Lap Windings

For a simplex lap winding

$$y_s \simeq S/p \quad . \quad . \quad . \quad . \quad . \quad . \quad (4.5)$$

and

$$y_c = 1 \quad . \quad . \quad . \quad . \quad . \quad . \quad (4.6)$$

The ends of any coil are thus brought out to adjacent segments, and the result of this method of connection is that all the coils of the armature are in sequence with the last coil connected to the first, thus forming a closed loop.

Example of Lap Winding. Fig. 4.6 shows such a winding in diagrammatic form. It represents a four-pole machine with 24 slots and 24 single-turn coils. (A practical winding would have more slots and still more conductors; small numbers have been used in this example for clarity.)

The conductors are shown in sectional elevation together with the connections in the overhang by adopting the following conventions. Connections at the commutator, or front, end of the armature are shown inside the armature circumference, and back-end connections are shown outside, full lines being used for top conductors and chain lines for bottom conductors.

For this winding: $p = 4$, $S = 24$, $C = 24$, $U = 2$, $t = 1$, $y_s = 24/4 = 6$ and $y_c = 1$.

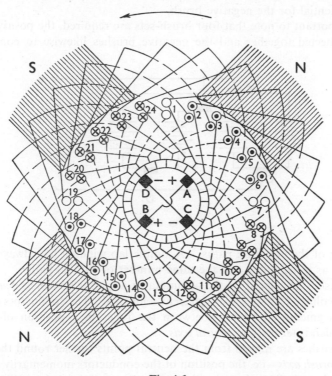

Fig. 4.6

Thus the top conductor of slot 1 is connected at the back of the armature to the bottom conductor of slot 7 forming a turn, and the ends of the coil are brought out to adjacent segments. The next coil in slots 2 and 8 is connected between the second of these segments and the next, with the result that the coils are in series. So the winding proceeds until all the coils are connected.

Direction of E.M.F. Entering the winding at slot 1 and proceeding round the winding we first pass through inactive conductors, but at slot 2 we find we are travelling against the e.m.f. and continue to do so for some time until we have completed one-quarter of the winding. At slot 8 the e.m.f. reverses in direction for the next quarter of the winding and so on.

The winding can thus be represented by an equivalent battery diagram consisting of four groups of cells in series (fig. 4.7).

Although the actual conductors move forward, this battery diagram always refers to the conductors under the poles, that is, it remains fixed in space. To use these batteries to deliver current to a load we must arrange connections at A, B, C and D, and we thus have four groups of cells in parallel. It must be emphasised that the tappings A, B, C and D must be fixed relative to the battery diagram, i.e. fixed in space, and that is the function of the brushgear and commutator.

Although the individual armature conductors pass around, the tapping is always made at the point of highest potential for the positive brush and at the lowest potential for the negative brush.

It is important to note that four brush-sets are required, the positive brushes being connected together and the negative brushes likewise to complete the

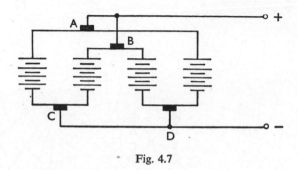

Fig. 4.7

paralleling of the armature paths. A simple lap winding has always as many brush-sets as it has poles, and the same number of parallel paths.

The brushes are placed on the commutator at points known as *neutral points* where no voltage exists between adjacent segments. The conductors connected to those segments lie midway between the poles in a position of zero flux density which is termed the *neutral axis*.

If the brushes are moved from the neutral points further round the commutator, the *brush axis*—i.e. the position of the conductors momentarily connected to the brushes—will not be coincident with the neutral axis but will differ by a small angle known as the *brush shift* forward or backward according to the direction of rotation.

4.1.4. Wave Windings

If, as an alternative to using a commutator pitch $y_c = 1$ and so producing a lap winding (fig. 4.8 (a)), a commutator pitch approximately equal to twice the pole pitch is used, then coils under consecutive pole pairs will be joined together in series thereby adding together their e.m.f.s (fig. 4.8 (b)).

After one circuit of the armature, the winding must not close on itself but progress to the conductor adjacent to the first and so connect up another set of coils in another circuit of the armature, continuing in this way until the winding is complete.

This type of winding is called a wave winding from the appearance of the end connections. To permit this progression a limit has to be placed on the value of C the number of commutator segments. If $y_c.p/2$ is equal to C the winding will close on itself in the first circuit of the armature and so, to connect to the adjacent conductor,

$$y_c.p/2 = C \pm 1 \quad . \quad . \quad . \quad . \quad . \quad (4.7)$$

As the values of y_c and C are necessarily integral it follows that the choice of a suitable value for C is restricted.

For example if $p = 6$, C may be 239 or 241 with $y_c = 80$, or 242 or 244 with $y_c = 81$, but 240 or 243 segments will not give a suitable winding.

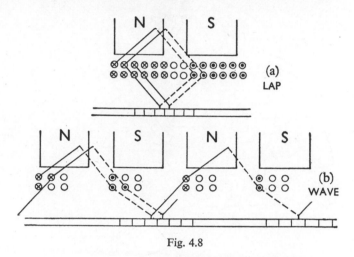

Fig. 4.8

Example of Wave Winding. The winding of fig. 4.9 has $p = 4$, $C = S = 21$, $U = 2$ and $t = 1$. The slot pitch $y_s \simeq 21/4 = 5$, with conductors 1 and 6 forming the first coil the ends of which are connected to segments **a** and **b**.

From equation (4.7)

$$y_c.2 = 21 \pm 1$$

$$y_c = 10 \text{ or } 11.$$

Both these commutator pitches will give a satisfactory winding, 10 being chosen in this example. The second coil to be connected is the coil in slots 11 and 16, and thus we see that between adjacent segments **a** and **c** there are $p/2$ coils. (If $y_c = 11$ had been chosen the segment **c** would have been on the other side of **a**.)

Tracing out the winding in the way in which it was done for the lap winding, at the same time observing the directions of conductor e.m.f., we find that the direction does not change until half the conductors have been connected, and therefore the e.m.f. diagram shows that the armature has only two paths in parallel (fig. 4.10).

Whereas a lap winding has as many paths as poles, a simplex-wave winding has only two parallel paths irrespective of the number of poles.

Only two brushes are essential for a wave winding, but brushes are usually placed in each neutral axis to give adequate contact area without having to use a very long commutator. The position and polarity of the brushes are shown in fig. 4.9.

Dummy Coils. A certain additional difficulty occasionally arises in the choice of C for a wave winding.

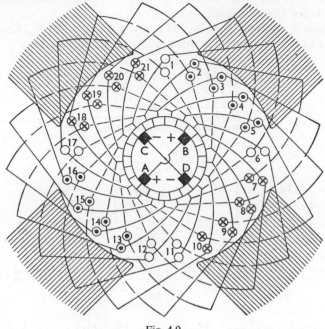

Fig. 4.9

In equation (4.7)

$$y_c \cdot p/2 = C \pm 1 \qquad \ldots \ldots \quad (4.7)$$

if p is 4 or a multiple of 4, then C must be odd.

But at the same time the value of C is governed by equation (4.2)

$$C = US/2 \qquad \ldots \ldots \quad (4.2)$$

U cannot at the same time be a multiple of 4 for this would make C an even

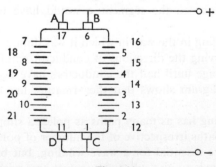

Fig. 4.10

number. (Making $U = 6$ will solve this difficulty but may not lead to a satisfactory number of slots.) On occasion, therefore, to overcome this difficulty the coils $C' = US/2$ placed in the slots are not all connected to the commutator. One coil has its ends cut short and insulated and is known as a dummy coil. The number of commutator segments and active coils is then

$$C = US/2 - 1$$

leading to a suitable commutator pitch. The use of dummy coils involves a slight asymmetry in the winding and should be avoided if possible.

4.1.5. Multiplex Windings

For most purposes simplex-lap or simplex-wave windings are employed, but occasionally a more complicated connection known as a multiplex winding may be desirable. The sole purpose of such a winding is to increase the number of parallel paths enabling the armature to carry a large total current, at the same time reducing the conductor current to improve commutation conditions. In the case of a ten-pole machine, using simplex windings, the designer is restricted to either two circuits (wave) or ten circuits (lap). The intermediate number of four circuits produced by a duplex-wave winding might prove to be a more suitable alternative.

A multiplex winding is also useful on occasion if a stock machine has to be rewound for a different voltage.

Duplex-lap Doubly Closed. This consists of two simplex-lap windings interleaved, and is obtained by making y_c equal to 2 provided that C is an even number. Since the two parts form two quite separate closed loops, the winding is termed *doubly closed*. The brushes must however cover at least three segments so that the two halves are always paralleled.

The windings will not be separate if C is odd and the winding is then termed *Duplex-lap singly closed.*

(If $C = 99$ and $y_c = 2$, the segments are connected as follows: 1–3–5 . . . 97–99–2–4 . . . 96–98–1.)

A multiplex-lap winding having m parallel sections (and a total number of parallel paths mp) is produced by making $y_c = m$. The number of closed loops is the highest common factor of m and C.

Multiplex-wave Windings. Multiplex-wave windings are obtained in a similar manner. If the equation (4.7) is modified to become

$$y_c.p/2 = C \pm 2 \qquad . \qquad . \qquad . \qquad . \qquad . \qquad (4.8)$$

a duplex-wave winding results with four parallel circuits.

For a multiplex-wave winding ($2m$ circuits),

$$y_c.p/2 = C \pm m \qquad . \qquad . \qquad . \qquad . \qquad . \qquad (4.9)$$

4.2. The E.M.F. Equation of a D.C. Machine

Let p = number of poles,
   a = number of parallel paths in the armature winding,
   ϕ = flux per pole (webers),
   N = speed (r.p.m.)
and Z = total number of armature conductors.

In one revolution the total flux cut by a single conductor

$$= \phi p \qquad \qquad \text{(4.10)}$$

The average rate of cutting flux (flux cut per second), which is therefore the average value of the generated e.m.f. in each conductor,

$$= \phi p \cdot N/60 \qquad \qquad \text{(4.11)}$$

In each of the parallel circuits between the brushes the number of conductors in series

$$= Z/a \qquad \qquad \text{(4.12)}$$

The total voltage between brushes, i.e. the generated e.m.f. of the machine,

$$E = (\phi p \cdot N/60)(Z/a)$$
$$= (p/a)(\phi N Z/60) \qquad \qquad \text{(4.13)}$$

4.3. Equipotential Connectors

It has been shown that the armature circuits in a lap winding of a multipolar machine are paralleled through the brushgear (fig. 4.7). Hence if slight differences occur in the generated e.m.f. in the parallel branches, relatively large circulating currents will be set up since armature resistance is small. These

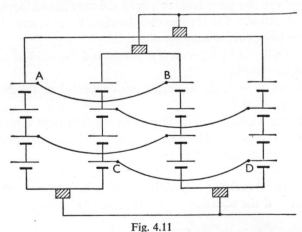

Fig. 4.11

currents, flowing through the brushes, result in considerable inequality of brush-arm currents, give rise to I^2R losses in the winding on no load, add to the losses on full load, both in the winding and in the brushes, and also introduce commutation difficulties. The differential e.m.f.s are due to variations in pole flux which are caused by small differences in air-gap lengths due to inaccurate registering of the bearings with the centre of the yoke, differences in the field coils or defects in castings.

Now, if the winding has an integral number of slots per pole pair, the winding is divided into $p/2$ symmetrical parts. Conductors separated by a double pole pitch should normally be at the same potential (fig. 4.11) and may thus be joined permanently by connections known as equipotential connectors. These take the form of rings at the back end of the armature under the overhang with tee-connections to the conductors at the coil noses. Alternatively, they may be arranged in a system of evolutes like the overhang of the main winding connected at the back of the commutator risers (fig. 4.12).

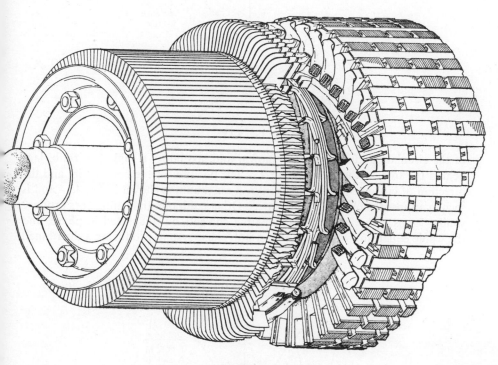

Fig. 4.12

In fig. 4.11 two such connectors are shown at AB and CD. The paralleling of the armature paths is thus completed internally, and although differential flux will still produce circulating currents, these currents flowing in AB and CD will no longer cause unequal brush-arm currents.

It will now be shown that the presence of these circulating currents through the equipotential connectors tend to diminish the out-of-balance fluxes, and the connections are therefore rightly called an *equalising winding*. In the four-pole machine of fig. 4.13 we will assume that the top N pole is stronger than the opposite N pole. The unbalance can be regarded as a superimposed two-pole field on the four-pole system as shown.

Two coils AC and BD are shown, separated by two pole pitches. We will assume that the maximum number of equipotential connectors have been used and consequently A will have been connected to B, and C to D. The figure-eight loop so produced has little resistance and is mainly reactive. Now the e.m.f. generated in the conductors as they cut this two-pole flux is shown in fig. 4.14, the total e.m.f. round the loop being the sum of these curves. The wave-form

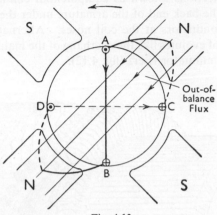

Fig. 4.13

of the circulating current is also shown, and, assuming a high L/R ratio, lags behind the total voltage wave by $\pi/2$. The position of the conductors and the direction of current when the current is a maximum is shown in fig. 4.14 and is seen to oppose the out-of-balance flux. Other equipotential connectors produce similar loops with similar a.c. circulating currents but displaced in phase, and the whole equalising winding is thus a polyphase system producing a distributed

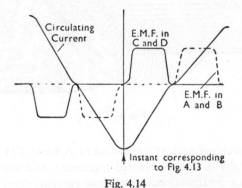

Fig. 4.14

m.m.f. wave whose axis is directed in the direction of the coil chosen by way of illustration.

This result could have been inferred from the *theorem of constant flux linkages*. If we assume the pair of coils and the equipotential connections to be resistance-less, then it is not possible for there to be any change of flux linking them as induced currents would be set up to prevent the change. Thus any two-pole flux, which would necessarily produce changing flux linkages with the coils as the armature rotates, cannot exist.

It is also interesting to observe that flux tends to be equalised in any machine having four poles even if equipotential connectors are not used. In fig. 4.15 (a) again the top right-hand N pole is assumed strong and the opposite one weak. The currents produced by the out-of-balance two-pole flux, i.e. the superimposed

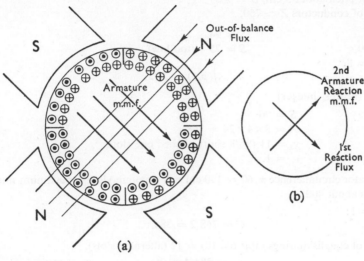

Fig. 4.15

circulating currents flowing around the armature and through the brush connections, will be as shown.

The m.m.f. axis of these currents is directed along the other pair of poles and these will also produce two-pole flux at right angles to the first.

Again we have circulating currents in the armature producing a second armature reaction at right angles (fig. 4.15 (b)). This second reaction opposes the original out-of-balance flux.

4.3.1. Rules for Equipotential Connectors

The number of slots per pole pair must be integral,

$$S/(p/2) = \text{integer} \quad . \quad . \quad . \quad . \quad . \quad (4.14)$$

The equipotential pitch y_{eq}, which is the distance in coils or segments between conductors connected to the same ring, must be integral, thus

$$y_{eq} = C/(p/2) \quad . \quad . \quad . \quad . \quad . \quad . \quad (4.15)$$

The phase pitch y_{ph}, which is the distance between conductors connected to adjacent rings, is usually integral though this is not an essential condition.

For symmetry

$$y_{ph} \text{ (number of rings)} = y_{eq} \quad . \quad . \quad . \quad . \quad (4.16)$$

EXAMPLE

An eight-pole, 100-kW, 440-V d.c. generator has an armature diameter of 85 cm and a commutator diameter of 60 cm. The total number of armature conductors is approximately 750. Choose a suitable winding and find (a) the number of slots, (b) the slot pitch, (c) the commutator pitch, (d) the equaliser pitch and number of equalising rings.

Armature circumference $\pi D = \pi.85 = 265$ cm.
For a slot pitch about 3 cm, $S \simeq 90$.
Number of conductors $Z \simeq 750$.

If $U = 8$,	$S = 94$.
$U = 10$,	$S = 75$ (too low).
Take $U = 8$.	

$$S/(p/2) = 23\cdot5.$$

Take 24 (nearest integer)

Therefore $S = 96$.
$$Z = 8 \times 4 \times 24 = 768.$$
$y_s = 11$ (96/8 short pitched one slot).
$y_c = 1$.

Commutator circumference $\pi.60 = 190$ cm will accommodate a maximum number of segments about 400.

Take $t = 1$:
$$C = 768/2 = 384.$$

Number of equalising rings (approx. 10) = 12 (alternate slots).
$$y_{eq} = 384/4 = 96.$$
$$y_{ph} = 96/12 = 8.$$

4.4. A.C. Windings

4.4.1. Generation of E.M.F.

The value of the e.m.f. generated in a winding can be determined in other ways. It is therefore worth while reviewing the simple lap and wave windings of the previous section, and examining the a.c. voltage generated in each conductor. Consider first the case of a simple two-pole lap winding in which the flux is sinusoidally distributed, that is to say, the flux density is a maximum at the centre of the pole falling to zero at the neutral axis in accordance with a sine wave.

Thus in fig. 4.16 the value of the flux density normal to the armature surface at the point P is given by

$$B_p = B \sin \theta \qquad \qquad (4.17)$$

Let $\omega =$ angular velocity of the armature (radians per second),
          $D_a =$ armature diameter
and $L_c =$ core length or length of conductor.

The e.m.f. in the conductor at P is given by equation (4.1).

Hence $e_p = B_p L_c u$
                         $= B \sin \theta L_c \omega (D_a/2)$

and since $\theta = \omega t$,

$$e_p = B\omega (L_c D_a/2) \sin \omega t \qquad \qquad (4.18)$$

which is a sinusoidal function of time, in other words, an alternating voltage. The numerical value of the voltage will be the same in all the conductors and the frequency will be the same, but the voltages will differ in phase. Conductor Q meets the flux ϕ degrees in advance of conductor P, hence

$$e_Q = B\omega L_c(D_a/2) \sin(\omega t + \phi) \quad . \quad . \quad . \quad . \quad (4.19)$$

At the instant shown in fig. 4.16 the e.m.f. of conductor **a** is zero, whereas **b** is in its maximum position, **c** is again zero, **d** at negative maximum and so on.

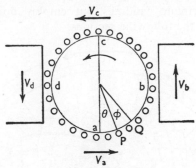

Fig. 4.16

The vectors corresponding to these voltages are shown in the figure and the vectors for the intermediate conductors obviously lie at intermediate angles.

The angle of advance due to a slot pitch

$$= \pi p/S \text{ radians} \quad . \quad . \quad . \quad . \quad . \quad (4.20)$$

Now when all the conductors are joined in series, as they are in a lap winding, the vectors form a regular polygon, which, in the limit, becomes a circle for a uniformly distributed winding (fig. 4.17).

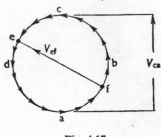

Fig. 4.17

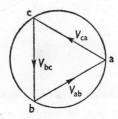

Fig. 4.18

Tapping points on the winding at **e** and **f** brought out via slip-rings thus provide a voltage whose vector is **ef** the diameter of the circle. In this way the ring winding can be used for an alternator.

The function of the commutator and brushgear is to maintain contact with the winding at the points **a** and **c** fixed in space. The voltage between the commutator brushes thus always corresponds to the vertical vector, that is, the vector in its maximum value position. The d.c. voltage at the commutator is thus equal to the maximum value of the a.c. voltage produced between diametrical tappings and is therefore $\sqrt{2}$ times the r.m.s. a.c. voltage.

The simple lap winding of fig. 4.16 can also be used to provide a three-phase supply. This is obtained by arranging three symmetrical tappings **a, b** and **c** (fig. 4.18), when the voltages V_{ab}, V_{bc} and V_{cd} will be as shown, the winding being in effect a delta-connected source. It is necessary that the number of slots per pole pair shall be divisible by 3. The windings of synchronous converters are of this type, six- and even twelve-phase connections being obtained by using more tappings. Conventional alternators and induction motors, however, do not usually have closed-circuit windings but employ double- and single-layer windings as shown in the following sections.

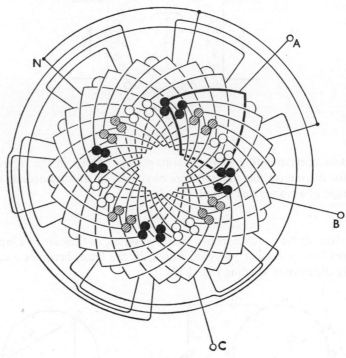

Fig. 4.19

4.4.2. Double-layer Windings for Three-phase

In this type of winding a double-layer lap or wave winding is first arranged precisely in accordance with the rules laid down for the d.c. machine. The slot pitch of each coil is approximately equal to a pole pitch, and adjacent coils are connected in series. The winding is then separated into six equal sections by removing six of the clips between coils. This has to be done for each pole pair in the lap case and presupposes that the total number of slots per pole is divisible by 3. (The possibility of using a fractional number of slots per pole per phase will be discussed later in Section 7.1.7.)

With a wave winding, provided C is a multiple of 6, six symmetrical sections will be obtained by removing six clips only irrespective of the number of poles.

The coil groups are known as phase bands, and these are shown together with their voltage vectors in the two-pole diagram of fig. 4.21.

Each phase is then completed by connecting together phase bands separated by a pole pitch, taking care to see that adjacent poles are connected in opposition. In fig. 4.21 connections link a_2a_4, b_2b_4 and c_2c_4, hence it will be seen that the

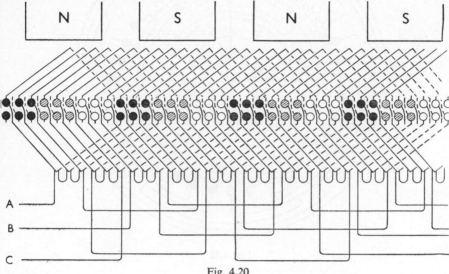

Fig. 4.20

voltages $V_{a_1a_3}$, $V_{b_1b_3}$ and $V_{c_1c_3}$ make a balanced three-phase system. The phase bands are usually connected in series, but parallel connections are possible for low-voltage heavy-current machines.

In fig. 4.19 is shown a winding diagram of a four-pole double-layer winding with two slots per pole per phase. The coils shown are fully pitched, but the

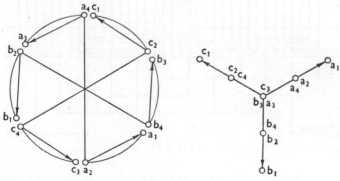

Fig. 4.21

span may be reduced with advantage. Each phase band has two coils in series and the interconnections between the phase bands are clearly shown. The start and finish of a phase can be arranged at any suitable gap between phase bands.

Fig. 4.20 is a developed diagram showing the connections of the coils for a multipolar machine with three slots per pole per phase.

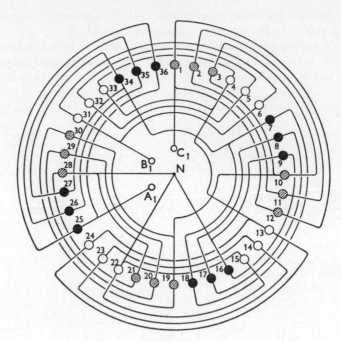

Fig. 4.22

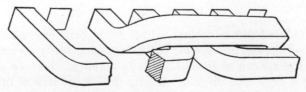

Fig. 4.23

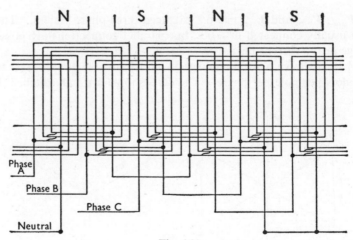

Fig. 4.24

4.4.3. Single-layer Windings

In this arrangement rectangular coils are generally though not necessarily used. Fig. 4.22 shows a winding with three slots per pole per phase.

The conductors of slot 3 and slot 10 form a coil, similarly slots 2 and 11, and also 1 and 12. The three coils fit outside each other and are termed concentric coils. These coils are connected in series and are the whole of the conductors of phase A in the first pole pair. Phases B and C are treated similarly. The main difficulty is the arrangement of the conductors in the overhang where a cross-over of the coils is needed. This is overcome by arranging the overhang in two tiers, bending one side of each coil so that it is lifted to pass over the intermediate conductors.

Fig. 4.24 shows the arrangement of the tiers. Coils forming the top tier on one side of the stator lie in the bottom tier on the other side. In the developed diagram, fig. 4.23, the top tier has been shown extended beyond the bottom for clarity.

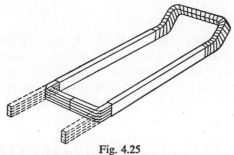

Fig. 4.25

When winding six-, ten- or fourteen-pole machines a special set of cranked coils is necessary in one place where coils pass from the top tier at one side to the bottom tier at the other.

Comparing the two types of winding, single-layer coils can be arranged in semi-closed slots (the coil is opened and pushed in the slots from one side, the coils then being reformed and reconnected by butt-welding, fig. 4.25).

Different sizes of former-wound coils are needed, but the slot has a better space factor. The end winding is more difficult to brace but gives better ventilation.

Double-layer windings are usually in open slots introducing more tooth ripple and pole-face loss, but their great advantage is that short chording and fractional slots may be used. The coils are all alike and the actual winding process is simpler.

4.5. The Magnetomotive Force of Distributed Windings

It is important to be able to determine the value of the flux produced by current in distributed windings and to find the manner in which flux density varies over the circumference of the core.

The air-gap, in the case of the induction motor, the round-rotor alternator, and many of the commutator machines, is uniform, except for the slotting, and consequently the permeance of this gap does not vary from point to point around the periphery.

But with other machines, the d.c. machine and the salient-pole alternator, though one side of the gap is plain, the other side consists of two regions: (a) the pole arc where the gap length is small, and (b) the interpolar arc, where the gap may be considered infinite.

There is a third class of machine in which there is saliency on both sides of the gap—the inductor alternator.

Now, in the first case, the uniform-gap machine, the variation of flux density over the armature periphery depends only on the distribution of the magneto-motive force of the windings.

With machines of the second class, the distribution of m.m.f. must first be found and then due allowance made for the variation of permeance.

It is necessary therefore to study first the m.m.f. produced by different winding arrangements.

4.5.1. M.M.F. Distribution Diagrams

Single Conductors spaced One Pole Pitch. In fig. 4.26 single conductors are shown each carrying a current I alternately in opposite directions, the spacing being the pole pitch τ. This corresponds to single coils, lap or wave connected.

Now if each conductor is considered to be divided into two parts, each carrying a current $I/2$, the winding can be described as a series of flat coils in the

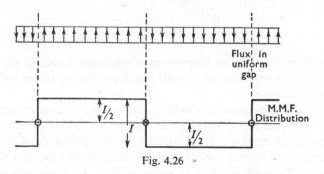

Fig. 4.26

centre of which the ampere-turns or the m.m.f. is $I/2$. Over the centre portion of the coil this m.m.f. is uniform and its direction changes from one coil to the next. The m.m.f. distribution diagram is thus a series of rectangles, the m.m.f. remaining constant between conductors and changing by the value of the conductor current from one side of the conductor to the other.

Distributed Winding—Isolated Coils. Fig. 4.27 shows three sets of conductors similar to those of the previous diagram overlapping each other, there being one conductor every 60°. The m.m.f. diagrams similarly overlap, and the total m.m.f. wave will thus be a stepped wave as shown. This may be traced by starting at conductor A which is the centre of the group and moving to the right, noting how the m.m.f. changes at each conductor by the amount of current in it.

Distributed Winding—Uniformly Spread. When there is a large number of coils, instead of the m.m.f. wave being stepped, a smooth transition may be assumed, and the diagram becomes triangular as shown in fig. 4.28. The maximum value of the m.m.f.—the apex of the triangle—will be $\Sigma I/2$, ΣI being the sum of the currents in the conductors spread over one pole.

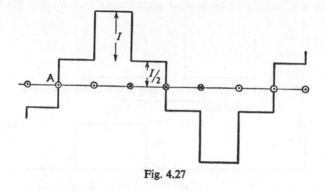

Fig. 4.27

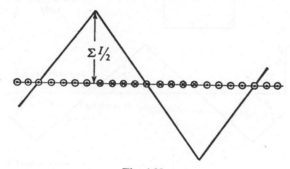

Fig. 4.28

Distributed Winding—Limited Spread. If the conductors only occupy a portion of the armature surface, the m.m.f. wave will be trapezoidal (fig. 4.29). This type of distribution is to be found with the rotor winding of a round-rotor alternator. Another example is that due to the instantaneous current in a single phase of an alternator stator winding.

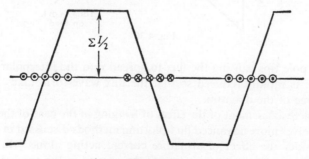

Fig. 4.29

4.5.2. Flux Wave-form of D.C. Machine

We are now in a position to build up the pattern of the flux wave-form of a d.c. generator on load. In fig. 4.30 (a) we have first the effect of the m.m.f. due to the field winding acting alone, which is the condition on no load. The field m.m.f. is a rectangular distribution, and this, combined with the uniform gap over the pole arc, results in an almost rectangular flux wave. Fringing takes

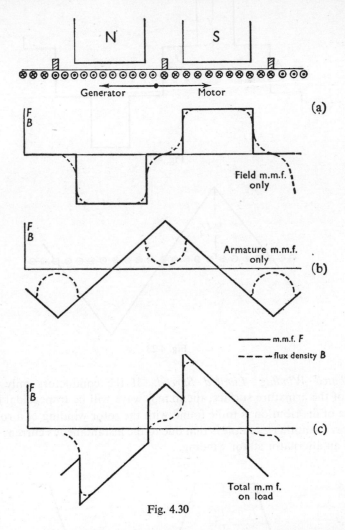

Fig. 4.30

place at the pole tips causing the flux to spread into the interpolar-arc, but the density there is rapidly reduced so that the flux wave-form takes the shape of the dotted line of the diagram.

The complete assessment of the effect of fringing in the case of the salient-pole machine involves more advanced flux-plotting methods discussed in Appendix B.

Now consider the effect of armature current acting alone. In spite of the rotation of the armature, the direction of the current in the conductors between the brushes under a given pole at any instant is the same; in other words the m.m.f. distribution remains fixed relative to the poles, and since the winding is distributed this m.m.f. wave will be triangular similar to that of fig. 4.28 (b).

It will be noted that the m.m.f. axis coincides with the brush axis, but though the m.m.f. here is a maximum, the flux at that point will be small since this is the region of the interpolar-arc. The dotted line in fig. 4.30 (b) again shows the flux wave-form.

Now, adding the two m.m.f. waves together and taking into account the variations of permeance of the gap, fig. 4.30 (c) shows the resultant of the main field and armature current together, this being the flux wave for the machine on load.

The armature m.m.f. is referred to as *armature reaction* and it is observed that, provided the brushes are situated at the neutral points, the result is a cross-magnetisation of the machine weakening one pole tip and strengthening the other. Granted symmetry, the total flux of the pole should be unchanged although the wave-form is distorted. There is, however, a tendency for one of the pole tips, and the teeth under it, to become saturated, which results in a slight reduction of the total flux.

The relation between the direction of armature current and the polarity of the main poles used in fig. 4.30 corresponds to the case of a generator with anti-clockwise rotation or of a motor with clockwise rotation.

The distortion of the field due to armature reaction may be summarised as follows for the two cases:

	Leading pole tip	Trailing pole tip
Generator	Weakened	Strengthened
Motor	Strengthened	Weakened

4.5.3. Three-phase Distributed Winding—60° Spread

The next case to be illustrated is the instantaneous m.m.f. pattern due to a three-phase distributed winding of the single-layer type previously described (p. 87). Each phase consists of a phase band of conductors under one pole spread over 60 electrical degrees forming coils by connection with a similar band of conductors 180° displaced, that is, under the next pole (fig. 4.22). In fig. 4.31 the three phases have been separated and the direction of current in the conductors shown illustrates in each case the conditions when the current in that phase is at its maximum positive value.

It will be seen that each diagram corresponds to case 4 (fig. 4.29), and the m.m.f. wave due to each current will be trapezoidal. The height of each trapezium increases and decreases with time according to the instantaneous value of the current.

Before the individual m.m.f. waves can be added together we must remind ourselves of the relation between the instantaneous values of the three-phase currents. Choosing the instant when the current in phase A is at its maximum positive value (fig. 4.31 (b)), the vector diagram of the three currents will be as shown for standard phase sequence from which it is noticed that the instantaneous value of the currents i_b and i_c will be negative and equal to $i_a/2$.

$$i_a = \sqrt{2}.I \quad . \quad . \quad . \quad . \quad . \quad . \quad . \quad (4.21)$$

$$i_b = i_c = -I/\sqrt{2} \quad . \quad . \quad . \quad . \quad . \quad (4.22)$$

These directions are now drawn in the conductor diagram and to illustrate

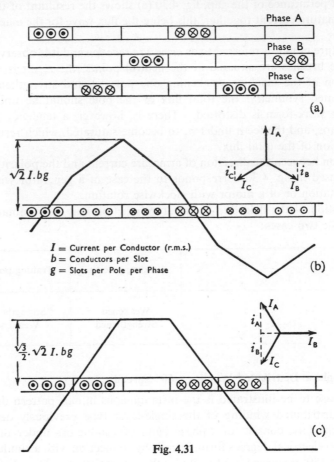

I = Current per Conductor (r.m.s.)
b = Conductors per Slot
g = Slots per Pole per Phase

Fig. 4.31

relative magnitudes smaller circles have been used for B and C. The axis of symmetry is seen to pass through the centre of phase band A, so, starting from that point, the ampere conductors are counted as we move to the right, and the m.m.f. is totalled as shown.

One-twelfth of a cycle later the current vectors will have advanced by 30° and the instantaneous currents are

$$i_a = -i_c = (\sqrt{3}/2)(\sqrt{2}.I)$$

and

$$i_b = 0 \quad . \quad . \quad . \quad . \quad . \quad . \quad . \quad (4.23)$$

These currents and their directions are shown in the conductor diagram and the m.m.f. wave is seen to be trapezoidal (fig. 4.31 (c)).

In comparing fig. 4.31 (b) with fig. 4.31 (c) the most important fact to be noticed is that the wave has moved forward by one-sixth of a pole pitch. If a diagram is drawn when the vectors have advanced a further 30°, i_c will be at a negative maximum and hence the diagram will revert to that of fig. 4.31 (b) but will be displaced by a further one-sixth pole pitch.

It is evident therefore that the m.m.f. wave advances at synchronous speed, one double pole pitch per cycle.

The shape of the wave changes a little between the limits of the two extreme forms shown, but it can be demonstrated that each shape consists mainly of the same fundamental sine-wave component, the difference being accounted for by

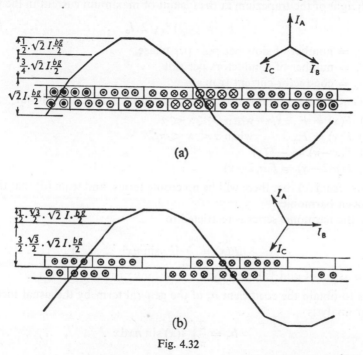

(a)

(b)

Fig. 4.32

the presence of smaller sine waves of shorter pole pitch which are known as *space harmonics*. These harmonics advance at their own synchronous speeds— one double pole pitch per cycle—and in some cases the direction of rotation is opposite to that of the fundamental. This accounts for the changing appearance of the total wave shape. Fourier analysis shows the magnitude of the fundamental sine wave to be

$$i = (4/\pi)(\sqrt{2}.I)(bg/2)(3k/2) \quad . \quad . \quad . \quad . \quad (4.24)$$

where I = current per conductor,
$\quad b$ = conductors per slot,
$\quad g$ = slots per pole per phase
and $\quad k$ = winding spread factor.

In fig. 4.32 (a) and (b) the m.m.f. diagrams are drawn for a double-layer winding which has been short-chorded by one-sixth. The second layer of conductors is thus displaced by the short-chording as shown. By comparison with the previous m.m.f. diagrams, it is seen that short-chording has also gone a long way to reduce the space harmonics and the waves are seen to resemble the fundamental sine wave much more closely.

4.6. Harmonic Analysis of M.M.F. Distribution of Three-phase Winding

The m.m.f. distribution, due to each phase, shown to be trapezoidal (fig. 4.33) can be represented by a Fourier series of sinusoidal waves as follows.

The height of the trapezium at the instant of maximum current in the phase is

$$F_m = (g/2)Z_s\sqrt{2}.I_c \quad \cdots \quad \cdots \quad (4.25)$$

where g = number of slots per pole per phase,

Z_s = number of conductors per slot

and I_c = conductor current (r.m.s.).

The function $F(x)$ representing the wave can be defined as follows:

(a) $F(x) = F_m . x/\alpha$ when $0 < x < \alpha$
(b) $F(x) = F_m$ when $\alpha < x < \pi/2$
(c) $F(x-\pi) = -F(x)$
(d) $F(\pi/2-x) = F(\pi/2+x)$

It follows from (c) that there will be no cosine terms, and from (d) that there will be no even harmonics.

Thus the harmonic series is restricted to

$$F(x) = \sum_{n=1}^{n=\infty} [b_n \sin nx] \quad \cdots \quad \cdots \quad (4.26)$$

where n assumes odd values only.

Thus to obtain the coefficient b_n of the general term by the usual methods of Fourier analysis

$$b_n = \frac{2}{\pi}\int_0^\pi f(x) \sin nx dx \quad \cdots \quad \cdots \quad (4.27)$$

and due to symmetry

$$b_n = \frac{4}{\pi}\int_0^{\pi/2} f(x) \sin nx dx \quad \cdots \quad \cdots \quad (4.28)$$

$$= \frac{4}{\pi\alpha}\int_0^\alpha F_m x \sin nx dx + \frac{4}{\pi}\int_\alpha^{\pi/2} F_m \sin nx dx$$

$$= \frac{4F_m}{\pi\alpha}\left\{\left[\frac{x(-\cos nx)}{n}\right]_0^\alpha + \int_0^\alpha \frac{\cos nx dx}{n}\right\} + \frac{4F_m}{\pi}\left[\frac{-\cos nx}{n}\right]_\alpha^{\pi/2}$$

$$= \frac{4F_m}{\alpha\pi}\left(\frac{-\alpha\cos n\alpha}{n} + \frac{\sin n\alpha}{n^2}\right) + \frac{4F_m}{\pi}\frac{\cos n\alpha}{n}$$

(n being odd)

$$= \frac{4F_m}{\pi\alpha n^2} \sin n\alpha \quad \cdots \quad \cdots \quad (4.29)$$

and putting $\alpha = \sigma/2$ we have (n being odd)

$$F = \frac{4F_m}{\pi}\left[\sum_{n=1}^{n=\infty}\frac{1}{n}\frac{\sin n\sigma/2}{n\sigma/2}\sin nx\right] \quad \cdots \quad (4.30)$$

The factor $(\sin n\sigma/2)/(n\sigma/2)$ will be recognised as $k_{s,n}$ the winding distribution factor for a uniformly distributed winding (equation (7.25)).

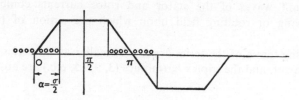

Fig. 4.33

Now in the three-phase distributed winding of fig. 4.31 the value of σ is $\pi/3$, the phases are displaced by $2\pi/3$ in space and the currents by $2\pi/3$ in time. The m.m.f. distribution of the three phases is thus

$$F_1 = \frac{4}{\pi}\{F_m \cos \omega t\}\left[\sum_{n=1}^{n=\infty}\frac{k_{w,n}}{n}\sin nx\right] \quad \cdots \quad (4.31)$$

$$F_2 = \frac{4}{\pi}\left\{F_m \cos\left(\omega t - \frac{2\pi}{3}\right)\right\}\left[\sum_{n=1}^{n=\infty}\frac{k_{w,n}}{n}\sin n\left(x - \frac{2\pi}{3}\right)\right] \quad \cdot \quad (4.32)$$

$$F_3 = \frac{4}{\pi}\left\{F_m \cos\left(\omega t - \frac{4\pi}{3}\right)\right\}\left[\sum_{n=1}^{n=\infty}\frac{k_{w,n}}{n}\sin n\left(x - \frac{4\pi}{3}\right)\right] \quad \cdot \quad (4.33)$$

The total m.m.f. of all three phases $F = F_1 + F_2 + F_3$ for which the nth harmonical term is

$$\frac{4}{\pi}\frac{F_m k_{w,n}}{n}\left[\begin{array}{l}\sin nx \cos \omega t + \sin n(x - 2\pi/3)\cos(\omega t - 2\pi/3)\\ \qquad + \sin n(x - 4\pi/3)\cos(\omega t - 4\pi/3)\end{array}\right]$$

$$= \frac{4}{2\pi}\frac{F_m k_{w,n}}{n}\left[\begin{array}{ll}\sin(nx - \omega t) & +\sin(nx + \omega t)\\ +\sin\{nx - \omega t - (n-1)(2\pi/3)\} & +\sin\{nx + \omega t - (n+1)(2\pi/3)\}\\ +\sin\{nx - \omega t - (n-1)(4\pi/3)\} & +\sin\{nx + \omega t - (n+1)(4\pi/3)\}\end{array}\right]$$

$$\qquad\qquad\qquad\qquad\qquad\qquad\qquad\qquad \cdots \cdots \quad (4.34)$$

Putting in turn $n = 1$, $n = 3$, $n = 5$, etc.,

$$F = \frac{3}{2}\frac{4}{\pi}F_m\left\{k_{w,1}\sin(x - \omega t) + \left(\frac{k_{w,5}}{5}\right)\sin(5x + \omega t) + \left(\frac{k_{w,7}}{7}\right)\sin(7x - \omega t) + \ldots\right\}$$

$$\qquad\qquad\qquad\qquad\qquad\qquad\qquad \cdots \cdots \quad (4.35)$$

or substituting for $k_{w,n}$

$$F = \frac{18F_m}{\pi^2}\left\{\sin(x - \omega t) + \left(\frac{1}{25}\right)\sin(5x + \omega t) - \left(\frac{1}{49}\right)\sin(7x - \omega t) + \ldots\right\} \quad (4.36)$$

The principal term of this series is $\sin(x - \omega t)$ which is a travelling or gliding wave (fig. 4.34).

At time $t = 0$ the distribution is sinusoidal as shown by the curve $y = \sin x$, but at a later instant t, $y = \sin (x - \omega t)$ which is a sine curve displaced from the former by the angle ωt.   This displacement increases uniformly with t, hence the wave moves forward with constant speed travelling a distance of two pole pitches per cycle.

This term is the main component of armature reaction in an alternator where it is seen to be advancing in step with the rotor field.   In an induction motor the m.m.f. waves of the stator and rotor currents combine to produce the moving or rotating field upon which the action of the machine depends.

The remaining terms of the series are much smaller as the series is seen to be rapidly convergent, and the triplex harmonics (3, 9, 15, etc.) are absent.

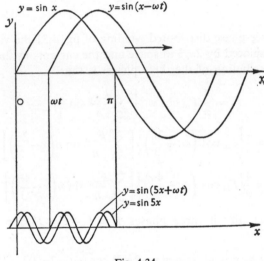

Fig. 4.34

The fifth harmonic term is $\sin (5x + \omega t)$.   Plotting this wave at $t = 0$ (fig. 4.34) we recognise it as a sinusoidally distributed field with *five times* as many poles as the fundamental field.

As t increases this field is seen to move *backwards* at a speed corresponding to two of its own pole pitches per cycle.

In the same way the term involving $n = 7$ has *seven times* the number of poles and moves *forward* at one-seventh the speed.

The series thus demonstrates the existence of multiple-field patterns superimposed, each moving with its own synchronous speed relative to the conductors.

The maximum amplitude of the fundamental wave

$$\hat{F}_1 = (3/2)(4/\pi)k_{\mathrm{w}}(gZ_{\mathrm{s}}/2)\sqrt{2}.I_{\mathrm{c}} \quad . \quad . \quad . \quad . \quad (4.37)$$

by equations (4.35) and (4.25).

The conductor current $I_c = I/a$, and the turns in series per phase

$$T = (gZ_s/2)(p/a) \quad . \quad . \quad . \quad . \quad . \quad . \quad (4.38)$$

Thus

$$(gZ_s/2)I_c = IT/p \quad . \quad . \quad . \quad . \quad . \quad . \quad (4.39)$$

the ampere-turns per pole per phase.

Hence

$$\hat{F}_1 = (3/2)(4/\pi)\sqrt{2}.k_w(IT/p)$$

$$= 2\cdot7k_w(IT/p) \text{ ampere-turns per pole} \quad . \quad . \quad . \quad (4.40)$$

CHAPTER 5

THE MAGNETIC CIRCUIT

5.1. Fundamental Principles

MAGNETIC-CIRCUIT problems arising in machines fall into two categories: (1) the assessment of the total ampere-turns on the main field windings required to produce the main gap flux, or the value of the magnetising current in the case of a transformer, and (2) the determination of the leakage fluxes due to individual winding currents. Such calculations are based on a series of approximations, and it is well if a brief revision of the fundamental principles is first made.

(a) The magnetic flux ϕ is a continuous function; magnetic lines cannot come to an abrupt end but form continuous loops around current.

(b) Flux density B varies from point to point in a field according to the manner in which the flux lines diverge. B also cannot change abruptly.

(c) Flux density B (Wb/m²) and magnetising force H (A/m) at a point are definitely related in any material. Experimentally derived B/H curves are available for various ferromagnetic materials.

For air,

$$H = 796\,000\,B \qquad . \quad . \quad . \quad . \quad (5.1)$$

(d) The line integral of H, that is, the integral of H taken around any complete line is equal to the current enclosed.

$$\oint H dl = \Sigma I \qquad . \quad . \quad . \quad . \quad . \quad (5.2)$$

To determine the precise value of ΣI which is necessary to produce given field conditions, the field should be plotted (*see* Appendix B) and the varying value of B determined along a flux line from which the corresponding value of H is found which must then be integrated.

If the plot of the field shows that the circuit can be divided into a number of sections in series, the value of B being reasonably constant within the individual sections, and if B_1 is constant over a length l_1, B_2 over l_2, etc., we shall have corresponding values H_1, H_2, H_3 and so on. The value of the integral $\oint H \cdot dl$ can then be found by simple summation:

$$I = \oint H dl = H_1 l_1 + H_2 l_2 + H_3 l_3 + \cdots \quad . \quad . \quad . \quad (5.3)$$
$$= F_1 + F_2 + F_3 + \cdots$$

This process corresponds to the finding of the total e.m.f. in an electric circuit problem by adding the voltage drops around a series circuit:

$$E = V_1 + V_2 + V_3 + \cdots \qquad . \quad . \quad . \quad . \quad (5.4)$$

In the magnetic circuit of the machine shown in fig. 5.1 the flux can be likened to the current in the electric circuit shown in fig. 5.2.   The ampere-turns of the coils are represented by the e.m.f. of the batteries and the values $H_1 l_1$, etc., by the voltage drops across the resistors.

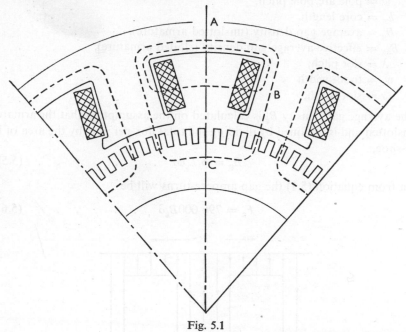

Fig. 5.1

From this it will be seen that just as there are two e.m.f.s associated with each loop and therefore each e.m.f. can be considered to be responsible for the current in half the circuit, so the m.m.f. of each field coil is equal to the sum of the Hl products along the line ABC from A to C.   This summation is made in tabular form to be shown later after the complication due to the leakage fluxes has been discussed.

The above circuit may be divided into the following sections: air-gap, poles, yoke, teeth and armature core.

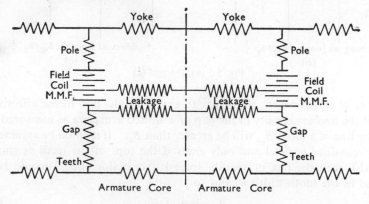

Fig. 5.2

5.1.1. The Air-gap

Let δ = radial length of the gap,
τ = pole pitch,
ψ = pole arc/pole pitch,
L_c = core length,
B_g = average gap density (unslotted armature),
B_{ag} = effective average gap density (slotted armature),
λ = slot pitch,
w_t = tooth width
and s = slot width.

The average gap density B_g is calculated on the assumption that the armature is unslotted and is obtained by dividing the total flux per pole by the area of the pole-shoe,

$$B_g = \phi/L_c\psi\tau \quad . \quad . \quad . \quad . \quad . \quad . \quad (5.5)$$

when from equation (5.1) the gap ampere-turns will be

$$F_g = 796\,000B_g\delta \quad . \quad . \quad . \quad . \quad . \quad . \quad (5.6)$$

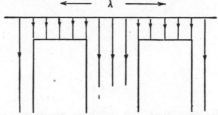

Neglecting the effect of slotting, B uniform
$B_{ag} = B_g$

(a)

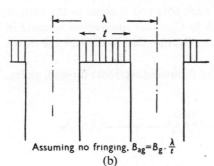

Assuming no fringing, $B_{ag} = B_g \cdot \dfrac{\lambda}{t}$

(b)

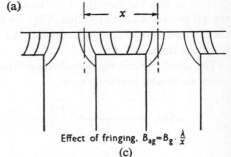

Effect of fringing, $B_{ag} = B_g \cdot \dfrac{\lambda}{x}$

(c)

Fig. 5.3 (a), (b) and (c)

The effect of the armature slotting is to cause a reduction in the effective gap area and the average density in the gap of a slotted armature as measured along the centre line of a tooth B_{ag} will be greater than B_g. If it could be assumed that the flux remained parallel and only entered the tops of the teeth as shown in fig. 5.3 (b), then the flux previously spread over a slot pitch λ would be concentrated in the tooth width w_t and so

$$B_{ag} = B_g.\lambda/w_t \quad . \quad . \quad . \quad . \quad . \quad (5.7)$$

A flux plot, made on the assumption that the iron surfaces are equipotentials, shows the tufted appearance of fig. 5.3 (c). B_{ag} will therefore not be quite as large as given by equation (5.7) but if the average width of the tuft is x

$$B_{ag} = B_g.\lambda/x \qquad . \quad . \quad . \quad . \quad . \quad (5.8)$$

where $x > w_t$.

It has been shown by Dr. F. W. Carter* that

$$x = w_t + fs \qquad . \quad . \quad . \quad . \quad . \quad . \quad (5.9)$$

where f is a function of the ratio slot width/gap length (s/δ) and this relationship is given by the curve in fig. 5.4 which Carter calculated.

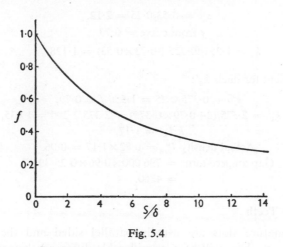

Fig. 5.4

Equation (5.7) thus becomes

$$B_{ag} = k_c B_g \qquad . \quad . \quad . \quad . \quad . \quad . \quad (5.10)$$

where

$$k_c = \lambda/(w_t + fs) \qquad . \quad . \quad . \quad . \quad . \quad (5.11)$$

k_c is known as *Carter's Air-gap Coefficient* and is obtained for any slotting and air-gap length by substitution in equation (5.11), first finding f from fig. 5.4 corresponding to the value of s/δ.

The effect of the ventilation ducts, which break up the stampings into packets, has a slight concentrating effect on the flux in the axial direction and so a second gap coefficient k_c' can be calculated treating the packets as teeth and the ducts as slots.

Summarising

$$B_g = \phi/L_c\psi\tau \qquad . \quad . \quad . \quad . \quad . \quad . \quad . \quad (5.5)$$

$$B_{ag} = k_c k_c' B_g \qquad . \quad . \quad . \quad . \quad . \quad . \quad (5.12)$$

and the air-gap ampere-turns

$$F_g = 796\,000 B_{ag}\delta \qquad . \quad . \quad . \quad . \quad . \quad (5.6a)$$

---

* J.I.E.E., Vol. 64, 1926, "The magnetic Field of the Dynamo-Electric Machine," F. W. Carter, M.A., Sc.D.

EXAMPLE

Find the ampere-turns required for the gap of a d.c. machine if:

$$\text{Apparent gap density } B_g = 0.82 \text{ Wb/m}^2$$
$$\delta = 0.25 \text{ in.}$$
$$w_t = 0.725$$
$$s = 0.53$$
$$\lambda = 1.255$$
$$\text{Width of packets} = 2.00$$
$$\text{Width of duct} = 0.375$$

Carter's coefficient for slotting k_c:

$$s/\delta = 0.53/0.25 = 2.12.$$
$$f \text{ from curve} = 0.73.$$
$$k_c = 1.255/(0.725 + 0.73 \times 0.53) = 1.128.$$

Carter's coefficient for ducts k_c':

$$s/\delta = 0.375/0.25 = 1.5; \quad f = 0.79.$$
$$k_c' = 2.375/(2 + 0.79 \times 0.375) = 2.375/2.295 = 1.035.$$
$$k_c k_c' = 1.17.$$
$$\text{Actual density } B_{ag} = 0.82 \times 1.17 = 0.96.$$
$$\text{Gap ampere-turns} = 796\,000 \times 0.96 \times 0.25/39.37$$
$$= 4860.$$

5.1.2. Armature Teeth

Since the armature slots are usually parallel sided and the teeth correspondingly tapered, there will be a considerable difference between the cross-sectional area of the teeth at the top and the bottom, particularly in a small machine.

It is consequently unsatisfactory to assume that B is uniform over the tooth portion of the magnetic circuit. The value of the tooth ampere-turns may be found graphically as follows.

Assuming in the first place that all the flux passes down the teeth and there is none in the slot then the value of B at various sections down the tooth is calculated. It is advisable to draw to scale one tooth and slot as shown in fig. 5.5.

The flux entering the tooth will be

$$\phi_t = B_g \lambda L_c \quad . \quad . \quad . \quad . \quad . \quad . \quad (5.13)$$

At point P where the tooth width is w_t, the density

$$B_t = \phi_t/w_t L_i = B_g(\lambda/w_t)(L_c/L_i) \quad . \quad . \quad . \quad (5.14)$$

where L_i is the nett iron length.

$$L_i = (L_c - \text{duct width})\,0.9 \quad . \quad . \quad . \quad (5.15)$$

0.9 being the *stacking factor* of the iron laminations.

The graph of B_t should then be plotted against distance from the bottom of the tooth, and from the B/H curve of the laminations the corresponding H values should also be plotted.   It will be noted that the H curve is a much more steeply rising graph.

Now since H is plotted against l the area under the graph should be measured and this will be $\int H.dl$ or the tooth ampere-turns.

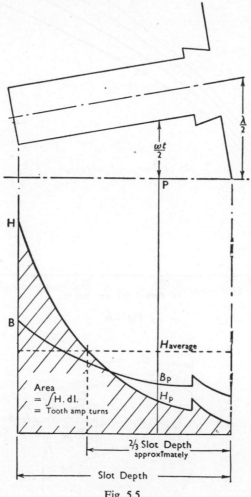

Fig. 5.5

For most purposes it will suffice if it is observed that the average value of H occurs about two-thirds of the way down the tooth (and not half-way down as might have been expected).   Thus, calculating H at this point and multiplying by tooth length, an approximate value of the tooth ampere-turns is obtained with much less labour.

Allowance for Slot Flux in Calculation of Tooth Ampere-turns.   At low values of tooth density it is safe to assume that all the flux passes down the teeth, but

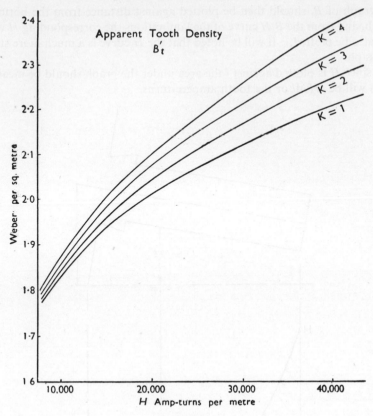

Fig. 5.6

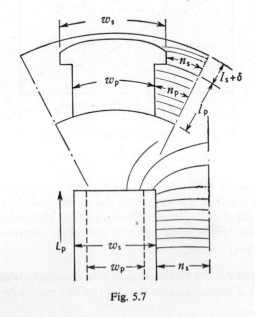

Fig. 5.7

when the teeth are saturated the flux which travels down the slots is not negligible.
  We can suppose that, at any particular slot depth, the total flux

$$\phi = \phi_t + \phi_s \quad . \quad . \quad . \quad . \quad . \quad . \quad (5.16)$$

where ϕ_s is the slot flux and ϕ_t the tooth flux.   Now if at this section the area of
the tooth is A_t and the slot area is A_s, then dividing by A_t we have

$$\phi/A_t = \phi_t/A_t + (\phi_s/A_s)(A_s/A_t) \quad . \quad . \quad . \quad (5.17)$$

ϕ_t/A_t is the actual density in the teeth B_{at} and ϕ_s/A_s the corresponding density
in the slot at this depth.
  At the same time ϕ/A_t is the fictitious tooth density we have hitherto been
using by assuming that all the flux passes down the teeth.   This we will term
the apparent tooth density $B_t{}'$.
  Rewriting equation (5.17)

$$B_t{}' = B_{at} + B_s . A_s/A_t \quad . \quad . \quad . \quad . \quad . \quad (5.18)$$
$$= B_{at} + B_s(k-1) \quad . \quad . \quad . \quad . \quad . \quad (5.19)$$

where $k = $ total area/iron area $= \lambda L_c/w_t L_i$.

  Now as the tooth flux and slot flux are in parallel across the section, the value
of H is the same for each; thus

$$B_s = H/796\,000 \quad . \quad . \quad . \quad . \quad . \quad (5.1)$$

and $$B_t{}' = B_{at} + H(k-1)/796\,000 \quad . \quad . \quad . \quad (5.20)$$

  The real density B_{at} is related to H by the magnetisation curve of the iron,
and, if this is known, curves of $B_t{}'$ can be drawn against H for several values of
k.   Such curves are shown in fig. 5.6.   The original magnetisation curve is the
one corresponding to $k = 1$ from which the others may be derived by adding
$H(k-1)/796\,000$ to each point according to equation (5.20).

5.1.3. Pole, Yoke and Core

  The calculation of the ampere-turns for these sections presents little difficulty.
In each case the flux density is found by dividing the flux in that part by the
area of its cross-section. H is then determined from the relevant B/H curve.
The flux in the pole and yoke is greater than the gap flux because of leakage.
In a first approximation a 20% leakage might be assumed when

$$\phi_p = 1 \cdot 2\phi \quad . \quad . \quad . \quad . \quad . \quad . \quad (5.21)$$

but for greater accuracy the leakage flux must be calculated separately.

5.1.4. Pole Leakage Flux

  The interpolar space can be likened to a large armature slot and consequently
the calculation of pole leakage flux is very similar to that of slot leakage flux
(Section 5.4.1).   The ampere-turns producing the leakage are those of gap plus
teeth plus core (F_{g+t+c}), thus

$$\phi_{\text{leakage}} = F_{g+t+c}\,\Lambda_l \quad . \quad . \quad . \quad . \quad . \quad (5.22)$$

where Λ_l is the total permeance of the leakage paths.

A working formula for the leakage flux of a salient-pole alternator, which should be compared with the results of Section 5.4.1 is given below:

$$\phi_{\text{shoe}} = F_{g+t+c}(l_s+\delta)\{2(L_p/n_s)+k_1\}/796\,000 \qquad . \quad . \quad (5.23)$$

$$\phi_{\text{pole}} = F_{g+t+c}0\cdot45l_p\{2(L_p/n_p)+k_1\}/796\,000 \qquad . \quad . \quad (5.24)$$

The dimensions w_s, w_p, n_s and n_p are shown in fig. 5.7. The factor k_1 allows for the flux fringing at the ends of the pole and depends upon the ratio w_s/n_s or w_p/n_p. The value of k_1 can be obtained from the curve in fig. 5.8.

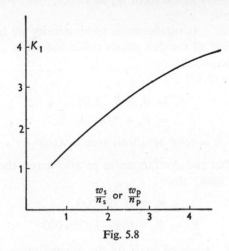

Fig. 5.8

5.1.5. Tabulation for Total No-load Ampere-turns

The total ampere-turns for the magnetic circuit required to produce a given gap flux ϕ can now be obtained by adding the results in a suitable tabular form such as shown below:

Part	Area	Length	Flux	B	H	$Hl = F$ ampere-turns
Core	$2A_c$	l_c	ϕ	B_c		
Teeth	$L_i\psi\tau(\omega_t/\lambda)$	l_t	ϕ	B_t'		
Gap	$L_c\psi\tau/k_ck_c'$	δ	ϕ	B_{ag}		
					$F_{g+t+c} =$	
Leakage flux $\phi_l = F_{g+t+c}\Lambda_l =$						
Pole	A_p	l_p	$\phi+\phi_l$	B_p		
Yoke	$2A_y$	l_y	$\phi+\phi_l$	B_y		
					Total no-load field ampere-turns =	

The ampere-turns for the gap, teeth and core are first evaluated and added together thus enabling the leakage flux to be calculated, and the table completed by adding the pole and yoke ampere-turns.

It must be remembered that the flux divides in the core and also in the yoke, hence twice the sectional area should be used in calculating flux density in these parts.

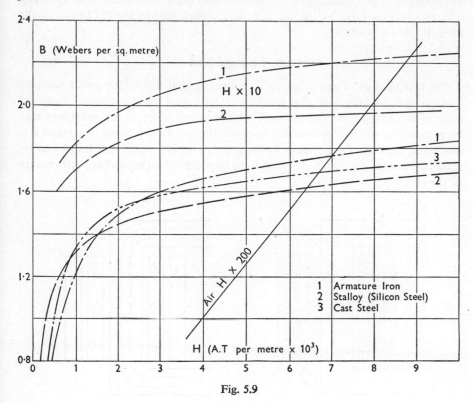

Fig. 5.9

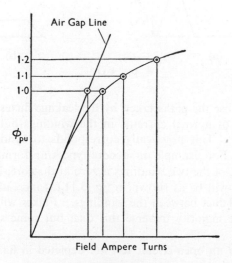

Fig. 5.10

5.1.6. Open-circuit Magnetisation Curve

Repeating the table for per-unit flux values of 1·0, 1·1 and 1·2 sufficient points are obtained to plot a satisfactory magnetisation curve for the machine (fig. 5.10). The gap ampere-turns at 1·0 per-unit flux should also be plotted to enable the air-gap line to be drawn.

5.2. Leakage Flux

The leakage flux of any winding is defined as that flux which under working conditions links only with that winding or with part of it, as distinct from the mutual flux which links two or more windings and which in a.c. machines may be responsible for energy transfer between them. In the transformer and a.c. machines, leakage fluxes cause voltage drops in the windings, known as reactance voltages, the values of which have important bearing on the performance of the machine.

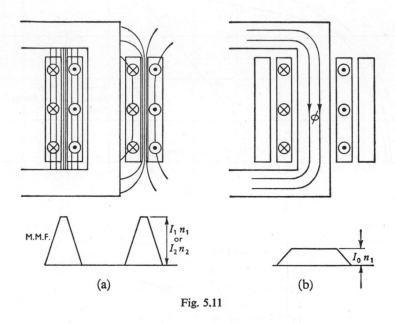

Fig. 5.11

In order to visualise the paths taken by the leakage fluxes it is convenient to consider the effect of normal currents in the windings but with the main or mutual flux absent. This practically corresponds to conditions present in a short-circuit test. For example in a core-type transformer on short-circuit test the total m.m.f. of the two windings is zero at the core, but the distribution across the winding will be as shown in fig. 5.11 (a) increasing from zero to a maximum in the oil duct between the windings. Fluxes will therefore be produced of which the majority traverse this duct but some spread out through the coils.

Conditions under an open-circuit test are depicted in fig. 5.11 (b) where we have the small magnetising current in only one winding responsible for the main flux. Normal operating conditions on full load can be represented by the superposition of the two diagrams.

5.2.1. Permeance of Leakage Paths

In the assessment of leakage fluxes the main paths of which are usually in air, iron surfaces are invariably taken as equipotentials and the calculation restricted to the air paths only.

The flux ϕ_x produced per ampere in a coil of n_x turns when the flux is restricted to a simple air path of length l and area a (fig. 5.12) is

$$\phi_x = n_x \Lambda_x \quad . \quad . \quad . \quad . \quad . \quad . \quad (5.25)$$

where Λ_x is the permeance of the air path.

$$\Lambda_x = \mu_0 a/l \quad . \quad . \quad . \quad . \quad . \quad . \quad (5.26)$$

$(\mu_0 = 4\pi/10^7)$.

The leakage inductance is then

$$L_x = n_x^2 \Lambda_x \quad . \quad . \quad . \quad . \quad . \quad . \quad (5.27)$$

assuming that all the flux links with all the turns.

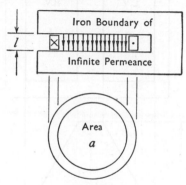

Fig. 5.12

Then leakage reactance

$$X_s = 2\pi f n_x^2 \Lambda_x \quad . \quad . \quad . \quad . \quad . \quad (5.28)$$

When the leakage paths are more complicated they are often found to be capable of division into parallel strips, each strip being associated with the length of conductor in part of the turn.

Then

$$\Lambda = \mu_0(a_1/l_1 + a_2/l_2 + a_3/l_3 + \ldots) \quad . \quad . \quad . \quad (5.29)$$

Moreover the areas a_1, a_2, etc., are usually the products of widths w_1, w_2, etc., and the lengths L_1, L_2, etc., of that part of the winding. Thus

$$\Lambda = \mu_0(L_1 w_1/l_1 + L_2 w_2/l_2 + \ldots) \quad . \quad . \quad . \quad (5.30)$$

$$= L_1 \lambda_1 + L_2 \lambda_2 + \ldots \quad . \quad . \quad . \quad . \quad . \quad (5.31)$$

where λ_1, λ_2, etc., are known as the specific permeances per unit length of the portion of the coil.*

---

* In terms of flux plotting (*see* Appendix B) the ratio w/l for a strip is really:
(number of squares in parallel)/(number in series.)

5.3. Leakage Reactances of a Core-type Transformer

Let L_1 = mean length of turn of L.V. winding,
a = radial depth of L.V. winding,
L_2 = mean length of turn of H.V. winding,
b = radial depth of H.V. winding,
L_3 = mean circumference of oil duct between windings,
c = radial depth of oil duct

and L_R = axial length of coil stack (often termed the reactance length).

These dimensions are shown in fig. 5.13. We will assume that the leakage flux is divided at the centre of the gap and that the flux on the right links with the H.V. winding and that on the left with the L.V. winding. This division is quite arbitrary and gives point to the fact that X_1 and X_2 are not really independent.

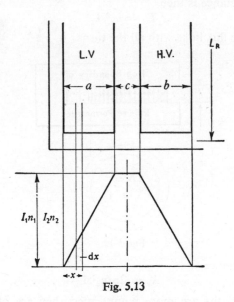

Fig. 5.13

By equation (5.26) the permeance of half the gap

$$\Lambda_c = \mu_0 L_c c/2L_R \qquad \cdots \cdots \quad (5.32)$$

Now flux generated in the sections **a** and **b** diminishes towards the inside of the L.V. winding and the outside of the H.V. winding with the diminishing m.m.f. and at the same time this flux links with a smaller number of turns.

Thus in an elementary strip dx wide the flux per ampere in the winding according to equation (5.25) will be

$$\phi_x = n_1(x/a)\mu_0(L_1 dx)/L_R \qquad \cdots \cdots \quad (5.33)$$

and as this only links with $n_1 x/a$ turns the equivalent flux links are

$$\{\phi_x n\} = n_1{}^2(x/a)^2\mu_0(L_1 dx)/L_R$$

The total flux links in this section

$$= n_1{}^2\mu_0\frac{L_1}{L_R}\int_0^a \frac{x^2}{a^2}\,dx$$

$$= n_1{}^2(\mu_0/L_R)(L_1a/3) \quad . \quad . \quad . \quad . \quad . \quad (5.34)$$

making the effective permeance of this section

$$\Lambda_a = (\mu_0/L_R)(L_1a/3) \quad . \quad . \quad . \quad . \quad . \quad (5.35)$$

The leakage reactance of the L.V. winding is thus

$$X_1 = 2\pi f n_1{}^2(\Lambda_a + \Lambda_c)$$

$$= 2\pi f n_1{}^2(\mu_0/L_R)(L_1a/3 + L_3c/2) \quad . \quad . \quad . \quad (5.36)$$

and similarly the reactance of the H.V. winding

$$X_2 = 2\pi f n_2{}^2(\mu_0/L_R)(L_2b/3 + L_3c/2) \quad . \quad . \quad . \quad (5.37)$$

The equivalent reactance referred to the L.V. winding

$$X_1' = X_1 + (n_1/n_2)^2 X_2 \quad . \quad . \quad . \quad . \quad . \quad . \quad (2.31)$$

$$= 2\pi f n_1{}^2(\mu_0/L_R)(L_1a/3 + L_2b/3 + L_3c) \quad . \quad . \quad . \quad (5.38)$$

The per-unit transformer reactance

$$x_{\text{p.u.}} = I_1 X_1'/E_1 = 2\pi f(I_1 n_1)(n_1/E_1)(\mu_0/L_R)(L_1a/3 + L_2b/3 + L_3c) \quad . \quad (5.39)$$

and since $E_1/n_1 = \sqrt{2}.\pi f BA$,

$$x_{\text{p.u.}} = \sqrt{2}(I_1 n_1)L_{\text{mt}}\mu_0(a/3 + b/3 + c)/BAL_R \quad . \quad . \quad (5.40)$$

where L_{mt} is an average length of turn used as an approximation for the separate values of L_1, L_2 and L_3.

5.4. Leakage Flux in the Induction Motor

Adopting the same principle as with the transformer and examining the leakage-flux pattern on a short-circuit test we find that there are a number of obvious leakage paths in parallel. These comprise: (a) slot leakage, (b) tooth-head leakage, (c) overhang leakage, (d) zigzag leakage, (e) harmonic leakage.

Slot leakage flux is shown at (a) in fig. 5.14. It crosses the slot from one tooth to the next, linking with that portion of the conductor below it by returning through the iron. The permeance of this section is thus determined by the dimensions of the slot. Tooth-head leakage is shown at (b). It is insignificant in the small gaps of an induction motor but needs to be allowed for in alternators where the gap is larger, particularly in a salient-pole machine where it can spread out much farther in the interpolar spaces.

Overhang leakage shown at (c) links the coils in the end winding and depends on the proximity of the conductors and their disposition relative to core and endshields.

Zigzag leakage is exclusive to induction motors and is due to flux crossing the gap in the manner shown at (d).

Harmonic leakage occurs when the winding distributions on stator and rotor are dissimilar. The main flux has then a harmonic content which does not correspond to the distribution of either winding and this excess flux has the effect of additional leakage reactance. Its calculation is beyond the scope of this book.

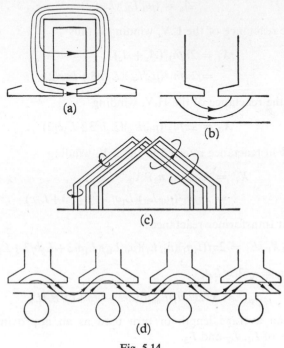

(a)

(b)

(c)

(d)

Fig. 5.14

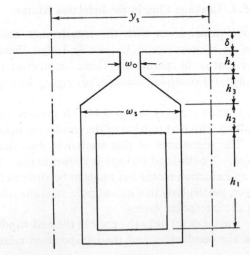

Fig. 5.15

5.4.1. Slot Permeance

Taking as an example the semi-closed slot (fig. 5.15) the slot flux divides into parallel paths of heights h_1, h_2, h_3, h_4. In the conductor section the leakage-flux density diminishes to zero as it does in the winding portion of the trans-former. The effective permeance is calculated in exactly the same way by integrating the flux links of an elementary strip dx over the height h_1.

Thus

$$\lambda_1 = \mu_0 \int_0^{h_1} \frac{x^2}{h_1^2} \frac{dx}{w_s} = \frac{\mu_0}{w_s} \frac{h_1}{3} \quad . \quad . \quad . \quad . \quad (5.41)$$

The specific permeances of the remaining strips are added, an average width being used for the section h_3.

The tooth-head permeance can also be included at this stage and is given by the final term.

Thus the slot permeance

$$\lambda_s = \mu_0 \left[\frac{h_1}{3w_s} + \frac{h_2}{w_s} + \frac{2h_3}{w_s + w_0} + \frac{h_4}{w_0} + \frac{\delta}{y_s} \right] \quad . \quad . \quad . \quad (5.42)$$

5.4.2. Overhang Permeance

This permeance is dependent on so many variables that exact mathematical solution is impossible. Many approximate formulae are used by designers, the following being an example of one which has wide use in practice.

If we assume that the two parts of the overhang form a square, then the per-meance of a single-turn coil with length of side a and periphery of conductor b is

$$\Lambda = \mu_0 4a \{0.366 \log (2a/b) + 0.11\} \quad . \quad . \quad . \quad (5.43)$$

when a is large compared with b.

Now since $L_e = 2a$, the specific permeance λ will be given by

$$\lambda = \mu_0 \{0.366 \log (L_e/b) + 0.11\} \quad . \quad . \quad . \quad (5.44)$$
$$\simeq \mu_0 \times 1$$

for a coil of normal proportions.

Considering now a group of g coils when there are g slots per pole per phase the total permeance for the group will be

$$\Lambda = g2L_e\lambda_e$$
$$= g2L_e\mu_0 \quad . \quad . \quad . \quad . \quad . \quad . \quad (5.45)$$

if we assume that there is no mutual flux. If on the other hand we assume that all the leakage flux links with all the turns, the effective permeance becomes

$$\Lambda = g^2 2L_e\mu_0 \quad . \quad . \quad . \quad . \quad . \quad (5.46)$$

Since these are the two extreme possibilities a more appropriate figure is likely to be:

$$\Lambda = g^{1.52}L_e\mu_0$$
$$= g2L_e\mu_0\sqrt{g}$$
$$= g2L_e\lambda_e$$

where the specific permeance for the overhang is thus taken as

$$\lambda_e = \mu_0\sqrt{g} \quad . \quad . \quad . \quad . \quad . \quad . \quad (5.47)$$

5.4.3. Zigzag Permeance

It will be assumed that the zigzag leakage flux travels in straight lines across the gap (fig. 5.16) and that the rotor and stator tooth pitches y_s are approximately equal. x is the distance between the centre lines of a stator tooth and a rotor slot at a given instant.

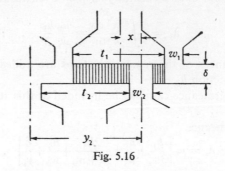

Fig. 5.16

The air-gap widths are thus

$$t_1/2+x-w_2/2 \quad \text{and} \quad t_1/2-x-w_2/2$$

or

$$m+x \quad \text{and} \quad m-x$$

where

$$m = (t_1-w_2)/2 = (y_s-w_1-w_2)/2 \quad . \quad . \quad . \quad . \quad (5.48)$$

The specific permeances are thus

$$\mu_0(m+x)/\delta \quad \text{and} \quad \mu_0(m-x)/\delta$$

and the specific permeance for the two gaps in series becomes

$$\lambda = (\mu_0/\delta)(m+x)(m-x)/(m+x+m-x) = \mu_0(m^2-x^2)/(2\delta m) . \quad . \quad (5.49)$$

Now as the rotor moves forward a distance of one-half the slot pitch, the permeance varies from a maximum when $x = 0$ to zero when $x = m$ and remains zero for the rest of the distance (fig. 5.17).

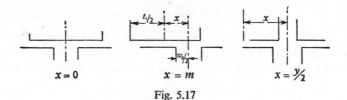

$$x = 0 \qquad\qquad x = m \qquad\qquad x = \tfrac{y}{2}$$

Fig. 5.17

The average value of λ is thus

$$\lambda = \frac{2}{y_s}\int_0^m \mu_0 \frac{m^2-x^2}{2\delta m}\mathrm{d}x$$

$$= \mu_0(2/3)m^2/y_s\delta$$

$$= \mu_0\{y_s-(w_1+w_2)\}^2/6y_s\delta$$

$$= \mu_0(y_s/6\delta)\{1-(w_1+w_2)/y_s\}^2 \quad . \quad . \quad . \quad . \quad (5.50)$$

The zigzag flux can be likened to the leakage flux in the duct between the windings of a transformer, and if in the same way we consider that half the flux links with each winding then the zigzag permeance becomes

$$\lambda_z = \mu_0(y_s/12\delta)\{1-(w_1+w_2)/y_s\}^2 \quad . \quad . \quad . \quad . \quad (5.51)$$

5.4.4. Leakage Reactance of Distributed Windings

For a double layer winding, let

t = turns per coil,

b = number of effective conductors per slot (number of wires/number in parallel) so that $t = b/2$,

p = number of poles,

a = number of parallel paths,

L_c = embedded length of conductors per slot,

L_e = length of end winding (fig. 5.14 (c)),

and g = slots per pole per phase.

The total permeance of the leakage paths associated with one turn

$$\Lambda_t = 2(L_c\lambda_s + L_e\lambda_e + L_c\lambda_z) \quad . \quad . \quad . \quad . \quad (5.52)$$

where λ_s, λ_e and λ_z are given by equations (5.42), (5.47) and (5.51). (In the case of fully pitched coils the first term should be doubled to allow for mutual flux linking with the other coil-side in the slot.)

The inductance of one coil

$$L_t = t^2\Lambda_t = (b^2/4)\Lambda_t \quad . \quad . \quad . \quad . \quad (5.53)$$

The number of coils in series

$$= (p/a)g \quad . \quad . \quad . \quad . \quad . \quad . \quad (5.54)$$

and the inductance of this group

$$= (p/a)gL_t \quad . \quad . \quad . \quad . \quad . \quad . \quad (5.55)$$

The winding consists of a such groups in parallel and the total effective inductance is therefore

$$L = (p/a^2)gL_t \quad . \quad . \quad . \quad . \quad . \quad (5.56)$$

Thus

$$L = (p/a^2)(gb^2/4)\Lambda_t \quad . \quad . \quad . \quad . \quad (5.57)$$

and the reactance

$$X = 2\pi f(pgb^2/4a^2)2(L_c\lambda_s + L_e\lambda_e + L_c\lambda_z) \quad . \quad . \quad (5.58)$$

CHAPTER 6

THE INDUCTION MOTOR

6.1. Construction

BY far the greatest number of electrical motors manufactured are induction motors, ranging from small single-phase fractional-horse-power motors to large machines delivering 10 000 h.p. and running direct from 11-kV mains. As a general-purpose approximately constant-speed motor for general industrial drives, the cage-rotor type has a remarkably simple and robust construction enabling it to operate in the most adverse circumstances and to give excellent service with little demands on maintenance.

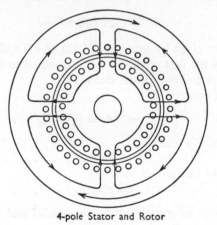

4-pole Stator and Rotor

Fig. 6.1

Excluding the single-phase fractional-horse-power class the induction motor consists of:

(a) A laminated steel stator core built up of silicon-steel punchings and assembled as a hollow cylinder in a fabricated or cast stator frame. A distributed three-phase stator winding is arranged in slots on the inner circumference similar in most respects to that of an alternator as described in Chapter 4.

(b) A laminated rotor core, cylindrical in form, this time with slots on the outer surface carrying the rotor winding. In small machines the laminations are circular discs keyed directly to the shaft, but in larger sizes form rings dovetailed to a framework known as the spider which is keyed to the shaft (fig. 6.1).

Rotor and stator are separated by a small air-gap, usually only 0·020 in. to 0·040 in., necessary for mechanical clearance.

The stator winding is connected to the main supply and must be insulated according to this voltage. The rotor winding is either (a) wound type or (b) cage type.

The wound-rotor type is a distributed winding somewhat similar to that of the stator, though usually a two-layer winding in a different number of slots is employed. It is of comparatively low voltage with rectangular strip conductors. The three phases are usually star connected and the ends of the windings are

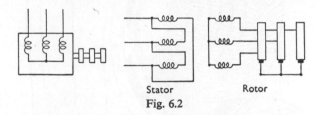

Stator   Rotor

Fig. 6.2

brought out to insulated slip rings. Under operating conditions the rotor winding is *short circuited* at the slip rings (fig. 6.2). This is done by switchgear connected to the brushes, or, with some manufacturers, a system of brush-lifting and short-circuiting gear is employed whereby cam mechanism is arranged to short-circuit the connections behind the rings when the external circuit is not required.

It is not always clear that a connection joining all three rings together is an effective short circuit on each phase. If the ring connections are regarded as a three-phase load of zero impedance (fig. 6.3) there should be no doubt on this point.

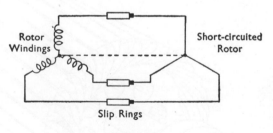

Rotor
Windings

Short-circuited
Rotor

Slip Rings

Fig. 6.3

The cage-rotor type has conductors usually uninsulated consisting of copper or aluminium bars in rotor slots connected at the ends by end rings to which they are brazed, welded or cast. Recent manufacturing developments of small machines include a centrifugal die-casting method of casting rotor bars, end rings, and fan blades in position on the rotor core, in one operation. An example of such a rotor is shown in fig. 6.6.

Again it must be appreciated that the end rings act as a short circuit on the individual rotor bars. This will be apparent from fig. 6.7 which is a developed diagram of the winding. It will be shown later that e.m.f. is generated in each

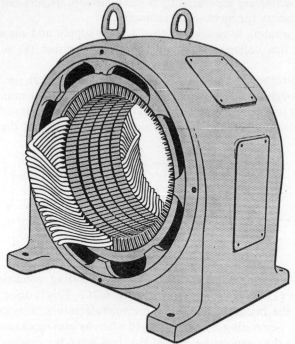

Fig. 6.4.—Induction Motor Stator with double-layer winding partly wound

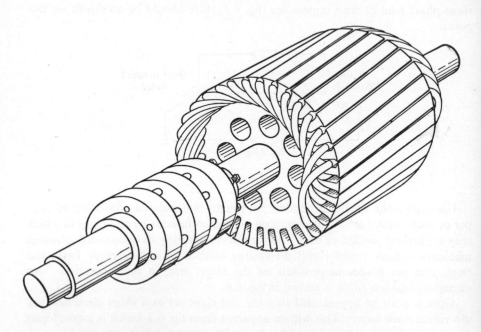

Fig. 6.5.—Wound Rotor for Induction Motor

rotor bar and, taking a pair of bars separated by a pole pitch, e.m.f.s in these bars are in phase opposition. Two such bars thus set up a series circuit and effectively short circuit each other as the equivalent battery diagram indicates. The complete rotor may be taken to be a superposed system of such pairs.

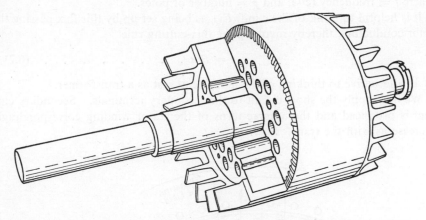

Fig. 6.6—Cage-type Rotor in part section showing cast aluminium bars and end rings

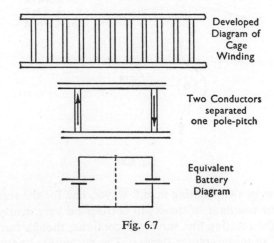

Developed Diagram of Cage Winding

Two Conductors separated one pole-pitch

Equivalent Battery Diagram

Fig. 6.7

6.2. Simplified Principle of Action

The induction motor, with its rotor at rest, will be seen to be a transformer with its secondary winding short-circuited. We will remove the short circuit temporarily (a practical possibility in the case of the wound rotor) and connect the stator to normal-voltage supply mains.

Magnetising current I_0 will then flow in the stator (primary winding) and an e.m.f. $E_{2,0}$ will be induced in each secondary phase (as in the case of a transformer). It will be appreciated that since the primary winding is a distributed three-phase winding, I_0 sets up a rotating m.m.f. wave (Section 4.6), which since the air-gap is uniform produces a corresponding rotating flux wave advancing a double pole pitch each cycle.

The revolutions per minute of this flux wave or rotating field is given by

$$N_s = 60f/(p/2) = 120f/p \quad . \quad . \quad . \quad . \quad . \quad (6.1)$$

where f = frequency (c/s), and p = number of poles.

It is helpful to think of the e.m.f. $E_{2,0}$ as being set up by this flux passing the rotor conductors, thereby invoking the flux-cutting rule

$$e = Blu \quad . \quad . \quad . \quad . \quad . \quad . \quad . \quad (6.2)$$

as an alternative to thinking of the machine at rest as a transformer.

We now apply the short circuit to the secondary terminals. Secondary current is produced and the ampere-turns of the stator winding correspondingly increase as with the transformer.

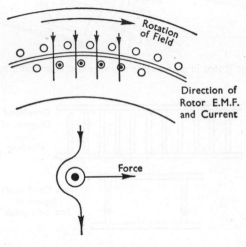

Fig. 6.8

There will now be two rotating m.m.f. waves, one for the stator and one for the rotor, but the resultant of these will correspond very nearly to that of the original I_0 and the rotating flux wave will continue, though somewhat reduced by the effect of primary voltage drops. The currents, although short-circuit currents, are not so excessive as in the case of a short-circuited transformer since leakage reactance is greater, but currents five to ten times full-load value are to be expected.

Now consider fig. 6.8.

At a given instant, when the rotating flux wave is in the position shown, if the rotor conductors lying in the path of the flux are carrying current, force will be exerted upon them. The direction of flux in this diagram is shown downwards and the field is moving left to right; the generated e.m.f. in the conductors will be directed towards the front (right-hand rule), and current will flow in the same direction at that instant. It follows therefore that the direction of mechanical force will be towards the right (left-hand rule), in other words causing the conductors to follow the movement of the rotating field.

Assuming that the total force on all the conductors is greater than the retarding mechanical forces of friction and the load, the rotor will begin to accelerate under the action of the net torque. As it does so it will begin to approach the speed of the field.

In other words, the field will now be passing the rotor conductors at a reduced rate, much slower than that which occurred when the rotor was at rest.

Rotor voltage will thus be considerably reduced and also the current. Ultimately these values fall so much—and with them the torque—so that there is no net torque available for acceleration and no further increase of speed takes place. The machine has now reached its normal running speed. At this stage the rotor has very nearly caught up the rotating flux.

The relative movement is such that the rotor is said to be slipping back through the field, and it must be stressed that it is this relative movement that is the cause of the generation of rotor voltage and current. Were the rotor to be driven at synchronous speed (i.e. that of the field) then there would be no induced e.m.f. and no current.

6.2.1. Slip

The ratio which determines the relative amount of this slipping back is known as the *slip* of the machine.

$$\text{Slip } S = (\text{synchronous speed—rotor speed})/\text{synchronous speed} \quad (6.3)$$

At normal load the slip of an induction motor is usually between 0·03 and 0·05.

At light load—the motor running freely—the slip is very small (about 0·005), and for many purposes the machine may then be considered to be running at full synchronous speed.

As load is applied, the natural effect of the braking torque is to cause the machine to slow down. As it does so, slip increases, and with it current and torque until the driving torque of the motor balances the retarding torque of the load. This determines the speed at which the machine runs on load.

The slip/horse-power output graph is almost linear over the normal-load range of the machine, but this does not continue indefinitely as will be seen in the next section.

6.2.2. Simplified Equations for Rotor Current

In this section and subsequently, the suffix 1 will be used for stator or primary quantities; suffix 2 for the rotor or secondary; suffix 0 will refer to standstill conditions and suffix S to when the slip is S.

Thus $E_{2,0}$ is the e.m.f. per phase in the secondary circuit at standstill.

It will also be assumed for the first part of this analysis that the rotating field is constant for all loads (a similar assumption was made in the case of the simplified theory of the transformer), that is, that voltage drops in the primary circuit can be ignored.

Since the three-phase machine is obviously symmetrical, and thus presents balanced three-phase load to the supply, star connection of both windings will be assumed and the circuit relations established for one phase only.

At slip S, the relative motion between the rotating field and the rotor is S times that at standstill with a result that

$$E_{2,S} = SE_{2,0} \qquad . \quad . \quad . \quad . \quad . \quad (6.4)$$

In addition, as the field is passing the pole pairs of the rotor at a slower rate, the rotor frequency

$$f_{2,S} = Sf_{2,0} = Sf_1 \qquad . \quad . \quad . \quad . \quad . \quad (6.5)$$

The rotor circuit, like the secondary of a transformer, has resistance R_2 and leakage reactance X_2.

Now it must be remembered that reactance is a term involving frequency ($X = 2\pi f \alpha$) so that X_2 is really $X_{2,0}$ a measured value at normal frequency. When the machine is running at slip S, since rotor frequency is reduced, the rotor leakage reactance $X_{2,S}$ is correspondingly reduced. Indeed $X_{2,S}$ vanishes at synchronous speed when $S = 0$.

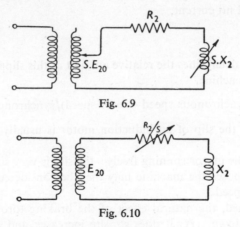

Fig. 6.9

Fig. 6.10

Since reactance is proportional to frequency,

$$X_{2,S} = SX_{2,0} \qquad . \quad . \quad . \quad . \quad . \quad (6.6)$$

Thus at any slip S the equation to rotor current is given by

$$I_{2,S} = E_{2,S}/Z_{2,S} = SE_{2,0}/(R_2+jX_{2,S}) = SE_{2,0}(R_2+jSX_2) \qquad (6.7)$$

and

$$I_{2,S} = SE_{2,0}/\sqrt{(R_2{}^2+S^2X_2{}^2)} \qquad . \quad . \quad . \quad . \quad (6.8)$$
$$= E_{2,0}/\sqrt{\{(R_2/S)^2+X_2{}^2\}} \qquad . \quad . \quad . \quad . \quad (6.9)$$

The secondary circuit can therefore be represented by either of the diagrams fig. 6.9 or fig. 6.10. In actual fact both voltage and reactance vary with S (equation (6.8), fig. 6.9), but the identical current is produced in a constant-voltage variable-resistance circuit (equation (6.9), fig. 6.10). The latter is simpler and has possibilities for development.

At this stage we must not lose sight of the fact that the rotating flux is due to the resultant of the two m.m.f. waves set up by the primary and secondary currents distributed in the conductors on either side of the air-gap.   At stand-still it is obvious that the two waves rotate together and thus combine to form a single rotating wave revolving at their common speed.

When, however, the rotor runs at slip S, that is, rotates at speed $N_S(1-S)$, the rotor frequency is Sf_1, and the m.m.f. wave of the rotor advances *relative to the rotor conductors* at a speed corresponding to the slip frequency Sf_1. This means that in space, relative to the stator conductors, it rotates at *full synchronous speed*.

In other words, no matter what the value of S, the two m.m.f. waves of stator and rotor still rotate together and their resultant can still be regarded as due to primary current I_0, the magnetising current, acting alone in the primary winding.

6.2.3. Simplified Equations for Torque

It is well known that when a current-carrying conductor lies at right angles to a magnetic field the force on the conductor

$$F = Bli \quad . \quad . \quad . \quad . \quad . \quad . \quad . \quad (6.10)$$

where B is the flux density of the field and l is the length and i is the current. This equation will apply to the force on the rotor conductors, but it must be remembered that both B and i are in this case alternating quantities which have the same frequency but are not necessarily in phase.

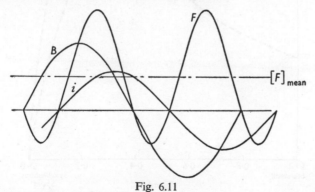

Fig. 6.11

If relative to a given rotor conductor

$$B = \hat{B} \sin \omega_2 t \quad . \quad . \quad . \quad . \quad . \quad (6.11)$$

and

$$i = \sqrt{2}.I_{2,S} \sin (\omega_2 t - \theta) \quad . \quad . \quad . \quad (6.12)$$

where θ is the angle of phase difference between them, then the force acting on unit length of the conductor,

$$F = \hat{B} \sin \omega_2 t \sqrt{2}.I_{2,S} \sin (\omega_2 t - \theta)$$

$$= (\sqrt{2}/2)\hat{B}I_{2,S}\{\cos \theta - \cos (2\omega_2 t - \theta)\} \quad . \quad . \quad (6.13)$$

which is illustrated in fig. 6.11 and is seen to consist of a mean value throughout the cycle, viz.,

$$[F]_{mean} = (\sqrt{2}/2)\hat{B}I_{2,S} \cos \theta \quad . \quad . \quad . \quad (6.14)$$

together with an alternating component at twice the rotor frequency.

The total force acting on the rotor conductor is equal to this average force multiplied by the total length of the conductors, the alternating component being of no consequence.

The rotor torque is thus

$$T = [F]_{\text{mean}}(L_c D_a/2)z_2 \quad . \quad . \quad . \quad . \quad . \quad (6.15)$$

where z_2 is the total number of rotor conductors

$$T = (L_c D_a/2)z_2(\sqrt{2}/2)\hat{B}I_{2,S}\cos\theta \quad . \quad . \quad . \quad . \quad (6.16)$$

$$= k'\Phi I_{2S}\cos\theta \quad . \quad . \quad . \quad . \quad . \quad . \quad . \quad (6.17)$$

where Φ which depends on $\hat{B}$ is the flux per pole and k' is constant.

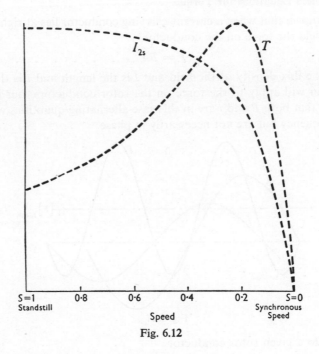

Fig. 6.12

Now $\cos\theta$ is equal to the rotor power factor since at the instant when B is a maximum the conductor at that point has maximum e.m.f. induced in it. Thus B and E_2 are in phase and the phase displacement between B and I_2 is the same as that between E and I_2.

Thus

$$\cos\theta = R_2/Z_2 \quad . \quad . \quad . \quad . \quad . \quad (6.18)$$

From equation (6.17)

$$T = k'\Phi(E_{2,S}/Z_{2,S})(R_2/Z_{2,S})$$

$$= k'\Phi . SE_{2,0}R_2/(R_2{}^2 + S^2 X_2{}^2) \quad . \quad . \quad . \quad . \quad (6.19)$$

$$= k'\Phi . E_{2,0}(R_2/S)/\{(R_2/S)^2 + X_2{}^2\} \quad . \quad . \quad . \quad (6.20)$$

Moreover, since both Φ and $E_{2,0}$ are approximately proportional to V_1,

$$T \simeq k''V_1^2 . (R_2/S)/\{(R_2/S)^2 + X_2^2\} \quad . \quad . \quad . \quad . \quad (6.21)$$

and again since

$$I_{2,S} = E_{2,0}/\sqrt{\{(R_2/S)^2 + X_2^2\}} \quad . \quad . \quad . \quad . \quad (6.22)$$

$$I_{2,S}^2 = E_{2,0}^2/\{(R_2/S)^2 + X_2^2\} \quad . \quad . \quad . \quad . \quad . \quad (6.23)$$

Therefore

$$T \simeq k'''I_{2,S}^2(R_2/S) \quad . \quad . \quad . \quad . \quad . \quad (6.24)$$

These equations for torque and rotor current when plotted to a base of speed or slip give rise to curves such as are shown in fig. 6.12, the values for which have been taken from the following example:

EXAMPLE

Plot the form of the current/slip and torque/slip curves of an induction motor for which $R_2 = 0.2\ \Omega$, $X_2 = 1.0\ \Omega$, neglecting stator voltage drops. Plot also the curves if resistance of (a) $0.2\ \Omega$, (b) $0.6\ \Omega$, is added to each of the phases at the slip rings.

S	R/S	$(R/S)^2$	$(R/S)^2 + X^2$	$\sqrt{\{(R/S)^2 + X^2\}}$	I varies as $\dfrac{1}{\sqrt{\{(R/S)^2 + X^2\}}}$	T varies as $\dfrac{R/S}{(R/S)^2 + X^2}$
0.050	4	16	17	4.123	0.242	0.235
0.100	2	4	5	2.236	0.447	0.400
0.133	1.5	2.25	3.25	1.803	0.555	0.462
0.200	1.0	1.00	2.0	1.414	0.707	0.500
0.250	0.8	0.64	1.64	1.281	0.781	0.488
0.333	0.6	0.36	1.36	1.166	0.858	0.440
0.500	0.4	0.16	1.16	1.077	0.928	0.345
0.800	0.25	0.062	1.06	1.031	0.970	0.235
1.000	0.2	0.04	1.04	1.020	0.980	0.192

The curves show that at full-load slip, when reactance is small, I and T are both approximately proportional to slip. As slip increases to unity at standstill, I increases, but it approaches a constant value since reactance and induced e.m.f. are both rising together.

Torque increases at first with slip to a maximum value known as the *stalling torque*. At higher slip values, torque then reduces, $\cos \theta$ diminishing so rapidly as to offset the increase of $I_{2,S}$ in equation (6.17).

This curve shows the characteristically poor starting torque of the simple cage-rotor induction motor in spite of its large starting current. Unless the resistance R_2 is carefully proportioned it is possible for the starting torque to be less than full-load torque. Such a machine, though capable of starting light and giving satisfactory performance on load, would not be capable of starting against full-load torque.

6.2.4. Effect of Variation of R_2

It is particularly important to note that in equations (6.22) and (6.24) both $I_{2,S}$ and T are functions of the fraction R_2/S.

It therefore follows that a variation of R_2 does not produce a new pair of values of I and T but merely alters the value of S at which the original values of I and T occur.

The curves of fig. 6.13 which show the effect of doubling and quadrupling R_2 have been derived in this manner, taking each point on the original curves of fig. 6.12 and replotting with twice and four times the slip value (note the corresponding points P_1, P_2, P_3).

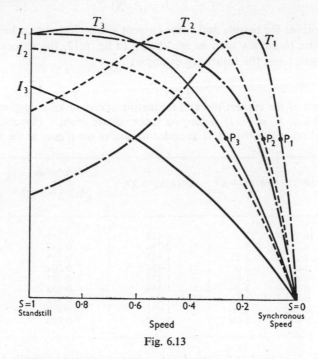

Fig. 6.13

6.2.5. Wound Rotor Type

By considerably increasing rotor resistance to R_2' so that

$$\frac{R_2'}{S_0} = \frac{R_2'}{1} = \frac{R_2}{S}$$

where S is full-load slip, full-load torque and full-load current are produced at standstill, and the torque and rotor current curves are elongated as shown in fig. 6.14.

As S is normally about 0.05, R' is of the order of $20R_2$. This, then, is the purpose of the wound-rotor-type induction motor. Additional resistance is added in series with the winding to limit the starting current and at the same time to improve the starting torque. If the machine is required to start against full-load torque, then the total starting resistance is arranged to give about one and a half times full-load torque with one and a half times full-load current. There is thus adequate excess torque for acceleration, and as the rotor does so the resistance is cut out step by step to maintain the current and the torque until finally all the external resistance is removed and the rings are short-circuited.

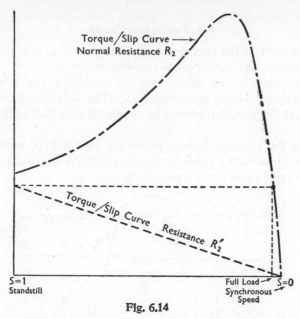

Fig. 6.14

6.2.6. Maximum Torque

We have seen (equation **6.21**) that

$$T = k''V_1^2 . (R_2/S)/\{(R_2/S)^2 + X_2^2\}$$
$$= k''V_1^2 . R_2S/(R_2^2 + S^2X_2^2)$$

For a maximum torque

$$\frac{dT}{dS} = 0 = \frac{(R_2^2 + S^2X_2^2)R_2 - R_2S(2SX_2^2)}{(R_2^2 + S^2X_2^2)^2}$$

$$0 = R_2^2 + S^2X_2^2 - 2SX_2^2$$

$$S^2X_2^2 = R_2^2$$

Thus $\qquad [S]_{T=\max} = \pm R_2/X_2$ . . . . **(6.25)**

The corresponding maximum torque value

$$[T]_{\max} = k''V_1^2 . R_2(R_2/X_2)/\{R_2^2 + (R_2^2/X_2^2)X_2^2\}$$

$$= k''V_1^2/2X_2$$ . . . . **(6.26)**

It is to be observed from these equations that:

1. The value of rotor resistance does not alter the value of the maximum torque but only the value of the slip at which it occurs.

2. The maximum torque varies inversely with rotor resistance and directly with the square of the applied voltage.

3. To obtain maximum torque at starting ($S_0 = 1$) rotor resistance must be made equal to rotor reactance.

6.3. Equivalent Circuits

The development of the complete equivalent circuit of the induction motor follows in the same way as that of the transformer.

Indeed it has already been shown that the machine at rest is a transformer with its secondary winding short-circuited. The induction-motor equivalent circuit (fig. 6.15 (a)) should therefore be compared with that of the transformer (fig. 2.22).

Once again the primary (stator) resistance and leakage reactance can be accounted for by including elements in series with an idealised machine. The magnetising circuit again forms a parallel branch.

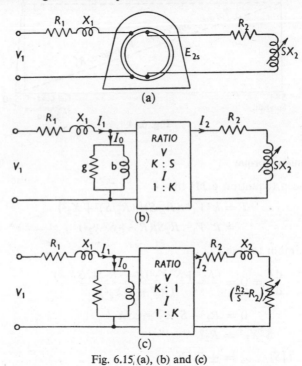

Fig. 6.15, (a), (b) and (c)

The main difference between the induction motor and the transformer lies in the fact that the secondary voltage $E_{2,S}$ varies with S and so does rotor reactance $X_{2,S}$.

The idealised machine in fig. 6.15 (b) is thus depicted as a ratio-change device in which voltage changes as $K:S$ and the current as $1:K$. The ratio K corresponds to the simple turns ratio n_1/n_2 of the transformer, but in the case of the induction motor some modification is introduced in the total winding voltages by the winding distribution factors.

Hence

$$K = k_1 n_1 / k_2 n_2 \qquad \cdots \cdots \quad (6.27)$$

Dividing voltage and impedance in the secondary circuit by S the current is unchanged and the equivalent circuit finally becomes that of fig. 6.15 (c), which is seen to be that of a transformer connected to a variable resistance load. The elements of this circuit are related to the dimensions of the conductors and the magnetic circuits of the main and leakage fluxes; consequently if these values can be computed from design dimensions the circuit is established for a particular machine.

The stator and rotor currents corresponding to a series of values of slip can thus be determined. Moreover, since the energy losses in the various resistances of the circuit represent the various sources of loss in the actual machine, the efficiency and performance characteristics can be found as subsequent examples will show.

For accurate analysis, the circuit in this form must be used. The relative values of X_1 and X_2 are larger than the corresponding ones to be found in the transformer, and also the magnetising admittance is relatively much larger due to the presence of the air-gap. In fact, magnetising current is usually of the order of one-quarter to one-third full-load current.

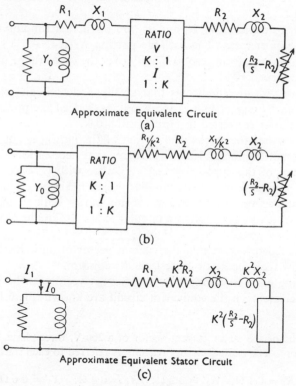

Approximate Equivalent Circuit
(a)

(b)

Approximate Equivalent Stator Circuit
(c)

Fig. 6.16 (a), (b) and (c)

6.3.1. Approximate Equivalent Circuit

Following the development of transformer equivalent circuits, the "exact" equivalent circuit of the induction motor will also be considerably simplified if the magnetising admittance is removed to the primary terminals as shown in fig. 6.16 (a).

9—E.M.

This enables referred values of resistance and leakage reactance to be used, and the circuit is reduced to that of either fig. 6.16 (b) or fig. 6.16 (c).

This step is not so readily justified as with the transformer owing to the relative magnitude of the magnetising current. The simplified circuit however leads to a much more elementary analysis and the results—though necessarily approximate—are usually sufficient to show the type of performance to be expected.

A more accurate analysis based on the "exact" equivalent circuit will be developed later.

6.4. The Locus of Stator Current

6.4.1. The "Circle" Diagram

The approximate equivalent circuit of fig. 6.16 (c) is seen to consist of two branches in parallel; one, a constant branch—the magnetising circuit—and the other a constant reactance in series with a variable resistance whose value depends upon S.

The resistances depicted by R_1 and R_2 are the actual winding resistance responsible for copper loss. The variable portion $K^2(R_2/S - R_2)$ is an effective resistance which varies from zero to infinity over the speed range from standstill to synchronous speed.

This effective resistance indicates that at slip S the circuit loses energy in other ways than by copper loss in the windings, indeed the power loss in this section is the power converted to mechanical work.

It is approximately the mechanical output of the machine, but it includes in addition the small friction and windage losses that necessarily take place.

Now a circuit of this type—constant reactance with variable resistance together with a parallel branch—is a familiar circuit in simple circuit analysis.

As the resistance varies, the current vector varies both in magnitude and direction in such a way as to follow a circular locus. (Circuits of this type have been analysed in Appendix A.)

We are thus led to expect that the current vector of an induction motor on load will follow such a pattern, as test results confirm.

The following example shows how the current vector can be plotted if the values of the elements in the equivalent circuit are known (fig. 6.17).

EXAMPLE

Plot the locus of the stator current vector of a 200-V, three-phase, star-connected induction motor. The resistances and reactances referred to each stator phase are as follows:

$$R_1 = 0{\cdot}1\ \Omega; \quad R_2' = 0{\cdot}2\ \Omega; \quad X_1 = 0{\cdot}4\ \Omega; \quad X_2' = 0{\cdot}6\ \Omega.$$
$$\text{Magnetising admittance } Y_0 = 0{\cdot}025 - \text{j}0{\cdot}1\ \mho.$$

Following the procedure of Appendix A an impedance scale is chosen and $\text{j}X_1$ and $\text{j}X_2$ set out to this scale. R_1 is added horizontally followed by R_2'/S.

When

$S =$	0·05	0·1	0·2	0·4	1·0
$R_2'/S =$	4	2	1	0·5	0·2

The locus of the impedance vector is thus obtained.

An admittance scale is now chosen to enable a circle of diameter $1/X = 1\cdot0\ \mho$ to be drawn of convenient size.

The admittance circle is now obtained and the various impedance points inverted to this locus.

The magnetising admittance $Y_0 = 0\cdot025 - j0\cdot1$ is now added at the origin and the final axes drawn.

To find current and power scales:

$$100\ \text{A} = VY/\sqrt{3}; \quad Y = 100\sqrt{3}/200 = 0\cdot866.$$

The 100-A point on the current scale will be opposite $0\cdot866\ \mho$.

$$10\text{kW} = V^2Y/1000; \quad Y = 10\ 000/(200\times200) = 0\cdot25.$$

The 10-kW point on the power scale will be opposite $0\cdot25\ \mho$.

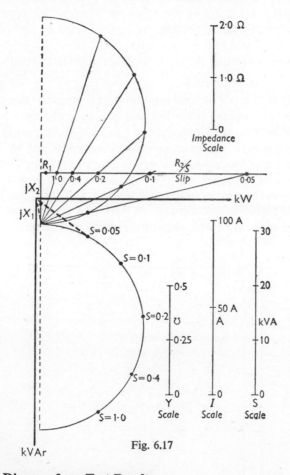

Fig. 6.17

6.4.2. Circle Diagram from Test Results

With the knowledge that the current locus is circular, the diagram can be drawn for a given machine if the position of two points only on the curve are known, these points being measured values obtained from testing when the machine is connected to normal-voltage mains.   It is advisable that these points should be as far apart as possible, so the obvious choice is that those corresponding to synchronous speed and standstill should be used.

These are to be obtained from the light-load test and the locked-rotor test respectively.

(a) *Light-load Test.*   The machine is started in the usual way and runs unloaded from normal-voltage mains.   Provision is then made to measure the no-load current I_0 and its power factor.   For this purpose it is usual to measure the power by the two-wattmeter method and to obtain the power factor from the ratio of the two wattmeter readings (Appendix C).

On this test it may be assumed that the machine is running almost at synchronous speed.   It is usually advisable to take a series of readings with various values of applied voltage, and the latter can generally be reduced to about one-third of the normal value before the machine develops an appreciable slip. Power is then plotted against voltage, this curve being of importance in the calculation of efficiency as will be seen later.

For the purpose of plotting the circle diagram only the normal-voltage point is required.

(b) *Locked-rotor Test.*   For this test the rotor must be clamped in some manner to prevent it rotating when the supply is switched on.   In the case of small machines full voltage may be applied for a very brief period, sufficient to read current and power, the greatest care being taken not to overheat the winding.   With larger machines, however, it is not usually possible to provide test plant of sufficient capacity and the risk of damage is greater.   It is usual therefore to restrict the current to about one and a half times full load, and the voltage must be reduced accordingly.   A series of readings of current and power factor are then taken with descending values of voltage.

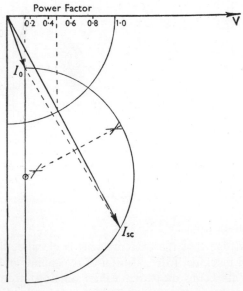

Fig. 6.18

Under the circumstances of this test the motor is in effect a short-circuited transformer and presents a practically constant impedance. The power factor is sensibly constant and the current almost linear with the voltage. Extrapolation thus enables the current and power factor to be found corresponding to full voltage even if this point is not actually measured.

The vectors I_0 and $I_{s.c.}$ can now be plotted in magnitude and direction, making use of a power-factor scale and graphical construction shown in fig. 6.18. We are then able to construct the circular current locus since its centre O must lie on the right bisector of this line joining the extremities of the two vectors and must also be vertically below the extremity of I_0.

The above method of plotting the vectors by drawing to a given length at a given angle (i.e. as polar quantities) will be improved upon and greater accuracy obtained if, instead of plotting current, a power scale is used. It is shown in Appendix A that convenient power scales can always be arranged for use with current charts of this type.

The vectors should therefore be plotted directly in rectangular coordinates using the values of kilowatts and reactive kilovolt-amperes obtained in the tests. The method of obtaining both components from wattmeter readings in a two wattmeter test is discussed in Appendix C.

6.5. Efficiency

Since

$$\text{efficiency} = \text{output/input} = (\text{input}-\text{losses})/\text{input} \quad . \quad . \quad (6.28)$$

it follows that if the losses can be determined corresponding to given currents, then the corresponding values of efficiency can be computed.

The chief sources of loss in the induction motor are as follows:

(a) Fixed losses—
    1. Iron loss.
    2. Friction and windage loss.
(b) Variable losses—
    3. Stator copper loss.
    4. Rotor copper loss.

The first two items are called "fixed losses", since when the machine is running on constant-voltage mains they vary little over the working range of load.

The stator iron loss depends on the value of the flux, and the friction and windage losses depend upon speed, but, since both flux and speed are sensibly independent of load, variations of these losses are of secondary importance. In contrast, the copper losses depend entirely on the load.

In addition to the above there are small losses collectively termed "stray" loss. This includes rotor iron loss and additional iron losses due to the leakage fluxes causing eddy currents in the stator frame and endshields.

6.5.1. (a) Fixed Losses

The sum of the losses (1) and (2) is practically the whole of the power on the no-load test described above.

There is included the small stator copper loss due to the no-load current I_0.

Rotor copper loss in this test is negligible as the rotor current is so very small. The power readings on the variable voltage test can be corrected by subtracting I^2R_1 from each value, assuming the equivalent-star resistance of the stator is known. They are shown in the tabulation of fig. 6.19 and the results when plotted form a curve as shown.

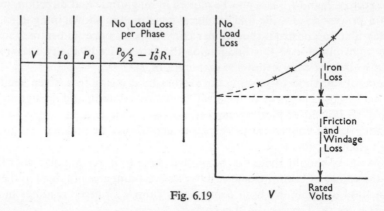

V	I_0	P_0	No Load Loss per Phase $P_0/3 - I_0^2 R_1$

Fig. 6.19

The curve shows an increase of loss with increase of voltage: it will be appreciated that the iron loss depends upon the flux which is almost proportional to voltage. Friction and windage will remain unchanged unless there is a variation of speed. Were it possible to reduce flux to zero the iron loss would be removed, and if the curve is extrapolated to the loss axis, a reasonable estimate of the friction and windage loss can be made.

This is done in fig. 6.19 and the total no-load loss at rated voltage is thus divided into its components.

6.5.2. (b) Variable Losses

Stator Copper Loss (3). The stator terminals are always accessible and the d.c. resistance of the stator windings can readily be measured by any suitable method: voltage drop, bridge or low-reading ohmmeter.

The a.c. resistance is strictly somewhat higher than this according to the amount of eddy-current loss in the copper; but this is usually ignored, and is in any case masked by the change of resistance with temperature.

For efficiency calculations the resistance should be measured hot, that is when the motor has settled down to its steady-state temperature on full load.

Rotor Copper Loss (4). Referring to the equivalent circuit of the motor on load (fig. 6.15 (c)) the total power intake to the rotor is the power delivered to the resistance R_2/S.

Thus

$$\text{rotor intake} = I_2^2 R_2/S \quad . \quad . \quad . \quad . \quad . \quad (6.29)$$

but

$$\text{rotor copper loss} = I_2^2 R_2 \quad . \quad . \quad . \quad . \quad . \quad (6.30)$$

and

$$\frac{\text{rotor copper loss}}{\text{rotor intake}} = \frac{I_2^2 R_2}{I_2^2 R_2/S} = S \quad . \quad . \quad . \quad . \quad (6.31)$$

An accurate knowledge of the slip S thus determines the fractional value of the loss in the rotor. Rotor copper loss is therefore frequently termed "slip loss".

Equation (6.31) can be derived in another way:

$$\text{rotor intake} = 2\pi N_s T \cdot 746/33\,000 \text{ watts} \quad . \quad . \quad . \quad (6.32)$$

where T is the gross torque (lb-ft) and N_s the synchronous speed in revolutions per minute. N_s must be used since the power is provided by the flux rotating at this speed. T includes both the output torque and the friction torque.

Now at the same time,

$$\text{rotor output} = 2\pi N_r T \cdot 746/33\,000 \text{ watts} \quad . \quad . \quad . \quad (6.33)$$

where N_r is the speed at which the rotor is actually revolving. Obviously the value of rotor output is less than the total rotor intake.

Subtracting equation (6.33) from equation (6.34) gives the loss in the rotor itself, hence

$$\text{rotor copper loss} = 2\pi(N_s - N_r)T \cdot 746/33\,000 \quad . \quad . \quad (6.34)$$

and dividing by equation (6.32)

$$\frac{\text{rotor copper loss}}{\text{rotor intake}} = \frac{N_s - N_r}{N_s} = S \quad . \quad . \quad . \quad . \quad (6.31)$$

Methods of measurement of slip will be discussed later.

6.5.3. Determination of Efficiency of an Induction Motor

The machine is conveniently loaded on a test bed by belting or directly coupling a d.c. generator of equivalent rating, and then loading the d.c. machine by a resistance load or paralleling with d.c. mains.

Load is increased until the stator current of the motor reaches the name-plate value. Readings of voltage, current and power are then made, preferably using the two-wattmeter method, and slip is determined by one of the following methods.

6.5.4. Measurement of Slip

Since

$$S = f_2/f_1 \quad . \quad . \quad . \quad . \quad . \quad . \quad (6.5)$$

the measurement of slip involves a comparison of stator and rotor frequency. In the usual case where f_1 is 50 c/s the rotor frequency is sufficiently low for the individual cycles to be counted. In the case of a wound-rotor machine, an indication of the rotor frequency is easily obtained by connecting a low-value centre-reading d.c. moving-coil voltmeter across the slip rings.

The voltmeter leads should have rounded ends of soft copper, and these may be lightly pressed without danger on adjacent slip rings as they revolve. There is usually sufficient voltage drop in the main brushes and their short-circuiting strap to provide an indication on the meter. The meter will follow the variations of the rotor current at such low frequencies and the pointer will oscillate.

If the number of oscillations, counted over a period of 20 sec, is $(N)_{20}$, then

$$S = \frac{f_2}{f_1} = \frac{(N)_{20}/20}{50} = \frac{(N)_{20}}{1000} \qquad . \quad . \quad . \quad . \quad (6.35)$$

With a cage-rotor-type motor it is not possible to employ a voltmeter so directly. If, however, a large flat search coil of many turns is placed centrally against the end plate on the non-driving end of the machine, it is sometimes possible to pick up sufficient voltage by induction from the leakage fluxes to obtain a reading. A larger 50-c/s voltage will also be induced, but this is too rapid to affect the instrument.

A commercial slip indicator has been developed using such a search coil employing a low-pass filter-amplifier to eliminate the fundamental frequency and then comparing f_2 and f_1 by means of a bridge circuit.

It is sometimes possible to obtain an indication by connecting a d.c. milli-voltmeter between the ends of the shaft.

If these methods fail, a stroboscopic method must be used. This employs the well-known principle that, if a rotating object is illuminated by the light of an intermittent source, it will appear to be stationary, provided the lamp flashes once and once only per revolution.

Modern stroboscopic lamps which are a form of neon-filled thyratron valve, can be arranged to discharge a capacitor once per cycle and to give an intensely bright flash lasting only a few microseconds.

If a symmetrical pattern is painted on the end of the motor shaft, e.g. in the case of a six-pole machine six segments might be used painted alternately white and black, this pattern will appear stationary when the machine is running at synchronous speed. At a slip S, the pattern will appear to rotate backwards. The speed of rotation of the pattern will be the slip speed (synchronous speed — rotor speed) which can be timed, and the value of S computed from equation (6.3).

6.5.5. Tabulation for Efficiency

Commencing with the total stator intake power measured on the load test, the losses are subtracted successively in the following manner. The remainder is thus the output power which can be expressed in horse-power if required, and efficiency can be computed by dividing output by input.

The following tabulation is self-explanatory:

Stator intake		=	watts
Stator copper loss $(3I_1^2 R_1)$	=		
Stator iron loss (from no-load test)	=		
Total stator loss	=	=	watts
Rotor intake (by subtraction)		=	watts
Rotor copper loss ($S \times$ rotor intake)	=		
Friction and windage loss (from no-load test)	=		
Total rotor loss	=	=	watts
Output		=	watts

Output horse-power =
Efficiency = output/input =

6.6. Determination of Performance from the Circle Diagram

We have seen in Section 6.4.2 that from the results of the open-circuit and locked-rotor tests on an induction motor the circle diagram can be constructed, that is, the diagram which shows how current, power and power factor change as load changes.

The intermediate values can be determined with reasonable accuracy, though it must be remembered that the method of drawing the circular locus is based upon the approximations which have been used in developing the approximate equivalent circuit of the machine.

It would be useful if further data could be obtained for each operating point. Particularly we should like to find the output power. This of course is best obtained by subtracting the losses from the input in the manner described in the previous section, but on the other hand if more approximate values will suffice, it is possible to arrange a simple graphical construction to be applied to the circle diagram enabling the output power to be read directly.

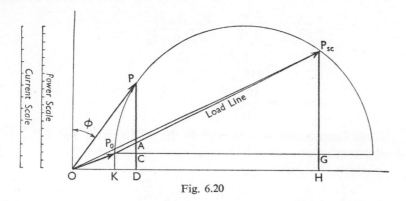

Fig. 6.20

It is customary, for this construction, to turn the power chart of fig. 6.18 through a right angle and so arrange for the power axis to be vertical.

For a given machine (fig. 6.20) let OP_0 be the no-load current, and $OP_{s.c.}$ the standstill current, from which the circle is constructed (Section 6.4.2).

Let P be a particular operating point for which OP is the current; PD (to the power scale) is the input power and $\cos \phi$ the power factor. Perpendiculars P_0K, PD and $P_{s.c.}H$, measured to the power scale, represent the power input at no load, the selected load point and standstill respectively. Strictly, $P_0K = CD = GH$ represents no-load loss, but if GH is taken to be the iron loss at standstill, subtracting this from $P_{s.c.}H$, the remaining power $P_{s.c.}G$ is the copper loss at standstill in both rotor and stator together. The copper loss corresponding to P will be much less than $P_{s.c.}G$ and the copper loss at P_0 will be almost negligible. Joining $P_0P_{s.c.}$ this line cuts PD at A. We will prove later that AC represents approximately the copper loss at P.

Thus, if AC is copper loss and CD no-load loss, AD represents total loss and, since PD is the input, the difference PA will be the output corresponding to the operating point P.

The line $P_0P_{s.c.}$ is termed the *load line*, vertical distances above the line to the circle representing output powers.

To prove that AC is approximately equal to the copper loss corresponding to the load point P, we proceed as follows.

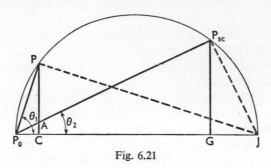

Fig. 6.21

In fig. 6.21, which is the circle portion only of fig. 6.20, by similar triangles

$$\frac{AC}{P_{s.c.}G} = \frac{P_0C}{P_0G} = \frac{P_0P \cos \theta_1}{P_0P_{s.c.} \cos \theta_2}$$

$$= \frac{P_0P \cdot P_0P/P_0J}{P_0P_{s.c.} \cdot P_0P_{s.c.}/P_0J}$$

$$= \frac{(P_0P)^2 \cdot}{(P_0P_{s.c.})^2}$$

Neglecting the no-load current, P_0P is the load current and $P_0P_{s.c.}$ is the standstill current, thus

$$\frac{AC}{P_{s.c.}G} = \frac{(P_0P)^2}{(P_0P_{s.c.})^2} \simeq \frac{OP^2 \cdot R_1'}{OP_{s.c.}{}^2 \cdot R_1'}$$

$$\simeq \frac{\text{copper loss on load}}{\text{copper loss at standstill}} \quad . \quad . \quad . \quad . \quad . \quad (6.36)$$

This final approximation indicates that the true load line joining $P_0P_{s.c.}$ is not quite a straight line but is slightly curved.

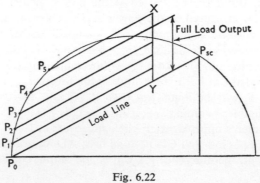

Fig. 6.22

6.6.1. Construction for given Load Points

We are now in a position to find the load points corresponding to given output values. For example if fig. 6.22 is the diagram for a motor rated at 40 h.p., a line XY is erected at any convenient point on the load line and the full-load output power 40×746 W is marked off along this line. Drawing parallel to the load line, the circle is cut at P_4 which is thus the same distance from the load line and is consequently the full-load operating point. Points corresponding to 25%, 50%, 75% and 125% load are also shown.

6.6.2. The Torque Line

We have seen from equation (6.32) that torque is proportional to rotor intake. Rewriting this equation

$$T(\text{lb ft}) = \frac{33\,000}{2\pi \cdot 746} \frac{\text{rotor intake (watts)}}{N_s(\text{r.p.m.})}$$

$$= \frac{7 \cdot 05 \text{ rotor intake (watts)}}{N_s} \quad . \quad . \quad . \quad . \quad (6.37)$$

Indeed the rotor intake can be taken as a measure of the torque since for a given machine N_s is constant, and this value is said to be the torque in *synchronous watts*.

To find torque from the circle diagram we must therefore find rotor intake and this will involve subtracting the stator losses only from the input. CD is the no-load loss, but AC is the copper loss of stator and rotor together. It is necessary to divide AC. This can be done for the standstill conditions by dividing $P_{s.c.}G$ at F making $P_{s.c.}F$ the rotor copper loss and FG the stator copper loss. The ratio of these lengths will be

$$P_{s.c.}F/FG = I_2{}^2 R_2 / I_1{}^2 R_1 = K^2 R_2 / R_1 \quad . \quad . \quad . \quad (6.38)$$

from equation (2.12).

The turns ratio K can be found in the case of a wound-rotor machine from an open-circuit test; with the machine at standstill normal stator voltage is applied and the rotor voltage is measured between the open-circuited rings:

then $\qquad\qquad\qquad K = V_{1,0}/V_{2,0} \quad . \quad . \quad . \quad . \quad . \quad (6.39)$

R_1 and R_2 are the measured d.c. resistances.

The loss ratio cannot be determined so easily for a cage-rotor machine. Stator copper loss must be calculated corresponding to $I_{s.c.}$ and the measured value of R_1, and this value measured off on the diagram as FG. The remainder is assumed to be rotor loss.

Following the approximate equivalent circuit which assumes the ratio of stator current to rotor current to remain constant, the loss ratio will also be constant. Consequently the line P_0F divides rotor copper loss from stator copper loss. The vertical distances above this line are thus rotor intake values, i.e. the torque in synchronous watts, and so P_0F is known as the *torque line*.

Fig. 6.23 shows the complete circle diagram, and the following table gives the data that can be obtained from it.   P is taken to be the rated full-load point and tangents have been drawn at R and U parallel to the load and torque lines respectively, thus establishing the maximum load and torque values.

AT FULL LOAD (*to the appropriate scales*)

OP	full-load current
PD	full-load input
PA	full-load output
CD	iron and friction loss
AB	rotor copper loss
BC	stator copper loss
PB	rotor intake (torque)
$\cos \phi$	power factor
PA/PD	efficiency
AB/PB	slip
RS/PA	instantaneous overload capacity, maximum load/full load
UV/PB	stalling/full-load torque
$P_{s.c.}F/PB$	starting/full-load torque

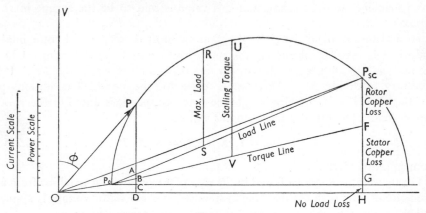

Fig. 6.23

6.7. The Induction Generator

6.7.1. Operation of the Induction Machine at Negative Slip

If an induction motor which is connected to constant voltage and frequency mains is mechanically coupled to a prime mover capable of driving the induction machine at a speed slightly higher than synchronism, it will be found that energy is returned to the a.c. mains, the machine thus becoming an induction generator.

As the prime mover causes the rotor speed to exceed synchronism, then by equation (6.3) the value of S becomes negative.   We must therefore re-examine the expressions for current and torque and consider the effect of substituting a negative value of S.   In the equivalent circuit (fig. 6.16 (c)) the induction motor is depicted as a transformer delivering power to an equivalent load resistance

$\{(R_2/S) - R_2\}$, which represents the power converted to mechanical work. For negative values of S, this load resistance is also negative, that is, it no longer absorbs power but is really a source, or in other words there is a transfer of energy from mechanical to electrical form.

The locus of stator current has been obtained by inverting the impedance locus of a constant reactance in series with variable resistance (fig. 6.17). This must

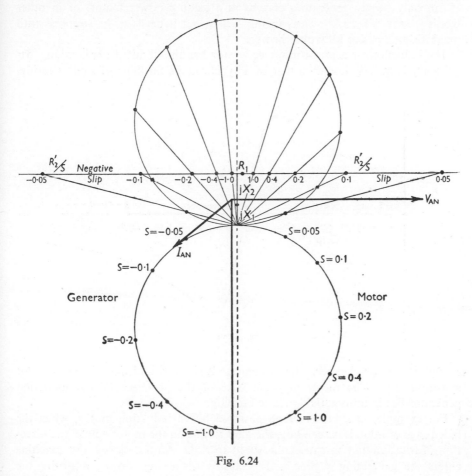

Fig. 6.24

now be extended for negative values of R_2'/S. Fig. 6.24 has been constructed to correspond to fig. 6.17 and it shows that as S becomes negative the impedance vector swings over to the second quadrant but that its locus is still a straight line. The current locus is thus the complete circle, and when the vector I_{AN} is on the left-hand side of the diagram it has a component in phase opposition to the voltage V_{AN}, thus corresponding to generator operation.

6.7.2. The Torque Equation

When the torque equation (6.20) is plotted for negative values of slip, the torque/speed curve of fig. 6.12 is extended as shown in fig. 6.25. The torque is negative at hypersynchronous speeds rising to a maximum value, after which it begins to fall again.   This maximum value of torque limits the range of operation of the machine as a generator.

It must be emphasised that the induction generator is only capable of supplying power to a system to which synchronous machines are connected, and it is not able to supply power to a simple resistance load connected across its terminals. It can only supply generating current at a leading power factor, or in other words it may deliver kilowatts to the system but it needs to be supplied with magnetising reactive kilovolt-amperes.

The induction or asynchronous generator has thus limited application.   Its efficiency is usually less than that of a synchronous machine of similar rating,

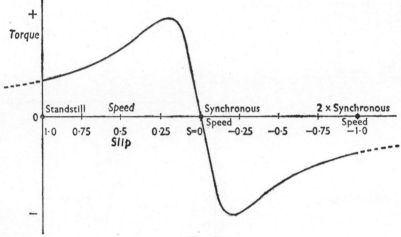

Fig. 6.25

though it may be cheaper.   Its switchgear is simpler, and there is no need for synchronising.   The most important use of the principle of the induction generator lies in automatic dynamic braking.

For example, in a lift or crane powered by an induction motor, when the laden cage or hook is descending, the load torque on the motor acts in the direction of rotation and so causes the speed to rise.   Automatically the machine enters the generating regime and produces a braking torque, returning the energy of the descending load to the supply.   This is accomplished with little change of speed and so the speed is practically the same in both directions. It is highly important to prevent shock loads from exceeding the maximum generating torque of the machine or causing the over-current trips to function during periods of regeneration.'

6.8. The "Exact" Circle Diagram

With small machines, where stator resistance and magnetising current are comparatively large, the use of the approximate equivalent circuit is not justified and a more exact method is advisable.

The following construction is developed from the "exact" equivalent circuit of fig. 6.15 (c). This is repeated in fig. 6.26. We now treat the first part of this circuit comprising the stator impedance Z_1 and magnetising admittance Y_0 as a four-terminal network in which the input and output voltages and currents are related by

$$V_1 = AV_2 + BI_2 \quad . \quad . \quad . \quad . \quad . \quad . \quad (6.40)$$

and
$$I_1 = CV_2 + DI_2 \quad . \quad . \quad . \quad . \quad . \quad . \quad (6.41)$$

The A, B, C, D constants corresponding to the L-type of connection of Z_1 and Y_0 are:

$$A = 1 + Z_1 Y_0 \quad . \quad . \quad . \quad . \quad . \quad . \quad (6.42)$$
$$B = Z_1 \quad . \quad . \quad . \quad . \quad . \quad . \quad (6.43)$$
$$C = Y_0 \quad . \quad . \quad . \quad . \quad . \quad . \quad (6.44)$$
$$D = 1 \quad . \quad . \quad . \quad . \quad . \quad . \quad (6.45)$$

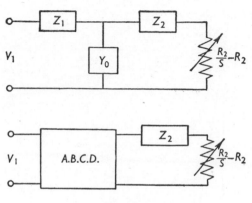

Fig. 6.26

The complex constant $A = Ae^{j\alpha}$ is the open-circuit voltage ratio of the network, and, with typical values of Z_1 and Y_0, we find A is a number slightly greater than 1 and α is a small negative angle.

Now it is shown in the Appendix (14.1.6) that a four-terminal network is equivalent to a perfect transformer with a complex ratio $A:1$, having a shunt admittance C/A connected on the input side and a series impedance B/A on the output side.

The equivalent circuit of the induction motor thus becomes that of fig. 6.27.

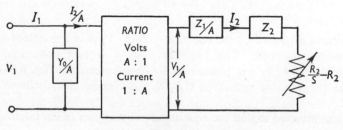

Fig. 6.27

The rotor current is given by

$$I_2 = (V_1/A)/\{(Z_1/A)+Z_2+(R_2/S-R_2)\} \quad . \quad . \quad . \quad (6.46)$$

The torque in synchronous watts (rotor input power) can be obtained from equation (6.29).

The stator current

$$I_1 = (V_1 Y_0 + I_2)/A \quad . \quad . \quad . \quad . \quad . \quad . \quad (6.47)$$

The loci of I_1 and I_2 are derived by the method of inversion given in the Appendix.

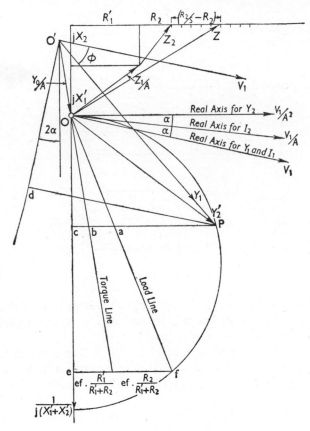

Fig. 6.28

I_2 is a current produced by the constant voltage V_1/A in a constant-reactance variable-resistance circuit. The impedance Z_1/A is first calculated and its components R_1' and jX_1' are plotted to an impedance scale (fig. 6.28). Z_2 is added, also the variable resistance $\{(R_2/S)-R_2\}$ giving the locus of the impedance Z.

This is then inverted to find the admittance of this part of the circuit which is seen to be a circle of diameter $1/j(X_1'+X_2)$.

The admittance Y_2' corresponding to a particular value of slip is given by the vector OP.

The corresponding value of I_2 can then be found from equation (6.46) by multiplying Y_2' by V_1A, and I_2/A by multiplying again by $1/A$. The line OP can be used to represent all these quantities if we chose a new reference axis and a new scale for each, and these axes will be inclined at α and 2α to the horizontal.

The admittance Y_0/A is now added at the origin to the new admittance scale $1/A^2$ times the original when O'P is the total admittance and also represents the current I_1 to a scale V_1 times this new admittance scale.

6.8.1. Power Values

The power supplied to the equivalent rotor circuit by the voltage V_1/A is equal to

$$P_2'+jQ_2' = (V_1/A)(\bar{V}_1/\bar{A})Y_2' = (V_1^2/A^2)Y_2' \quad . \quad . \ (6.48)$$

P_2' is thus represented by the line Pc to a scale V_1^2/A^2 times the admittance scale for Y_2'.

The total input power,

$$P_1+jQ_1 = V_1^2Y_1 \ . \ . \ . \ . \ . \ (6.49)$$

and P_1 is represented by the line Pd to a scale V_1^2 times the admittance scale for Y_1. These power scales are the same, since the admittance scale for Y_1 is $1/A^2$ times the scale for Y_2.

Now if the operating point f corresponds to standstill ($S = 1$), the load line and the torque line can be drawn as for fig. 6.23 and the following power values obtained from the diagram:

Pd = input power,
Pa = output power

and Pb = input power to the rotor or the torque in synchronous watts.

6.9. Double-cage Rotors

An induction motor which has a low-resistance rotor will have relatively small rotor copper loss and slip at full load, but its starting torque will also be low. On the other hand if the ratio R_2/X_2 is increased, the starting torque is improved at the expense of its running characteristics. If the rotor is equipped with two independent cages, the one having a higher resistance/reactance ratio than the other, a compromise may be achieved. A double-cage rotor has conductors in specially shaped slots (fig. 6.29). The two conductors are separated from each other by a relatively deep and narrow portion of the slot; the bars are independent in some designs or they may be joined in the die-cast aluminium-rotor type. The end rings also may be separate or combined.

The conductors at the bottom of the slot form the low-resistance cage or the main running cage whilst those at the top of the slot are of smaller cross-section and have a higher resistance. The end rings of this cage are also of reduced cross-section and may be of a higher-resistance alloy. This is termed the starting cage.

10—E.M.

Two such examples of rotor slotting are shown in fig. 6.29. Slot **a** is for a cast-aluminium-type cage for a 40-h.p. machine and slot **b** is for a 60-h.p. 12-pole machine with separate cages. In this case the bottom bars and the end rings are of copper, with the top cage made entirely of brass having three times the resistivity of copper.

A further modification adopted by another leading manufacturer is shown in fig. 6.30. The starting cage is a high-resistance cage at the top of the slots as before, but the running winding consists of a number of short-circuited single-turn coils of high-conductivity copper. By varying the pitch of these coils the designer has considerable control over the reactance/resistance ratio of the winding and consequently over the starting current and the torque/speed characteristic.

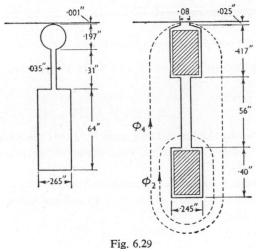

Fig. 6.29

It will be seen from fig. 6.29 that the leakage reactances of a double-cage rotor, X_2, X_3, X_4, are due to the following leakage fluxes:

ϕ_2, flux linking only with the running winding;
ϕ_3, flux linking only with the starting winding;
ϕ_4, flux linking with both windings.

With the slotting shown in the figure, ϕ_3 is negligible, being confined to the end rings, but if the conductors were in alternate slots ϕ_3 would be present and ϕ_4 reduced.

6.9.1. Equivalent Circuit

The equivalent circuit of a double-cage-rotor machine is shown in fig. 6.31. The two cage impedances $R_2'+jX_2'$ and $R_3'+jX_3'$ are effectively in parallel between the points **a** and **b** with the reactance X_4 in series. If common end rings are used, a resistance R_4/S must be included in series with X_4'.

Primary impedance and the magnetising admittance are accounted for as in the single-cage machine.

From the equivalent circuit, the performance of the machine can be predicted.

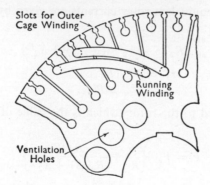

Fig. 6.30

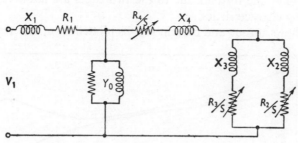

Fig. 6.31

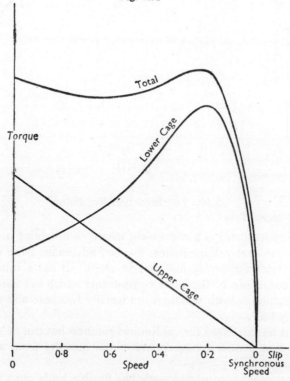

Fig. 6.32

Neglecting X_3' the equivalent rotor currents are given by

$$I_2' = V_{ab}/\{R_2/S + jX_2'\}$$
$$= V_{ab} \cdot (R_2'/S - jX_2')/\{(R'_2/S)^2 + X_2'^2\} \quad \cdots \quad (6.50)$$

and
$$I_3' = V_{ab}/(R_3'/S)$$
$$= V_{ab} \cdot S/R'_3 \cdot \quad \cdots \quad \cdots \quad (6.51)$$

and the power supplied to the rotor (which is the value of the gross torque in synchronous watts) by

$$P = V_{ab}{}^2 \left\{ \frac{S}{R'_3} + \frac{R_2'/S}{(R_2'/S)^2 + X_2'^2} \right\} \quad \cdots \quad (6.52)$$

This expression has been plotted in fig. 6.32 assuming that V_{ab} remains constant, and it shows how the torques due to the two cages are additive and give improved starting characteristics.

Fig. 6.33 shows torque and current graphs plotted from test results.

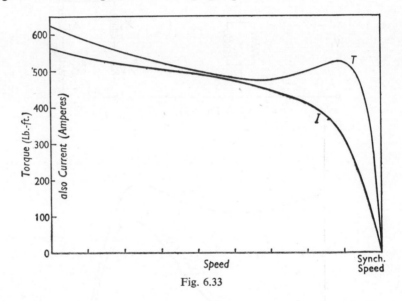

Fig. 6.33

6.10. The Induction Regulator

6.10.1 Single-phase Type

An induction regulator is a convenient means of obtaining a variable output voltage from constant-voltage mains, its chief advantage lying in the fact that the voltage varies uniformly and not in steps. It has a stator and a rotor unit usually consisting of the same components which are used in induction-motor construction. Both windings are usually two-pole and are spread over approximately 120°.

The rotor is not arranged for continuous rotation but can be rotated through half a revolution usually by worm-and-pinion gearing from a handwheel or pilot motor drive.

Slip rings are therefore unnecessary but flexible leads must be used for the rotor connections.

The rotor winding is usually connected to the supply and the stator forms the secondary winding. The flux is alternating, and when the rotor is in the position shown in fig. 6.34 (a) with the axes of the stator and rotor winding coincident, maximum secondary voltage is produced. As the rotor is rotated through 90°

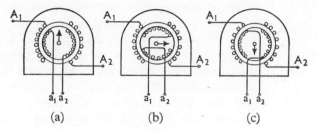

Fig. 6.34 (a), (b) and (c)

the flux linking with the secondary winding is reduced to zero and the secondary voltage similarly reduced (fig. 6.34 (b)).

A further rotation of 90° causes the secondary voltage to rise again to maximum value (fig. 6.34 (c)), but its phase will be displaced by 180°.

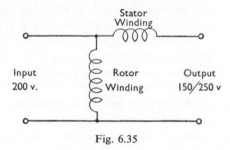

Fig. 6.35

The regulator is most advantageously arranged as a variable auto-transformer to "buck" or "boost" the input voltage. With the connections as shown in fig. 6.35 and a turns ratio of 4:1 the stator winding produces a voltage variable 0–50 V. The output voltage will be varied from 150 V to 250 V as the rotor is rotated through 180°.

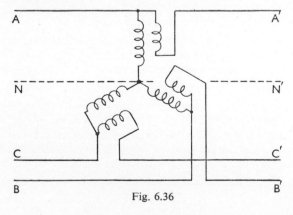

Fig. 6.36

6.10.2. Three-phase Regulator

A similar result is obtained from a three-phase supply using a three-phase regulator, but the voltage is varied in a different way.   This regulator has three-phase distributed windings on both stator and rotor cores, similar to the wound-rotor induction motor with the rotor winding connected to the supply.

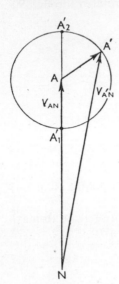

In this case the rotor m.m.f. produces rotating field. The voltage induced in the stator windings does not therefore vary in magnitude as the rotor is turned slowly through 180°. Altering the rotor position by turning the rotor in the direction in which the field rotates advances the phase of the secondary voltage relative to the primary.

The equipment may thus be termed a phase-shifting transformer and as such is a useful piece of laboratory equipment for a.c. meter testing and similar applications. It is also used to advance the phase of the grid voltages of grid-controlled mercury-arc rectifiers.

When the apparatus is arranged as a booster (fig. 6.36) the secondary voltage is added to that of the primary as shown in the vector diagram fig. 6.37.

Fig. 6.37

As the rotor axis changes, the vector $V_{AA'}$ rotates relative to the phase voltage of the supply V_{AN} and over 180° of rotor displacement the output voltage varies from a minimum $V_{A'_1N}$ to a maximum $V_{A'_2N}$.

Induction regulators of this type are used in distribution networks to boost the voltage of a feeder or alternatively to compensate for variable input voltage, and have many applications in laboratories and testing plants where variable voltage is required.

CHAPTER 7

THE SYNCHRONOUS GENERATOR

7.1. Generation of E.M.F.

7.1.1. Flux Distribution Curve

THE curve of distribution of flux in the air-gap of an alternator (fig. 7.1) is not usually so rectangular as in a d.c. machine, but it is never perfectly sinusoidal unless the machine has a salient-pole rotor with specially shaped pole shoes graduating the air-gap, or a cylindrical rotor with a sinusoidally distributed field winding.

The figure shows two poles of a salient-pole-type machine. Assuming in the first place that the rotor is stationary, if τ is the pole pitch and S is the distance measured between a point P in the gap and the quadrature axis (the centre line between poles), B_P, the flux density in the gap, may be represented by a Fourier series, that is,

$$B_P = \sum_{n=1}^{n=\infty} B_n \sin (n\theta + \psi_n) \quad . \quad . \quad . \quad . \quad (7.1)$$

where
$$\theta/2\pi = S/2\tau \quad . \quad . \quad . \quad . \quad . \quad (7.2)$$

This series is a rapidly converging one with the exception that prominence may be given to certain harmonics due to the slotting of the stator. The general series can usually be simplified. Since the N and S poles of the machine are essentially similar

$$B(\theta) = -B(\theta + \pi) \quad . \quad . \quad . \quad . \quad . \quad (7.3)$$

and the expansion never contains even harmonics. Furthermore, the flux is usually symmetrical about the pole axis and then

$$B(\theta) = B(\pi - \theta) \quad . \quad . \quad . \quad . \quad . \quad (7.4)$$

and under these conditions $\psi_n = 0$ for all values of n.

7.1.2. E.M.F. Equation

When the rotor rotates at uniform speed, the poles moving from right to left in fig. 7.1, the flux passes the armature conductors with velocity $u = dS/dt$ and the e.m.f. generated in an armature conductor at P by the flux-cutting rule will be

$$e = B_P L_c u \quad . \quad . \quad . \quad . \quad . \quad . \quad (7.5)$$

$$= B_P L_c . dS/dt \quad . \quad . \quad . \quad . \quad . \quad (7.6)$$

Now, since the pole moves forward a distance of 2τ during each cycle,

$$u = dS/dt = 2\tau f \qquad \ldots \ldots \ldots \quad (7.7)$$

where f is the frequency, and therefore from equation (7.2)

$$d\theta/dt = 2\pi f = \omega \qquad \ldots \ldots \ldots \quad (7.8)$$

and if ω is constant

$$\theta = \omega t \qquad \ldots \ldots \ldots \ldots \quad (7.9)$$

Now reverting to equation (7.5) the e.m.f. in conductor P varies as B_P, hence from equation (7.9) the wave-form of the conductor e.m.f. to a time base will be identical with the space wave-form of the flux distribution.

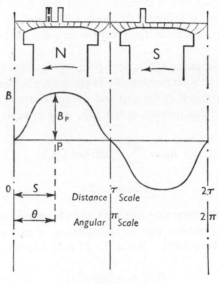

Fig. 7.1

Thus

$$e_P = L_c u \sum_{n=1}^{n=\infty} B_n \sin (n\omega t + \psi_n) \qquad \ldots \ldots \quad (7.10)$$

and similarly the e.m.f. in a conductor at Q spaced an angular distance β from P

$$e_Q = L_c u \sum_{n=1}^{n=\infty} B_n \sin \{n(\omega t + \beta) + \psi_n\} \qquad \ldots \ldots \quad (7.11)$$

It will be shown later that although all the harmonics present in the flux wave also appear in the conductor wave-form, by suitable winding arrangements these harmonics can largely be eliminated from the terminal voltage. Conversely no harmonics will appear in the e.m.f. wave which are not present in the flux wave. It is not normally necessary therefore to adopt expensive methods of removing harmonics from the flux wave.

7.1.3. Flux per Pole

The total flux per pole is equal to the average flux density over the whole pole pitch multiplied by the gap area (τL_c); thus the total flux per pole which is due to the nth harmonic is

$$\phi_n = [B_n \sin n\theta]_{\mathrm{mean}} L_c\tau \quad . \quad . \quad . \quad . \quad . \quad . \quad (7.12)$$

$$= (L_c\tau/\pi)\int_0^\pi B_n \sin n\theta d\theta$$

$$= (2/\pi)(B_n/n)L_c\tau \quad . \quad . \quad . \quad . \quad . \quad . \quad (7.13)$$

and
$$B_n = (\pi/2)(n\phi_n/L_c\tau) \quad . \quad . \quad . \quad . \quad . \quad . \quad (7.14)$$

From equation (7.10) the value of the nth harmonic in the conductor voltage will be

$$e_n = L_c u B_n \sin (n\omega t + \psi_n) \quad . \quad . \quad . \quad . \quad (7.15)$$

and from equation (7.7) and (7.14)

$$e_n = L_c 2\tau f(\pi n\phi_n/2L_c\tau) \sin (n\omega t + \psi_n)$$
$$= \pi n f\phi_n \sin (n\omega t + \psi_n) \quad . \quad . \quad . \quad . \quad . \quad (7.16)$$

7.1.4. E.M.F. in Full-pitched Coil

The e.m.f. in a coil of N turns is equal to $N(e_P - e_Q)$, where e_P and e_Q are the e.m.f.s in the conductors in the opposite coil sides. Thus for a fully pitched coil, that is a coil whose sides are separated by a full pole pitch ($\beta = \pi$ in equation (7.11)), the value of the fundamental frequency component of the e.m.f. (from equation (7.16))

$$e_P = \pi f\phi_1 \sin \omega t$$
$$e_Q = \pi f\phi_1 \sin (\omega t + \pi)$$
$$e_P - e_Q = 2\pi f\phi_1 \sin \omega t$$

and the r.m.s. value of the fundamental component of the coil voltage

$$E_1 = \sqrt{2} . \pi f\phi_1 N \quad . \quad . \quad . \quad . \quad . \quad (7.17)$$

and similarly for the nth harmonic

$$E_n = \sqrt{2} . \pi n f\phi_n N \quad . \quad . \quad . \quad . \quad . \quad (7.18)$$

7.1.5. Pitch Factor

If the pitch of the coil is less than π by an angle ϵ, then the e.m.f.s in the coil sides will not be in exact phase opposition and the coil e.m.f. will be less than $2N$ times the conductor voltage.

The vector difference $E_P - E_Q$ is shown in fig. 7.2, and from the geometry of this vector diagram

$$| E_P - E_Q | = 2E_P \cos \epsilon/2 \quad . \quad . \quad . \quad . \quad (7.19)$$

The vector diagram only refers to the fundamental frequency component, and the effect of short pitching a coil reduces the coil voltage given by equation (7.17) in the ratio

$$k_p = \cos \epsilon/2 \quad . \quad . \quad . \quad . \quad . \quad (7.20)$$

which is known as the *pitch factor*.

Now with respect to the nth harmonic in the flux wave the reduction in the effective pitch angle is relatively n times as great as for the fundamental (fig. 7.2), so the pitch factor for the nth harmonic

$$k_{p,n} = \cos n\epsilon/2 \quad . \quad . \quad . \quad . \quad . \quad . \quad . \quad (7.21)$$

This usually causes a much greater reduction of voltage than the corresponding value for the fundamental.

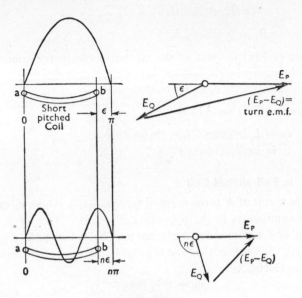

Fig. 7.2

If $\cos n\epsilon/2 = 0$, this particular harmonic will be completely suppressed. For example:

PITCH FACTOR FOR AN 80% PITCHED COIL

Order of harmonic.	1	3	5	7	9	11	13	15	17
Pitch factor .	0·955	0·585	0	0·585	0·955	0·955	0·585	0	0·585

Short pitching by one slot in a pole pitch of six (83·4% coil) successfully reduces both the fifth and seventh harmonics, and, as triplex harmonics do not appear in the line voltage of a star-connected alternator, this value is very effective in improving the voltage wave-form of the machine.

PITCH FACTORS FOR A WINDING WITH 9 SLOTS PER POLE

Order of harmonic.	1	3	5	7	9	11	13	15	17
Pitch factor:									
Coil short-chorded 1 slot .	0·985	0·866	0·643	0·342	0	0·342	0·643	0·866	0·985
Coil short-chorded 2 slots .	0·940	0·500	0·174	0·766	1·0	0·766	0·174	0·500	0·940

7.1.6. Spread Factor

The total voltage of a winding is obtained by connecting coils in series, and as successive coils are necessarily displaced from each other by a slot pitch, the total voltage of the group, which is the vector sum of the individual coil voltages, is necessarily less than their arithmetical sum. There is thus a second factor which reduces the total e.m.f., the *spread factor*

$$k_s = \frac{\text{vector sum of coil e.m.f.s}}{\text{arithmetical sum of coil e.m.f.s}} \qquad . \quad . \quad . \quad (7.22)$$

Thus if N is now the total number of turns of a complete phase winding, equation (7.17) becomes

$$E_1 = \sqrt{2}.\pi k_p k_s \phi_1 f N \quad . \quad . \quad . \quad . \quad . \quad (7.23)$$

The spread factor of a winding differs for each individual harmonic, and, as the value of the factor is quite small for certain harmonics, considerable improvement in the terminal voltage wave-form results.

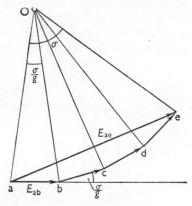

Fig. 7.3

For a winding in which the coils of one phase are distributed over an angle σ (usually $\pi/3$ for a three-phase winding) with g being the number of slots per pole per phase, that is the number of alternative positions of the coils, then the phase displacement between adjacent coils will be σ/g for the fundamental and $n\sigma/g$ for the nth harmonic.

The total voltage of the phase band will thus be the vector sum of the coil voltages **ab**, **bc**, **cd**, etc. (fig. 7.3), that is **ae**.

Thus $k_{s,n}$, the spread factor for the nth harmonic,

$$= ae/g.ab$$
$$= \{2.ao.\sin(n\sigma/2)\}/\{g.2.ao.\sin(n\sigma/2g)\}$$
$$= \{\sin(n\sigma/2)\}/\{g\sin(n\sigma/2g)\} \quad . \quad . \quad . \quad . \quad . \quad . \quad (7.24)$$

and as $g \to$ infinity,

$$k_{s,n} = \{\sin(n\sigma/2)\}/\{n\sigma/2\} \quad . \quad . \quad . \quad . \quad . \quad . \quad . \quad (7.25)$$

The following table shows the spread factor for the fundamental and harmonics of a three-phase winding spread over 60°.

Slots/pole/phase	2	3	4	∞
$n = 1$	0·966	0·96	0·957	0·955
$n = 3$	0·707	0·666	0·653	0·636
$n = 5$	0·259	0·218	0·205	0·191
$n = 7$	0·259	0·178	0·158	0·136
$n = 9$	0·707	0·333	0·271	0·212
$n = 11$	0·966	0·178	0·126	0·087
$n = 13$	0·966	0·218	0·126	0·074
$n = 15$	0·707	0·666	0·271	0·127
$n = 17$	0·259	0·960	0·158	0·056
$n = 19$	0·259	0·960	0·205	0·050

($k_{s,n}$ for the rows)

7.1.7. Use of a Fractional Number of Slots per Pole per Phase

The above table shows the degree of suppression of harmonics in a well-distributed winding. Such a wide distribution is not possible in slow-speed multipolar machines which have only a short pole pitch. With these, two or three slots per phase is the maximum that is possible.

When g is equal to 2, prominence is given to the 11th and 13th harmonics; for g equal to 3, the 17th and 19th are large (in general for three-phase windings the order of the outstanding harmonics is given by $6g \pm 1$). The effective spread of the winding is increased by the use of fractional values of g.

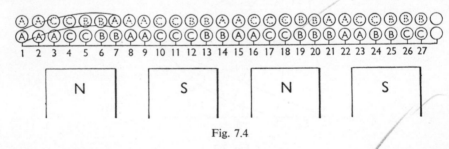

Fig. 7.4

For example, a three-phase machine which has $2\frac{1}{4}$ slots per pole per phase means that there are 27 slots to an adjacent group of 4 poles with 9 coils in series for each phase. These coils must be grouped symmetrically, and so there will be two coils together under three consecutive poles, with three together under the fourth pole. This arrangement is shown in fig. 7.4. Now each of the nine coils differs in angular position from the others. The slot pitch in this case is

$$\lambda = (2/27) 360° = 26\tfrac{2}{3}°,$$

and hence the position of the slots occupied by phase A is:

Slot	1	2	3	8	9	15	16	22	23
Angular displacement from slot 1	0	$26\tfrac{2}{3}°$	$53\tfrac{1}{3}°$	$6\tfrac{2}{3}°$	$33\tfrac{1}{3}°$	$13\tfrac{1}{3}°$	40°	20°	$46\tfrac{2}{3}°$

The value of k_s corresponds to $g = 9$, and such a winding can be considered infinitely spread. The use of fractional pitch is only possible with double-layer windings. It assists considerably, as shown above, in improving the wave-form of the machine but in addition it gives the designer a much greater latitude in his choice of the total number of slots to be used.

On the other hand it is necessary that the whole of the *g* coils (the numerator of the fraction) shall be connected in series, and therefore the number of possible parallel paths in the winding is limited.

It is also necessary to observe the balance rule, viz. the denominator of the fraction must not be a multiple of the number of phases or it will be found impossible to obtain the correct angular displacement between the phases of the winding.

7.2. The Alternator on Open Circuit

When an alternator is driven at constant speed, the terminal voltage on open circuit as given by the equation (7.23) depends upon the flux per pole which in turn depends upon the value of the rotor m.m.f. or excitation current. The latter relation is depicted by the magnetisation curve which is a very similar curve to that derived for a d.c. machine. If the reluctance of the magnetic circuit is confined to the air-gap and the reluctance of the iron portion can be neglected, then the magnetisation curve will be a straight line. This is plotted

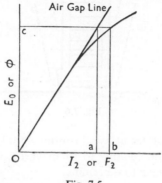

Fig. 7.5

in fig. 7.5 as the air-gap line. In practice the ampere-turns required to drive flux through the rest of the magnetic circuit is small and only becomes apparent at the higher flux values as saturation approaches. Thus in fig. 7.5, corresponding to a flux **oc**, the air-gap ampere-turns are **oa**, the iron ampere-turns are **ab** and the total m.m.f is **ob**.

Saturation is not so pronounced with an alternator of the rotating-field type as with a d.c. machine, nor is there marked residual flux.

7.3. The Alternator on Load

When the alternator is loaded the stator currents modify the magnetic conditions in the machine and may cause changes in the terminal voltage unless correcting action is taken. The effects of the stator current are as follow:

1. *Armature Resistance voltage.* The voltage drop per phase in armature resistance equal to $I_1 R_1$ may be allowed for by vector subtraction in the same

way as for the transformer.   With large machines this has only a small per-unit value and its effect can often be neglected.

2. *Modification of the Flux due to Stator m.m.f.*   A flux plot of the magnetic field of an alternator on open circuit shows the flux to consist of two well-defined components:

   (a) the mutual flux or effective flux which links both rotor and stator turns;
   (b) rotor leakage flux, mainly fringing from pole tip to pole tip, that is, flux which, although contributing to the pole density, does not induce e.m.f. in the stator coils.

Now when stator current flows, this current being a polyphase current in a distributed winding sets up a rotating m.m.f. wave (Section 4.6).

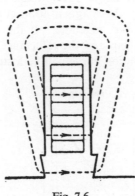

Fig. 7.6

The stator m.m.f. F_1 rotates at synchronous speed, that is, in step with the rotor poles, but its position relative to them varies with the power factor of the load.   This we shall have to determine.

There are then three components of the resultant flux:

   1. mutual flux, differing from the open-circuit value;
   2. rotor leakage flux as before (assuming the rotor m.m.f. is unchanged);
   3. stator leakage flux.

This latter is flux linking only with the armature conductors and not traversing the main-field circuit.   As with the transformer, such leakage flux is responsible for reactance-voltage drops and the winding is said to possess *leakage reactance*.

The stator leakage takes place mainly in the slot portion (*see* Chapter 5), the line linkages being depicted in fig. 7.6, but, in addition, leakage flux also exists encircling the conductors in the overhang of the coils.

The equivalent circuit of an alternator on load (for simple steady-state conditions) is thus that of fig. 7.7.   The resistance R and leakage reactance X_1 are "lumped" and shown causing voltage drops in the external circuit.   An internal e.m.f. due to the mutual flux is postulated.   But the mutual flux is now set up by the resultant of rotor and stator m.m.f. and thus differs from the open-circuit value.

The influence of the stator m.m.f. on the mutual flux is referred to as *armature reaction*.

The shape of the flux wave may also be changed and harmonics may be introduced (particularly the third).

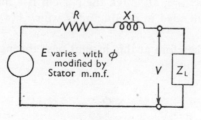

Fig. 7.7

7.3.1. Vector Diagram of an Alternator on Load.   The Potier Diagram for a Round-rotor Machine

At this stage the round-rotor machine only will be considered.   The theory developed for this type of machine will at a later stage be modified so as to apply to the salient-pole alternator.   A two-pole round-rotor machine is depicted in fig. 7.10.   If the terminal voltage is V and the load current I, then from the equivalent circuit of fig. 7.7 the internal e.m.f. must be

$$E = V + I.R + I.jX_1 \quad . \quad . \quad . \quad . \quad . \quad (7.26)$$

which is illustrated in the vector diagram fig. 7.8.

Now in fig. 7.9, the magnetisation curve of the machine, we see that to produce an e.m.f. E, an m.m.f. F_e is required.

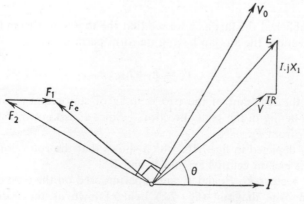

Fig. 7.8

We now refer to the space diagram of the machine showing the stator and an instantaneous position of the rotor.   The instant we have chosen is the instant when the stator m.m.f. F_1 is directed along the horizontal axis which corresponds to the condition that currents in conductors P and P' are at a maximum value.   Note that F_1 has been chosen to be in line with the vector of I_1, and as I_1 rotates in the time vector diagram (fig. 7.8) F_1 does the same in the space diagram (fig. 7.10).

Now the time diagram shows E to be in advance of I by an angle θ slightly greater than the power-factor angle of the load. The voltage in the conductor P is not a maximum, therefore, although the current is a maximum. There will be maximum e.m.f. generated in conductor Q which lies at an angle θ ahead of P.

The flux axis must therefore at this instant pass through Q in order to produce maximum rate of cutting.

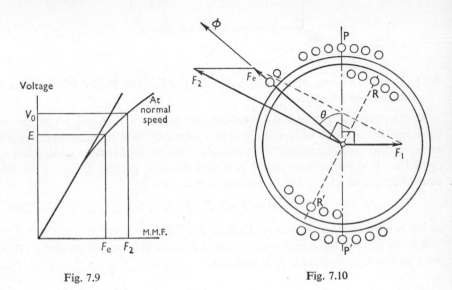

Fig. 7.9   Fig. 7.10

Having established the flux axis we see that the total effective m.m.f. F_e must act in this direction, the air-gap having uniform permeance.

But

$$F_e = F_1 + F_2 \quad . \quad . \quad . \quad . \quad . \quad . \quad (7.27)$$

that is, F_e is the resultant of the two m.m.f.s of stator and rotor, which are obviously not acting in the same direction. Since F_1 is known, F_2 is found by subtracting F_1 from F_e.

F_2 is finally depicted in fig. 7.10, which shows that the rotor conductors are actually at this instant centred around R and R'.

The m.m.f. vectors F_1, F_2 and F_c are superimposed on the time diagram, the resulting composite diagram (fig. 7.8) being known as the *Potier diagram*. Built up in this way the Potier diagram shows us how to determine the excitation required to produce a given terminal voltage V under given load conditions.

Finally, the no-load voltage corresponding to this excitation can be obtained from the magnetisation curve, and the open-circuit voltage V_0 compared with V to find the *per-unit regulation*, i.e. the per-unit rise in voltage as the load is removed.

EXAMPLE

The magnetisation curve of a round-rotor alternator is given by:

Per-unit voltage on open circuit $E_{p.u.}$.	0	0·28	0·55	0·75	0·9	1·0	1·08	1·15	1·20
Per-unit rotor current $[I_2]_{p.u.}$.	.	0	0·2	0·4	0·6	0·8	1·0	1·2	1·4	1·6

The resistance of the stator is 0·02 per unit and the leakage reactance 0·2 per unit. Stator m.m.f. on full load is equivalent to a rotor current of 0·2 per unit.

Find the rotor current and per-unit regulation at full load, 0·8 power factor lagging. In the Potier diagram (fig. 7.8):

$$V = 0·8 + j0·6.$$
$$I(R+jX) = 0·02 + j0·2.$$
$$E = 0·82 + j0·8.$$
$$E = 1·145, \text{ whence } F_e \text{ from the O.C. curve} = 1·4.$$
$$E = 1·145 (0·716 + j0·7).$$

$$F_e = 1·4 (-0·7 + j0·716).$$
$$= -0·98 + j1·0.$$
$$F_1 = -0·2.$$
$$F_2 = F_e - F_1 = -1·18 + j1·0.$$
$$F_2 = 1·54.$$

$$E_0 = 1·185, \text{ from the O.C. curve.}$$

Rotor current: 1·54 per unit.
Regulation: 0·185 per unit.

7.3.2. To Draw the Potier Diagram from Test Results

The lengths of the component vectors required for the construction of the Potier diagram can be obtained from the following tests.   In each of these, the

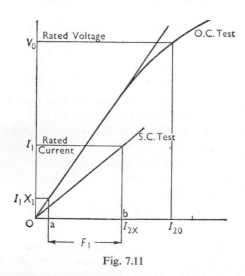

Fig. 7.11

machine is driven at constant rated speed by a prime mover and as no power output is required the driving machine may be small.

Open-circuit Test.   With the stator terminals open-circuited, the rotor field current I_2 is varied and readings taken of the terminal voltage V_0.   Plotting V_0

11—E.M.

against I_2 the result is the magnetisation curve of the machine. The lower part of the curve is usually practically a straight line, and this when extended becomes the air-gap line.

Short-circuit Test. After the excitation has been removed the line terminals are short-circuited through ammeters to read stator current. Maintaining normal speed, excitation is increased slowly until normal full-load current flows in the stator. The results of the two tests are shown in fig. 7.11.

Now, in the short-circuit test, if $I_{2,x}$ is the excitation producing rated stator current, and, if stator resistance is neglected, the Potier diagram for this condition reduces to that of fig. 7.12. Since $V = 0$, $E = I.jX_l$, and moreover F_e is seen to be small. F_1 and F_2 are practically in opposition and very nearly equal to each other.

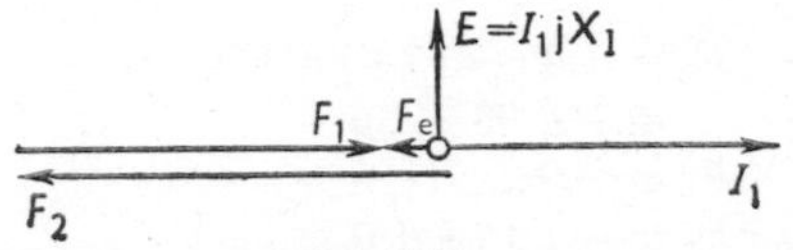

Fig. 7.12

Assuming for the moment that X_1 has been computed from the dimensions of the leakage-flux paths, we see in fig. 7.11 that **oa** is the excitation required to produce a voltage IX_1 on open circuit. **oa** then is a measure of the effective ampere-turns F_e in fig. 7.12. Now **ob** is equal to $I_{2,x}$ which is the rotor current value corresponding to F_2. The difference **ab** is then a measure of F_1 expressed as an equivalent rotor current.

EXAMPLE

A 4000-kVA, three-phase alternator with cylindrical rotor has the following open-circuit characteristic:

| Per-unit field current . | . | . | . | 0·4 | 0·8 | 1·2 | 1·6 |
| Per-unit voltage on open circuit . | | . | . | 0·48 | 0·88 | 1·08 | 1·2 |

The leakage reactance is 0·12 per unit, and full-load current flows in the short-circuited armature when the field current is 0·85 per unit.

Determine the equivalent per-unit field current corresponding to armature reaction.

Leakage reactance = 0·12.
Field current corresponding to reactance drop on O.C. test from curve = 0·1.
Field current on short-circuit test = 0·85.
Armature reaction F_1 (as in fig. 7.11)

$$= 0·85 - 0·1$$
$$= 0·75.$$

The Zero-power-factor Load Test. To determine the value of the leakage reactance additional data is required and this can be supplied from a zero-power-factor load test. As with the open-circuit test, readings of terminal voltage are taken as excitation is varied, but this time the alternator is loaded by means of reactors or alternatively by an under-excited synchronous motor.

The stator current must be kept constant at rated value throughout the test and zero lagging power factor maintained.

Plotting V against I_2 gives a curve which is found to be similar to the open-circuit magnetisation curve but which has been displaced downwards and to the right (fig. 7.13). The reason for this can be seen from the Potier diagram corresponding to the point P.

We see from this that at zero power factor, neglecting resistance, $I_1 j X_1$ is in phase with V and F_e is the numerical difference between F_2 and F_1. The zero-power-factor curve is the locus of P whose co-ordinates are V and F_2, whereas the open-circuit curve is the locus of P′ with co-ordinates E and F_e.

Thus P is displaced downwards from P′ by $I_1 X_1$ and to the right by F_1. These displacements can thus be found by comparing the curves.

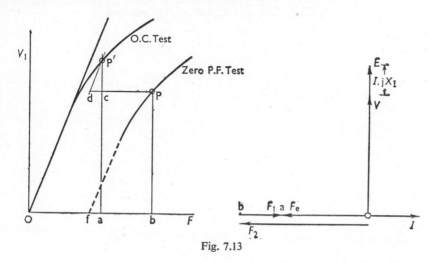

Fig. 7.13

Commencing at the point P in fig. 7.13 **Pd** is drawn horizontally equal to **of** and a line is drawn through **d** parallel to the air-gap line. This cuts the open-circuit curve at P′, whence P′**c** is equal to IX_1 from which X_1 may be found, and **ab** is the excitation corresponding to F_1 the armature reaction.*

EXAMPLE

An 11-kV, three-phase, cylindrical-rotor-type alternator has the following open-circuit characteristic at rated speed:

| Per-unit line voltage . | 0·26 | 0·52 | 0·8 | 1·00 | 1·16 | 1·29 |
| Per-unit field current . | 0·25 | 0·50 | 0·75 | 1·00 | 1·25 | 1·50 |

The excitation to produce full-load current on short circuit is 0·62 per unit, and when the machine supplies full-load kilovolt-amperes at 11-kV and zero power factor the

---

* Points P and P′ do not quite represent identical magnetic conditions in the two tests although the simple theory outlined above suggests this. The gap flux is approximately the same, but the much increased rotor m.m.f. on the zero-power-factor test also produces a higher proportion of rotor leakage flux. This may cause saturation of the rotor part of the magnetic circuit and demand still greater rotor-ampere-turns. The presence of rotor leakage flux results in the two curves having slightly differing shapes, and the corresponding points P and P′ are difficult to identify. The value of X_1 determined, using the construction described above, is slightly greater than the stator leakage reactance and is sometimes termed the "Potier" reactance.

excitation is 1·75 per unit compared with the excitation at 11 kV on the open-circuit characteristic.

Neglect resistance.

Determine:

(a) the per-unit synchronous reactance;
(b) the per-unit leakage reactance;
(c) the armature reaction as in equivalent per-unit field current at full load.

From graph plotted as in fig. 7.13:

(a) per unit excitation from air-gap line at $1·0_{p.u.}E$
$$= 0·95.$$
$$\therefore \ Z_s \text{ (from 7.34)} = 0·62/0·95 = 0·65 \text{ per unit.}$$

(b)
$$dP = 0·62$$
$$cP = 0·45$$
$$cP' = 0·19.$$
Leakage reactance = 0·19 per unit.

(c)   Armature reaction $F_1 = 0·45$ per unit.

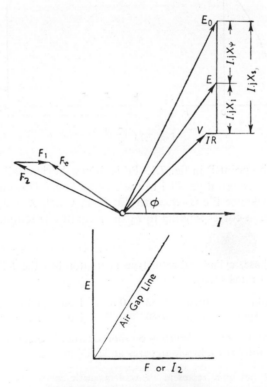

Fig. 7.14

7.3.3. Synchronous Reactance

It is often convenient to neglect the saturation of the iron parts of the magnetic circuit and to consider the magnetisation curve to be linear, that is to consist solely of the air-gap line. Such an assumption is well justified when the machine operates at reduced voltage or under fault conditions when the machine delivers a large lagging current and the flux is considerably reduced by armature reaction.   The Potier diagram of fig. 7.8 then becomes that of fig. 7.14.   Since E_0 is now proportional to F_2 and E is proportional to F_e, by similar triangles E_0 lies along IjX_1 produced.

Thus in fig. 7.14:

$$E_0 = V + I(R + jX_s) \quad . \quad . \quad . \quad . \quad . \quad . \quad (7.28)$$

where

$$X_s = X_1 + X_\phi \quad . \quad . \quad . \quad . \quad . \quad (7.29)$$

X_s is a reactance value greater than the stator leakage reactance X_1 by the value X_ϕ, which is known as the *magnetising reactance*.

For many purposes therefore it is sufficient to assume that an alternator (with constant excitation) can be represented by a *constant* internal e.m.f. E_0 together with series resistance and reactance.

The value of X_s is known as *synchronous reactance*, and $Z_s = R + jX_s$ is the *synchronous impedance*.

Fig. 7.15 compares alternative equivalent circuits of the alternator in terms of the Potier diagram and of synchronous reactance respectively.

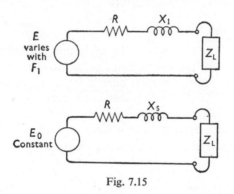

Fig. 7.15

7.3.4. Determination of Synchronous Reactance from Open−and Short-circuit Tests

In fig. 7.16, **oa** is the field current corresponding to normal voltage on open circuit *taken from the air-gap line*.   The short-circuit curve is extrapolated to **oa,** the current at that point being the short-circuit current $I_{s.c.}$ On the assumption that V remains constant within the machine, then

$$V/I_{s.c.} = Z_s \quad . \quad . \quad . \quad . \quad . \quad (7.30)$$

and

$$X_s = \sqrt{(Z_s^2 - R^2)} \quad . \quad . \quad . \quad . \quad . \quad (7.31)$$

The per-unit value of the synchronous impedance

$$z_s = IZ_s/V \quad . \quad . \quad . \quad . \quad . \quad . \quad (7.32)$$

which is

$$= I/(V/Z_s)$$

or

$$z_s = I/I_{s.c.} \quad . \quad . \quad . \quad . \quad . \quad . \quad (7.33)$$

Furthermore by similar triangles in (fig. 7.16),

$$I/I_{s.c.} = \text{ob}/\text{oa} \qquad . \quad . \quad . \quad . \quad . \quad . \quad (7.34)$$

Thus per-unit synchronous impedance is equal to the ratio of the field current corresponding to full-load current on the short-circuit test to the field current corresponding to normal open-circuit voltage on the air-gap line.

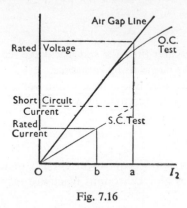

Fig. 7.16

7.3.5. Short-circuit Ratio

The short-circuit ratio is the ratio of the excitation current corresponding to rated armature voltage on the open-circuit saturation curve to the excitation current required to give rated armature current on short circuit.

The short-circuit ratio is thus nearly but not exactly equal to the reciprocal of the per-unit synchronous impedance.

The value of the short-circuit ratio of a large modern round-rotor alternator is of the order of 0·55 and about twice that figure for a salient-pole water-wheel alternator.

7.4. Vector Diagram of the Salient-pole-type Alternator

7.4.1. Two-axis Theory

In developing the vector diagram for the round-rotor machine it has been assumed that the flux is dependent upon the effective m.m.f. F_e which is the vector sum of F_1 and F_2. This is true because the permeance of the air-gap is uniform and the effective flux

$$\Phi = \Lambda(F_1 + F_2) \qquad . \quad . \quad . \quad . \quad . \quad (7.35)$$

With a salient pole machine the gap permeance is not uniform but varies from a maximum at the pole centre (known as the direct axis) to a minimum between the poles (the quadrature axis). Now the rotor m.m.f. always acts along the direct axis producing flux in a permeance Λ_d, but the position of F_1 depends on the load power factor (fig. 7.8). At unity power factor F_1 acts approximately along the quadrature axis where the permeance Λ_q is less, and at zero power factor it lies along the direct axis where its effectiveness is greater.

When F_1 lies at an intermediate angle it should be resolved into components F_d and F_q which act along the direct and quadrature axes respectively. The resultant flux will then be given by

$$\Phi_e = \Lambda_q F_q + \Lambda_d(F_d + F_2) \quad \cdots \cdots \cdots \quad (7.36)$$
$$= \Lambda_d\{(\Lambda_q/\Lambda_d)F_q + F_d + F_2\} \quad \cdots \cdots \quad (7.37)$$
$$= \Lambda_d F_e \quad \cdots \cdots \cdots \cdots \quad (7.38)$$

where
$$F_e = kF_q + F_d + F_2 \quad \cdots \cdots \cdots \quad (7.39)$$
and
$$k = \Lambda_q/\Lambda_d \quad \cdots \cdots \cdots \cdots \quad (7.40)$$

k is known as the *cross-reaction coefficient* the value of which depends mainly on the ratio "pole arc/pole pitch" and is always less than unity.

The effective m.m.f. F_e is thus the vector sum $F_2 + F_d$ together with only a fraction of F_q to allow for its reduced effectiveness.

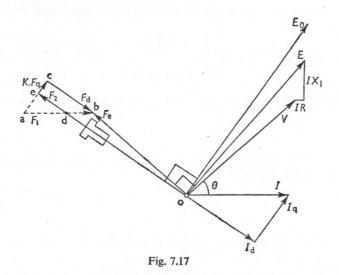

Fig. 7.17

In fig. 7.17 the internal voltage

$$E = V + I(R + jX_1)$$

is shown together with the effective m.m.f. F_e obtained from the magnetisation curve. The direction of F_e establishes the flux axis. It is now required to divide I into components I_d and I_q along the direct and quadrature axes. This is difficult at the moment since we are unsure of the exact position of the direct axis.

Assuming however that this is the line **od**, I can be resolved to I_d and I_q (fig. 7.17). F_2 acts along **od** and F_d can be drawn parallel with it and proportional to I_d. F_q proportional to I_q acts in quadrature and F_q and F_d together form F_1.

But only the fraction kF_q is required, and the figure shows how F_2, kF_q and F_d together make up F_e according to equation (7.39).

Now in the right-angled triangle **acb**, $\mathbf{ac} = F_q$, $\mathbf{bc} = F_d$, $\mathbf{ab} = F_1$ and $\mathbf{ec/ac} = k$

the cross-reaction coefficient.   From the geometry of this triangle it is seen that the point **d** divides the hypotenuse **ab** so that

$$db/ab = ec/ac = k.$$

This then shows how the position of the direct axis can be initially established. The procedure is as follows.

Commencing with F_e, F_1 is added and then **ab** is divided at **d** in the ratio **db/ab** $= k$, establishing **od** as the direct axis.   A perpendicular is dropped from **a**, meeting **od** produced at **e**, whence **oe** is equal to F_2 the required rotor m.m.f.

7.4.2. Synchronous Reactances X_d and X_q of the Salient-pole Machine

For the round-rotor machine we saw that, in the absence of saturation, the effect of armature reaction could be replaced by an additional reactance X_ϕ, making

$$X_s = X_1 + X_\phi \qquad . \quad . \quad . \quad . \quad . \quad . \quad (7.29)$$

from which

$$E_0 = V + IR + IjX_s \quad . \quad . \quad . \quad . \quad . \quad (7.28)$$

In the same way then we expect to find for a salient-pole-type machine, if saturation is neglected,

$$E_0 = V + IR + I_d jX_d + I_q jX_q \qquad . \quad . \quad . \quad . \quad (7.41)$$

where each of the components of current have an associated synchronous reactance, the values being

$$X_d = X_1 + X_\phi . \quad . \quad . \quad . \quad . \quad . \quad . \quad (7.42)$$

and

$$X_q = X_1 + kX_\phi \quad . \quad . \quad . \quad . \quad . \quad . \quad (7.43)$$

The effect of the cross-reaction coefficient reducing armature reaction in the quadrature axis makes X_q less than X_d.

X_d is termed the *direct axis synchronous reactance.*

X_q is termed the *quadrature axis synchronous reactance.*

It is interesting to observe that although equation (7.41) appears to be the equation for the voltage drops in an equivalent circuit, no such equivalent circuit can be constructed since I_d and I_q are two components of current and X_d and X_q are differing reactances.

The vector diagram corresponding to this equation is given in fig. 7.18 and corresponds exactly with the diagram of fig. 7.17, the m.m.f. vectors being replaced by reactance drops proportional to them in accordance with equations (7.42) and (7.43).

In fig. 7.18 the direct axis is determined by adding the vector IjX_q to $V + IR$. The line **oc** is then the direct axis.   The next step is to divide the current I into its components I_d and I_q from which $I_d jX_d$ and $I_q jX_q$ can be found and added in turn to obtain the open-circuit voltage E_0.   Continuing further, the corresponding value E_0' for the round-rotor machine will be obtained by extending the line IjX_q and making it equal to IjX_d.

It is significant that numerically there is very little difference between E_0 and E_0'. This means that from the point of view of voltage regulation, the simpler diagram for the round-rotor machine can often be used for the salient-pole case with reasonable accuracy. The marked effect produced by the saliency is the reduction of the internal angle α.

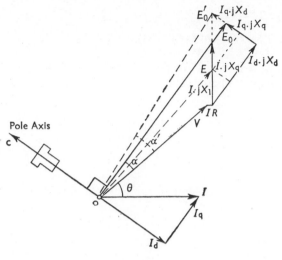

Fig. 7.18

7.4.3. Determination of X_d and X_q by Test

According to the equivalent circuit of fig. 7.15, the alternator is to be regarded as having a constant internal voltage depending on excitation in series with a synchronous impedance. It follows therefore that if the internal voltage is removed, (the machine is still driven at synchronous speed but is unexcited), and then an external voltage is applied, the current that flows will be such that

$$V/I = Z_s \simeq X_s \quad . \quad . \quad . \quad . \quad . \quad (7.44)$$

For a salient-pole machine, then, if the speed is arranged to be just short of synchronism the stator m.m.f. due to I will move slowly relative to the poles. Thus the value of V/I will be observed to vary from a maximum when the m.m.f. lies in the direct axis to a minimum in the quadrature axis.

These maximum and minimum values establish Z_d and Z_q from which X_d and X_q can be found.

It is important that only a small current should be used in this test (no more than 0·5 per unit) in order to ensure an absence of saturation and hence that the results correspond to the air-gap line.

EXAMPLE

An alternator has a direct-axis synchronous reactance of 0·8 per unit and a quadrature-axis synchronous reactance of 0·5 per unit.

Draw the vector diagram for full load at a lagging power factor of $0\cdot8$ and find the per-unit open-circuit voltage.

Neglect saturation.

In the vector diagram of fig. 7.18:

$$V = 0\cdot8 + j0\cdot6.$$
$$IjX_Q = j0\cdot5.$$
$$V + IjX_Q = 0\cdot8 + j1\cdot1.$$
$$= 1\cdot36\,(0\cdot588 + j0\cdot81).$$
$$\therefore\ I_Q = 0\cdot588\,(0\cdot588 + j0\cdot81).$$
$$I_d = 0\cdot81\,(0\cdot81 - j0\cdot588).$$
$$I_QjX_Q = 0\cdot5\,.\,0\cdot588\,(-0\cdot81 + j0\cdot588) = -0\cdot238 + j0\cdot173.$$
$$I_djX_d = 0\cdot81\,.\,0\cdot8\,(0\cdot588 + j\,.\,0\cdot81)\quad=\quad0\cdot381 + j0\cdot525.$$

$$V = 0\cdot8 + j0\cdot6.$$

$$E_0 = 0\cdot943 + j1\cdot298.$$
$$E = 1\cdot60.$$

CHAPTER 8

THE SYNCHRONOUS MOTOR

8.1. Synchronising

8.1.1. Paralleling D.C. Machines

IN a generating station, arrangements have to be made for machines to be connected in parallel for the purpose of sharing the common load. The paralleling connections are known as bus-bars and the generators are connected to the bars through circuit breakers, isolating switches and metering panels.

Let us first consider the case of d.c. generator No. 1 (fig. 8.1) connected between the bus-bars **be** and **hf** and supplying current to the load **ef**. If, at the time of peak load, the current rises above the rating of generator No. 1, it becomes necessary to run up set No. 2 and to connect this generator in parallel so that this machine can supply part of the current required. We will examine in detail the necessary conditions for this operation to be carried out. These are only two, namely that the voltage and polarity of the incoming machine should be

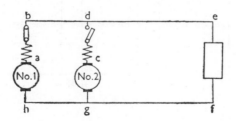

Fig. 8.1

the same as that of the machine already on load. It is not necessary for the two machines to be of the same size.

The generators are represented in the figure by constant-voltage sources in series with their armature resistances, thus for generator No. 1 already on load

$$E_{ha} = V_{ab} + V_{ef} \quad . \quad . \quad . \quad . \quad . \quad . \quad (8.1)$$

or
$$E_1 = I_{ab} R_1 + V \quad . \quad . \quad . \quad . \quad . \quad . \quad (8.2)$$

Generator No. 2 will be connected in parallel when the switch **cd** is closed. The prime mover driving this machine is started and brought up to speed and the excitation of the generator is then adjusted to make

$$E_{gc} = V_{dg} \quad . \quad . \quad . \quad . \quad . \quad . \quad . \quad (8.3)$$

or
$$E_2 = V \quad . \quad . \quad . \quad . \quad . \quad . \quad . \quad (8.4)$$

This also involves making sure that if **d** is positive to **g** then g' must also be positive with respect to **c**, i.e. that the polarity of the incoming machine is correct. The voltage drop across the open switch will therefore be zero, and it can be closed without causing current to flow in this part of the circuit, i.e. in machine No. 2, or altering the existing conditions in any way. Machine No. 2 is then said to be "floating" on the bus-bars.

If the excitation of generator No. 2 is now increased slightly,

$$E_{gc} = V_{cd} + V_{ef} \quad . \quad . \quad . \quad . \quad . \quad . \quad (8.5)$$

or

$$E_2 = I_{cd}R_2 + V \quad . \quad . \quad . \quad . \quad . \quad . \quad (8.6)$$

Thus the current I_{cd} is set up.

Now

$$I_{ab} + I_{cd} = I_{ef} \quad . \quad . \quad . \quad . \quad . \quad (8.7)$$

so that as I_{cd} increases, I_{ab} will automatically be reduced.

From equation (8.2) it will be seen that the bus-bar voltage V tends to rise. This may be reduced to normal again by reducing E_1. In other words, after the

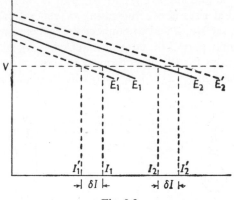

Fig. 8.2

second machine has been paralleled, load can be transferred from one machine to the other by decreasing the excitation of the one and increasing the excitation of the other. To raise the bus-bar voltage, the excitation of both machines must be increased.

Equations (8.2) and (8.6) may be represented graphically by the sloping lines in fig. 8.2. If the common terminal voltage is V, then the two currents in the machines will be I_1 and I_2.

The effect of an increase of excitation is to raise the open-circuit voltage and consequently the whole of the characteristic curve. Thus, in the figure, E_2 is increased to E_2' and E_1 correspondingly reduced to E_1', the new characteristics being shown in dotted line.

For the same bus-bar voltage the new currents will be I_1' and I_2', from which it will be seen that the current δI has been transferred from one generator to the other.

In the above case it has been tacitly assumed that the speed of the prime mover remains constant at all loads, that is, that the engine is controlled by a very sensitive governor mechanism.   In practice, when the load on the generator increases, speed tends to fall, and will do so by an amount sufficient to cause the governor gear to operate, increasing the engine power and torque to balance the retarding effect of the increased load.

The speed/load characteristic of the governor thus adds to the effect of armature resistance in reducing the terminal voltage of the generator on load. The overall terminal-voltage/load-current characteristic is thus a curve similar to those depicted in fig. 8.2, the value of E_1 being the no-load voltage and the slope being dependent on the combined effects of armature resistance and of the governor sensitivity.

It should be noted also that for a d.c. generator running in parallel with others, its e.m.f. can be increased—and therefore its share of the load—either by increasing its excitation, or by increasing the speed of the prime mover.

8.1.2. Paralleling A.C. Machines

A somewhat more elaborate procedure is necessary when a.c. generators are to be paralleled though the same fundamental switching conditions apply.   The voltage across the switch of the incoming machine must be reduced to zero, and it can then be closed without causing any change in the current distribution.*

The corresponding case for the a.c. machine is illustrated in fig. 8.3.   The phase voltages of generator No. 1 are given in the vector diagram (fig. 8.4 (a)), whilst those of the incoming machine No. 2 are in fig. 8.4 (b).   It is well to remember that these two sets of vectors cannot be drawn on the same diagram unless the frequencies are identical.   If the frequency of the incoming machine is

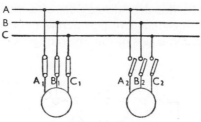

Fig. 8.3

very nearly but not exactly equal to the first, then if the vectors of fig. 8.4 (b) are superimposed on those of fig. 8.4 (a) the former will not be stationary but will rotate at the difference frequency.

It will now be seen (fig. 8.4 (c)) that the voltages across the blades of the open switch A_1A_2, B_1B_2, C_1C_2 will not be zero unless:

1. the voltages of the two machines are equal, $V_{A_1N} = V_{A_2N}$;
2. the frequencies of the two machines are equal;
3. the sequence of the phases of the two machines are the same;
4. the voltage vectors coincide.

The last condition will not in practice be maintained for any considerable length of time.   It is not possible to adjust the two frequencies to maintain exact

* It is profitable to examine this statement in the light of Thévénin's theorem.

equality (unless the alternators are mechanically coupled) and hence the voltages across the switch will rise and fall slowly as A_2, B_2 and C_2 move relative to A_1, B_1 and C_1.

The process of synchronising therefore involves first adjusting the voltage and frequency of the incoming machine so as to make them as nearly as possible equal to those of the "on load" machine, and then closing the switch at the instant when the voltage across it is zero. To ascertain correctly the instant of zero voltage a piece of equipment known as a synchroscope is required.

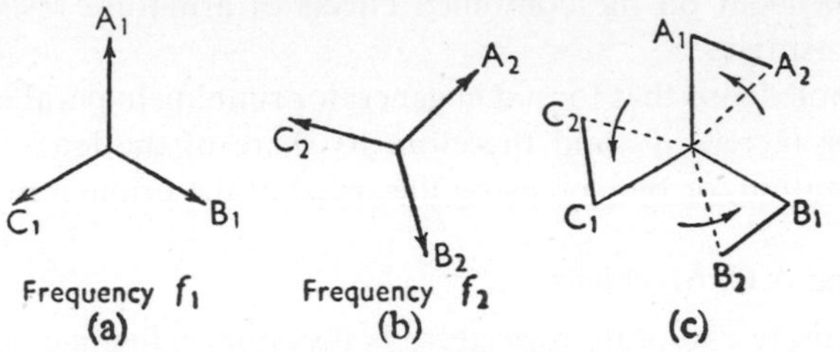

Fig. 8.4

8.1.3. Synchroscopes

Dark-lamp method. If lamps are connected across the blades of the switch, as in fig. 8.5, the brilliancy of the lamps will vary as the voltages A_1A_2, B_1B_2 and C_1C_2 rise and fall. In the first place the fact that they all rise and fall together will indicate that the sequence of the phases of the incoming machine is correct. The frequency of this machine should be adjusted until the rate of rise and fall is quite slow and a dark period of about four seconds is observed. The switch may then be closed in the middle of a dark period. The vector diagram shows that the maximum voltage across the lamps is twice the phase voltage of the machine, and lamps of suitable rating (usually two in series) must be used.

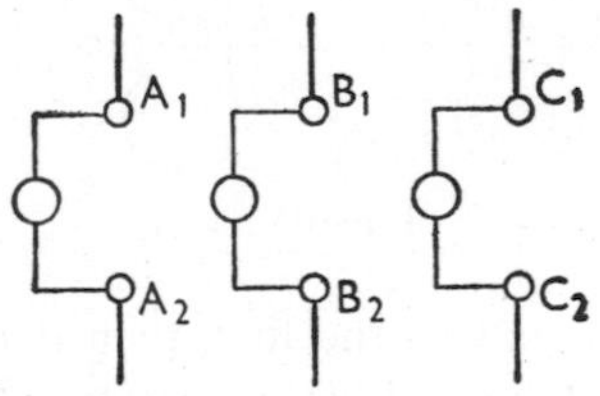

Fig. 8.5

Once the phase sequence has been established, and if the connections have not been changed, it is not necessary subsequently to employ three sets of lamps; one set will suffice as shown in fig. 8.6 (a), together with voltage transformers for use on an H.V. system.

Bright-lamp Method. If the connections of one of the transformer secondaries of fig. 8.6 (a) is reversed as shown in fig. 8.6 (b), then the correct instant for closing the switch is when the voltage across the lamp is at its maximum value.

The brightest point in the cycle is possibly more easy to distinguish than the middle of a dark period and avoids confusing the latter with a lamp failure.

Cross-connected Lamps.   When three sets of lamps are connected (fig. 8.6 (c)) with lamp (1) between A_1 and A_2, lamp (2) between B_1 and C_2 and lamp (3) between C_1 and B_2 the lamp voltages rise and fall successively.   The dark period of lamp (1) indicates the instant of synchronism and at that instant

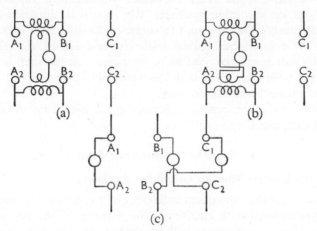

Fig. 8.6 (a), (b) and (c)

lamps (2) and (3) will be equally bright.   If they are mounted at the corners of an equilateral triangle they give the appearance of rotation, in one direction if the incoming machine is slow and in the other if it is fast.

Mechanical Synchroscope.   This instrument consists of two sets of coils, a rotor and a stator unit (fig. 8.7), the rotor being mounted in the centre of the stator.   The stator has two coils at right angles which are fed with currents in

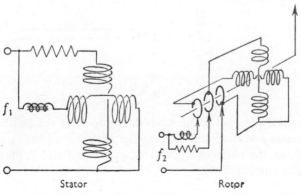

Fig. 8.7

quadrature in time through a resistance and reactor phase-splitting circuit. The series impedances are of the order of hundreds of ohms, and the terminals are connected across the "on load" machine.   A rotating field is thus set up at the centre of this system at the frequency of the supply.

The rotor unit has similar coils, but these are mounted on a spindle carrying a pointer. Slip rings are arranged to pass current to the coils, at the same time allowing the rotor to rotate freely. The terminals of this system with series impedances similar to those of the stator are connected across the "incoming machine". Relative to the rotor coils there will thus be a rotating field at the frequency f_2 of the incoming machine. The two rotating fields interact and lock together causing the rotor unit to rotate at the difference frequency. The rotation of the pointer thus indicates the rise and fall of voltage across the synchronising switch and the position of the pointer on the shaft is so arranged relative to the coils that when it points vertically upwards ("12 o'clock") it indicates the correct instant for closure.

Other forms of synchroscope are described in Electrical Engineering (General) (Dover and Chapman).

8.2. The Synchronous Motor

8.2.1. The Synchronous Machine on Infinite Bus-bars

We now consider the subsequent behaviour of a synchronous machine after it has been synchronised with another in the manner of the previous section. Certain simplifying assumptions will be made. The machine will be represented by a constant-voltage source (for a given excitation) in series with a constant synchronous impedance. The "on load" machine to which it has been connected will be assumed to have a much greater rating; that is to say, its synchronous impedance will be much smaller and can be neglected. The bus-bar voltage and frequency will thus remain constant in spite of changes taking place in the machine which is the subject of the investigation. Under such circumstances the bus-bars are termed infinite bus-bars.

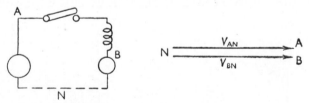

Fig. 8.8

The single-phase diagram of fig. 8.8 is drawn to show the bus-bar A, with the supply as a constant-voltage source, together with the incoming machine at B. On synchronising, the voltages V_{BN} and V_{AN} are equal and in phase; the switch is closed and no current flows.

8.2.2. Synchronous Motor on No-load

If now the driving torque of the prime mover is removed, the machine will tend to slow down and the vector V_{BN} will tend to fall back in relation to V_{AN}. An angle α will appear between them, $d\alpha/dt$ being the difference in their angular velocities. This means that a voltage drop V_{BA} is set up across the impedance of the circuit and current flows according to the vector diagram (fig. 8.9).

The current in the circuit

$$I_{BA} = V_{BA}/Z_s \qquad \qquad (8.8)$$

and lags behind V_{BA} by the angle $\theta = \tan^{-1} X_s/R$ which is usually nearly $\pi/2$. This current can be represented either by the vector I_{BA} or by I_{AB}.

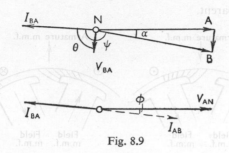

Fig. 8.9

The following angles are important:

$\alpha =$ angle between V_{AN} and V_{BN} = load angle.

$\theta =$ angle between V_{BA} and I_{BA} = impedance angle.

$\psi =$ angle between V_{BN} and I_{BA}.

$\phi =$ angle between V_{AN} and I_{AB}.

Now this circuit is a simple loop with two sources and so the powers developed by the sources will be as follows:

$$\text{output of source A} = V_{AN}I_{AB} \cos \phi \qquad \qquad (8.9)$$
$$\text{output of source B} = V_{BN}I_{BA} \cos \psi \qquad \qquad (8.10)$$

and the power in the "load" Z

$$= V_{BA}I_{BA} \cos \theta$$
$$= (IZ)I(R/Z) = I^2R, \text{ the copper loss} \qquad (8.11)$$

Now under the assumed conditions the angle ϕ is small, consequently source A is operating at practically unity power factor. But in equation (8.10) ψ is nearly 180° and $\cos \psi$ is negative. This source is "delivering negative power", indicating that it is really receiving rather than supplying energy. Evidently, then, this power is associated with a driving torque produced by the machine itself tending to prevent the machine from slowing down.

The load angle α will only increase therefore (and with it I_{BA}) until this power is equal to the mechanical power that was removed in shutting down the prime mover. The machine will then continue to run in synchronism but with this small load angle α.

8.2.3. Production of Driving Torque

A simplified diagram (fig. 8.10) is useful in attempting to show the presence of this driving torque due to I_{BA}. The figure shows on the left a portion of machine A with the rotor poles moving clockwise. The direction of the e.m.f.

12—E.M.

in the conductors under the poles will be in the direction given and as this machine operates with angle $\phi \simeq 0$ this direction also represents current. The armature reaction field will be directed along the quadrature axis in the direction of the arrow and will rotate with the poles as previously described. The main flux is thus distorted as indicated in the figure, and the retarding action of this should readily be apparent.

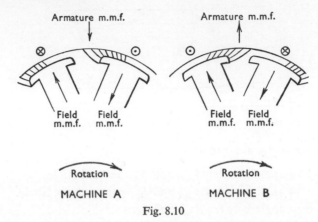

Fig. 8.10

Now in the case of machine B we have seen that the current is practically in antiphase with the generated e.m.f. The conductor e.m.f.s will be identical with those of machine A; the current, however, will be in the reverse direction. The result is that the armature reaction m.m.f. of the motor is the reverse of that of the alternator, and the flux will tend to be concentrated towards the leading pole tip.

That this flux tends to pull the pole forward, i.e. to produce a driving torque is now evident.

8.2.4. Effect of Increase of Load

Having established that a machine, once synchronised, will continue to run as a motor at synchronous speed after the prime mover has been uncoupled, the mechanical losses being supplied electrically, we next consider the effect of applying a mechanical load. We can now anticipate that mechanical load on the rotor will cause a tendency to slow down; the load angle α will increase, so will I_{BA}, and more electrical power will be converted to mechanical power. The machine will continue to run at synchronous speed but it will regulate its own input by increasing its angle of lag according to the load demand. The exact relation between current, power and α must now be determined.

8.2.5. Current Locus with Increasing Load

Expanding equation (8.8):

$$I_{BA} = V_{BA}/Z_s = (V_{BN} - V_{AN})/Z_s = V_{BN}/Z_s + (-V_{AN}/Z_s) \quad (8.12)$$

and the current I_{BA} can thus be regarded as the superposition of two short-circuit currents.

With V_{BN} and V_{AN} numerically equal as in fig. 8.11 (a), the bus-bar voltage V_{AN} is taken as the reference so that as the load angle varies the vector V_{BN} rotates, the locus of the point B being circular. V_{AN}/Z can now be drawn to a current scale and will be inclined to V_{AN} by the impedance angle θ and the vector $-V_{AN}/Z$ is the reverse of this. V_{BN}/Z will similarly lag behind V_{BN} by the angle θ so that the locus of V_{BN}/Z will be as shown. Drawing this vector from the extremity of the vector $(-V_{AN}/Z)$ the current vector I_{BA} is determined according to equation (8.12).

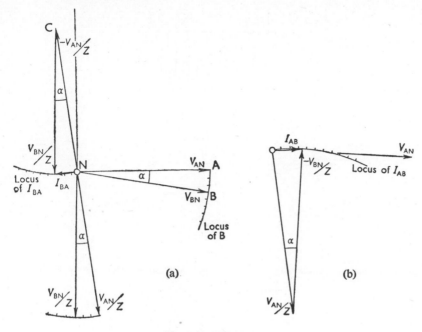

Fig. 8.11 (a) and (b)

The locus of the extremity of I_{BA} is thus a circle of radius V_{BN}/Z with its centre at the point C. The current vector subtends the angle α at C, and the manner in which it increases with α is clearly shown from the locus. It should be remembered that the projection on V_{AN} of I_{BA} (the in-phase component of current) is a measure of the power input to the motor. The horizontal axis can be scaled in kilowatts as indicated in Appendix A.

The full implications of this locus will be discussed later. If alternatively the current vector I_{AB} is required, the construction for its locus is shown in fig. 8.11 (b).

It must also be remembered that throughout this analysis it has been assumed that Z_s remains constant under all conditions.

8.2.6. Effect of Variation of Field Current

An industrial type of synchronous motor is usually equipped with its own exciter, a directly coupled shunt generator from which the field current is obtained. In many cases the exciter is overhung from the end plate of the

main machine.   A regulator in the exciter field circuit controls the exciter
voltage and consequently the field current of the synchronous motor.   We will
now trace the effect of increasing the field current of a synchronous motor on
load.   The magnetisation curve shows the relation between V_{BN} and I_f, consequently the first effect of an increase of I_f to I_f' is that V_{BN} increases to V_{BN}'.
The original vector diagram of fig. 8.11 is redrawn in fig. 8.12 and shows

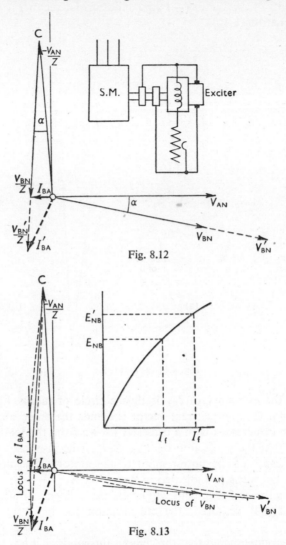

Fig. 8.12

Fig. 8.13

$(-V_{AN}/Z)$ and V_{BN}/Z together with the current I_{BA} for a given angle α.   Now
as I_f increases to I_f' and V_{BN} to V_{BN}' there is no immediate change in the load
angle so that I_{BA} is seen to change to I_{BA}'.   It is observed that the main change
which occurs is that the current is increased in magnitude and advanced in
phase.   The in-phase component of current remains practically constant.   The
very small increase in value which does occur tends to accelerate the machine

and so reduce α, the result of which is shown in fig. 8.13. This current locus is a straight line at right angles to the voltage axis and corresponds to constant input power conditions which must result since the mechanical load is in no way changed.*

The important fact to be appreciated at this stage is that:

INCREASED EXCITATION CAUSES LEADING POWER FACTOR.

DECREASED EXCITATION CAUSES LAGGING POWER FACTOR.

8.2.7. Power-factor Correction

These features make the synchronous motor a most useful industrial machine. Its speed is constant at all loads (provided mains frequency remains constant), which is an important factor in many operations such as textile drives where a variation of motor speed can cause a variation in the product.

It can always be adjusted to operate at unity power factor for optimum efficiency and economy, but, moreover, if the rating of the machine will allow, it may be over excited and take current at a leading power factor. In this way it provides leading reactive kilovolt-amperes to the system, improving the power factor of the complete installation. The following example is typical of such a condition.

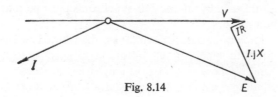

Fig. 8.14

EXAMPLE

A process drive is supplied by a 2500-h.p., three-phase, 4400-V induction motor having a full-load efficiency of 0·93 and a power factor of 0·87. A synchronous motor having a rating of 3000 kVA is installed to provide additional drive and its input is found to be 1750 kW. The resistance and synchronous reactance are 0·006 per unit and 0·35 per unit, and the magnetisation curve at rated speed is as follows:

Field current (A)	.	.	11·5	23	34·5	47·5	67	115
O.C. line voltage (V)	.	.	1000	2000	3000	4000	5000	6000

Determine the synchronous-motor field current required to improve the power factor of the total load to unity.

$$\text{Induction motor kVA} = \frac{2500 \times 0\cdot746}{0\cdot93 \times 0\cdot87} = 2300.$$

kVAr to be supplied by synchronous motor $= 2300 \times 0\cdot493 = 1135.$

kW   „   „   „   „ $= 1750.$

* Strictly, it is the output power which has the constant value and the input power will increase slightly at the higher current values due to increased copper losses. It is shown in Appendix A that the locus corresponding to constant output is a portion of a large-diameter circle.

Synchronous motor current (fig. 8.14) per unit

$$I = -1750/3000 + j1135/3000 = -0.583 + j0.378.$$
$$IR = -0.0035 - j0.002\ 27.$$
$$IjX = 0.132 - j0.204.$$

$$V = 1.000 + j0.$$

$$E = 1.1355 - j0.2063.$$
$$E = 1.155 \text{ (per unit)}.$$
$$= 5080 \text{ V}.$$

$$I_f = 70 \text{ A from curve.}$$

8.2.8. Starting

The synchronous motor must first be brought up to synchronous speed before it is capable of operating with load angle α in the manner previously described. A small direct-coupled induction motor, known as a pony motor, may be used for this purpose unless the motor is required to start against full-load torque. The induction motor must have two poles less than the main machine and so be capable of raising the speed of the latter to synchronous speed. Excitation is then applied to the main motor, and the process of synchronising is carried out by means of a synchroscope.

This method is not very satisfactory and not suited to industrial needs. Modern machines are usually of the self-synchronising type and are arranged to start as induction motors.

Cage windings, known as damper windings, distributed in slots in the pole faces are always fitted to synchronous motors for a purpose to be described in the next chapter, and so these may also be employed for starting.

With the field winding open-circuited the stator is first connected to a reduced voltage by means of an auto-transformer starter. A rotating field is produced, inducing currents in the cage winding and developing induction-motor torque. The machine accelerates as an induction motor, but cannot reach synchronism since all induction motors run with a small slip. When the maximum speed is reached, the field switch is closed connecting the field windings to the d.c. excitation bus-bars, and as the current builds up in the inductive field system, synchronising torque is developed over part of the slip cycle. Provided the original slip is not too great, or the inertia of the system excessive, this should be sufficient to cause the final acceleration required to reach synchronous speed and the rotor is said to pull into step. The auto-transformer tapping is now quickly changed and the machine runs on full voltage ready for load to be applied.

At the moment of starting, when the rotor is at standstill, a large e.m.f. is induced in the field winding, and for this reason the number of field turns of a machine arranged for self-synchronising must not be too large; also damping resistances may be connected in parallel. If the machine has its own directly coupled exciter, the field windings may sometimes remain connected to it. The exciter voltage cannot commence building up until its own critical speed is reached, and the subsequent delay usual with all d.c. generators enables the main machine to reach slip speed before the excitation is effectively applied.

As the exciter builds up, the main machine synchronises automatically and the stator is then switched to full voltage.

Large synchronous motors, and especially those designed for starting against full-load torque, employ three-phase wound-rotor-type windings in place of the cage windings in the pole faces. These are connected to slip rings and external starting resistances exactly in the manner of wound-rotor induction motors, enabling high starting torque to be obtained. The starting resistance is cut out step by step, and when the rings are short-circuited the starting winding forms a very efficient damper winding.

8.3. The Synchronous Induction Motor

The conventional, and most efficient, synchronous motor is the salient-pole type, but a round-rotor-type machine can also be used. In this case the motor can have a distributed two-phase or three-phase winding of normal induction-motor construction which is used not only as a starter and damping winding but also to carry the excitation current.

The exciter may be connected in various ways, one of which is shown in fig. 8.15 where it is connected between one of the slip rings and the other two which are short-circuited under running conditions. At the instant of starting the exciter is unexcited, and when the starting resistances are cut out the machine

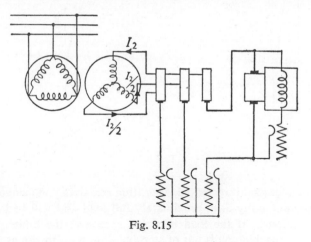

Fig. 8.15

first runs as a normal induction motor. After a short delay, the exciter voltage builds up, and field current is produced flowing through one phase of the rotor winding to the star-point where it divides between the other two phases in parallel, each of which therefore carries half the exciter current. The direct current flowing in the rotor conductors is thus identical with that of fig. 4.31 (b) which shows the instantaneous currents due to a three-phase a.c. supply at the instant of maximum current in one of the phases. The corresponding rotor m.m.f. is shown in the same figure to be almost sinusoidally distributed, and consequently as this field is established the machine pulls into step as previously described and the machine becomes a synchronous motor.

8.3.1. The Synchronous Induction-motor Circle Diagram

The locus of the vector of stator current I_{AB} in a synchronous motor has been described in fig. 8.11 (b). I_{AB} is the resultant of two vectors V_{AN}/Z_s and $-V_{BN}/Z_s$. Now in this case V_{AN}/Z_s is the current taken by the machine when running at synchronous speed with applied voltage V_{AN} but without excitation. This current is practically I_0, the no-load current of the machine as an induction motor. The current V_{BN}/Z_s is the short-circuit current in the stator I_X when driven at synchronous speed and thus depends on the value of the excitation.

In fig. 8.16 this locus is shown superimposed upon the circle diagram for induction-motor operation derived by the methods of Chapter 6. The locus indicates that at light load the synchronous motor will operate at a leading

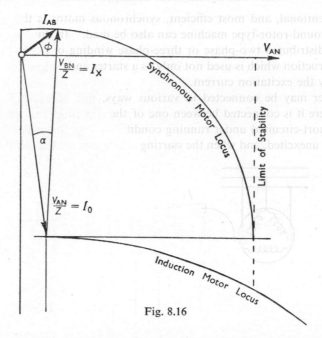

Fig. 8.16

power factor and if load is increased, excitation remaining unchanged, the power factor will become unity at approximately full load and will be lagging under overload conditions. If the load becomes excessive, the limit of stability is reached and the machine pulls out of step but continues to run as an induction motor until the excess-load torque is removed when it should resynchronise automatically.

The overload capacity of the machine as a synchronous motor (i.e. the position of the limit of stability) is seen to depend on the value of I_x, which is almost proportional to the excitation. The value of I_0 must also be large unless considerable variation of power factor and load angle can be tolerated over the working range. For this reason a synchronous induction motor has a longer air-gap than is usual with induction machines, improving its performance as a synchronous machine at the expense of its induction-motor characteristics.

CHAPTER 9

PARALLEL OPERATION OF SYNCHRONOUS MACHINES

9.1. Generator Operation

THE operation of a synchronous machine on infinite bus-bars will now be extended to include the generating regime.   Once more we consider the machine of fig. 8.8, but now, after paralleling, instead of shutting down the prime mover as in the previous section, we increase its driving torque.   The rotor of the machine will tend to accelerate, the poles advancing beyond their synchronous position, and the vector V_{BN} will now lead V_{AN} by angle α.

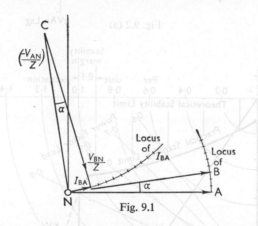

Fig. 9.1

The locus diagram of fig. 8.11, which showed the effect of the rotor lagging, is now extended for leading values of α (fig. 9.1). I_{BA} is now almost in phase with the bus-bar voltage V_{AN}, hence the machine is now delivering power to the bars, and α takes up a stable value when the alternator load balances the increased power of the prime mover.

9.1.1. Operation Chart

The locus of fig. 9.2 refers, shall we say, to one of the turbo-alternators of a power station, the excitation of which has been adjusted to make the generated e.m.f. of the machine equal to the bus-bar voltage (this is known as $1 \cdot 0$ per-unit excitation), and it shows how the current will change as the steam supply to the turbine is increased.   The current vector increases in length and progressively leads the bus-bar voltage vector.

Other loci can be drawn for differing values of V_{BN} (i.e. for differing per-unit excitations), and these will also be circles with centre C but with differing radii.

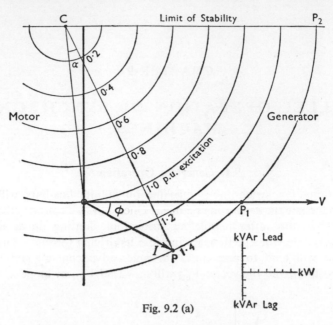

Fig. 9.2 (a)

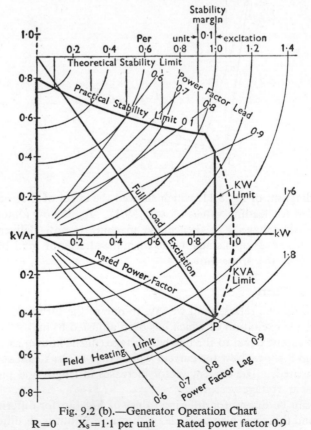

Fig. 9.2 (b).—Generator Operation Chart
R=0 X_s=1·1 per unit   Rated power factor 0·9

From the family of curves (fig. 9.2 (a)) the excitation and the load angle corresponding to any given current can be found. For example, it is seen that to operate at lagging power factor an excitation greater than 1·0 per unit must be used. The in-phase and quadrature components of I are a measure of the kilowatts and reactive kilovolt-amperes supplied by the machine, and corresponding power scales are devised to read these values directly. The diagram is thus known as an *operation chart*.

Suppose the machine is operating at point P, generating current I at power factor $\cos \phi$ (the necessary excitation is 1·4 per unit). If the steam supply to the turbine is increased, excitation remaining constant, α will increase and the operating point will move around the circular locus of 1·4 per-unit excitation, the kilowatt load increasing but the reactive kilovolt-amperes diminishing. At P_1 the power factor is unity. If the driving torque continues to increase, the load will do likewise until the point P_2 is reached. Here the kilowatt output (and retarding torque) is a maximum, and any further increase in α would result in a decrease in the retarding effect of alternator load. At this point then the machine would break from synchronism. The line CP_2 is the *limit of steady-state stability*.

9.1.2. Operation Chart Limits

In fig. 9.2 (b) an operation chart has been drawn for a machine with a synchronous reactance of 1·1 per unit and zero resistance. The length of OC is therefore $1/1·1 = 0·91$, enabling the excitation circles to be drawn. The full-load operating point P corresponds to the rated power factor of 0·9. Practical operation of the machine as an alternator on infinite bus-bars is restricted to the portion of the figure bounded by:

(a) the zero-power axis;
(b) the field heating limits—an excitation circle corresponding to full-load excitation;
(c) the kW limit—if imposed by the maximum power of the prime mover;
(d) the kVA limit—a circle of unit radius about O;
(e) the practical stability limit.

Limit (e) is obtained by subtracting an assumed stability margin (say 0·1 per-unit power) from each point on the theoretical stability limit. At all excitations on the practical limit the machine will therefore have a power in hand of 0·1 per unit before the actual stability limit is reached.

9.2. Comparison of the Potier Diagrams for Generator and Motor Operation

Although it is usually satisfactory to assume that synchronous impedance remains constant it will be advisable at this stage to re-examine the Potier diagram which enables allowance to be made for saturation. The Potier diagram for a generator has already been explained and the same method will now be applied to the motor case.

The diagram of fig. 7.8 relating to a round-rotor machine has been redrawn in fig. 9.3 with the slight modification that the terminal voltage V has been taken as the reference vector in the horizontal direction. This is more convenient since V is now the bus-bar voltage and remains constant.

The diagram for the generator delivering a load current I at a lagging power factor $\cos\theta$ is developed as explained on p. 160 in order to find the rotor m.m.f. F_2. This vector is seen to lie ahead of the no-load pole axis by the load angle α.

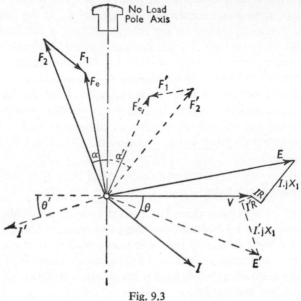

Fig. 9.3

If on the other hand the rotor is retarded and the machine operates as a motor, it is required to find the rotor excitation when the load current is I', a *motoring* current at a *leading* power factor $\cos\theta'$. The voltage drops in resistance and leakage reactance are added to V in their correct angular relation to I' to find the generated voltage E', and the corresponding effective m.m.f. F_e' is obtained from the magnetisation curve. F_e is erected at right angles to E', and F_1' subtracted to obtain F_2' which lies behind the no-load pole axis by the angle α'.

Constructions corresponding to figs. 7.17 or 7.18 for the salient-pole machine can equally well be applied to motor operation when the current vector is in the opposite quadrant to the generator case.

EXAMPLE

Draw and explain the Potier diagram for a cylindrical rotor-type alternator on load at a lagging power factor. Compare this diagram with the corresponding one for the same machine when operating as a synchronous motor on load at a leading power factor.

An 11-kV, three-phase, cylindrical-rotor synchronous machine has the following open-circuit characteristic at rated speed:

Line voltage	.	.	.	8300	10 300	12 000	13 500	14 600
Field current (amperes)	.			60	80	100	120	140

At full-load current, armature resistance drop is 2% (0·02 per unit), armature leakage reactance drop 20% (0·2 per unit) and the armature reaction is equivalent to a field current of 35 A. Find the excitation required when the machine operates as a synchronous motor on 11-kV mains with full-load current at a power factor of 0·6 leading.

$$V = 11.$$
$$IR = -0.22\ (0.6+j0.8) = -0.13-j0.18.$$
$$IjX = -2.2\ (-0.8+j0.6) = +1.76-j1.32.$$

$$E = 12.63-j1.50.$$
$$E = \sqrt{(12.63^2+15^2)} = 12.72\ \text{kV}.$$

From graph $F_e = 108.5$ A.

$$F_e = 108.5\left(\frac{1.5}{12.72}+j\frac{12.63}{12.72}\right) = 12.8+j107.7.$$
$$F_1 = -35\ (0.6+j0.8) = -21-j28.$$
$$F_2 = F - F_1 = 33.8+j135.7.$$
$$F_2 = 140\ \text{A}.$$

The Potier diagrams for the generator and motor cases are shown in fig. 9.3.

9.3. Power/Angle Relation

The relation between the power P and the angle α will now be derived.

Writing V for V_{AN} the bus-bar voltage, and E for V_{BN} the generated e.m.f., the vector diagram corresponding to the operating point P in fig. 9.2 is redrawn in fig. 9.4.

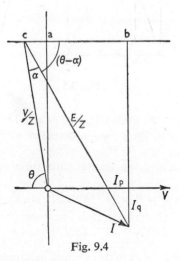

Fig. 9.4

The in-phase current
$$I_p = ab$$
$$= cb - ca$$
$$= (E/Z) \cos (\theta-\alpha)-(V/Z) \cos \theta$$
$$= (V/Z)\{(E/V) \cos (\theta-\alpha)-R/Z\} \quad . \quad . \quad . \quad . \quad (9.1)$$

Power $P = VI_p$
$$= (V^2/Z)\{(E/V) \cos (\theta-\alpha)-R/Z\} \quad . \quad . \quad . \quad . \quad (9.2)$$

If R is sufficiently small to be neglected, which is usually the case, $\theta = 90°$.

$$P = (V^2/X)(E/V) \sin \alpha \quad . \quad . \quad . \quad . \quad . \quad (9.3)$$

Note that

$$V^2/X = \text{short-circuit volt-amperes}$$
$$= \text{rated volt-amperes}/(x \text{ per unit})$$

and
$$E/V = \text{per-unit excitation.}$$

The graph of equation (9.3) is shown in fig. 9.5, the power/angle diagram.

9.3.1. Synchronising Power

The stability of the machine at any point on the operating chart relies on the fact that, if α is given a small increase due to some disturbance, additional electrical power output causes a torque unbalanced by driving torque, producing

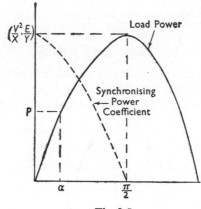

Fig. 9.5

retardation and a return to the original value of α.   This excess torque is known as *synchronising torque*, and the power associated with it as the *differential* or *synchronising power*.

For a round-rotor machine, neglecting saturation and stator resistance, the load power

$$P = (V^2/X)(E/V) \sin \alpha \quad . \quad . \quad . \quad . \quad (9.3)$$

and
$$dP/d\alpha = (V^2/X)(E/V) \cos \alpha \quad . \quad . \quad . \quad . \quad (9.4)$$

The synchronising power ΔP due to $\Delta \alpha$, a small increment of α,

$$\Delta P = (dP/d\alpha)\Delta \alpha \quad . \quad . \quad . \quad . \quad . \quad (9.5)$$
$$= (V^2/X)(E/V) \cos \alpha \, \Delta \alpha \quad . \quad . \quad . \quad . \quad (9.6)$$

$dP/d\alpha$ is termed the *synchronising power coefficient* and is expressed in megawatts per electrical radian (if required per mechanical degree of rotor displacement, the expression must be multiplied by $(2\pi/360)(p/2)$).

The synchronising torque corresponding to ΔP

$$\Delta T \text{ (lb ft)} = \Delta P \text{ (watts)} \times 33\ 000/(746.2\pi N_s) = 7.05.\Delta P/N_s \qquad (9.7)$$

where N_s is the synchronous speed in revolutions per minute.

In m.k.s. units, $\Delta T \text{ (newton-metres)} = \Delta P/\omega_{s,m} \quad \cdot \quad \cdot \quad \cdot \quad \cdot \quad (9.8)$

where $\omega_{s,m}$ is the angular velocity of the shaft in radians per second.

It is clear from equation (9.4) that the synchronising power coefficient is greatest at no load ($\alpha = 0$) and diminishes to zero when $\alpha = \pi/2$, the limit of stability (fig. 9.5). It also increases with the excitation and varies inversely with the reactance.

9.4. Oscillations in Machines on Infinite Bus-bars

Equation (9.6) shows that the synchronising power ΔP is proportional to $\Delta\alpha$ for small displacements. In this respect the *synchronous tie* can be likened to a long flexible shaft, the two ends of which normally rotate in synchronism, but if one is given a slight deflection relative to the other, thereby twisting the shaft, torque is set up tending to restore the original alignment.

Now if at one end of the shaft there is a flywheel and this is deflected by a small angle, on being released it is well known that the flywheel will oscillate with a free torsional oscillation which persists until damping forces absorb the original energy of deflection. The periodic time of this oscillation is related to the moment of inertia of the masses and to the stiffness of the shaft. Such an oscillation may take place superimposed upon a steady angular velocity.

Similar conditions arise in a synchronous machine running in parallel with others, since the rotor necessarily has considerable inertia. If, due to a sudden load change, the rotor is displaced by $\Delta\alpha$, the synchronising torque will act in a similar manner to the torsion of the shaft, and the rotor will oscillate before settling down at the new load angle unless heavy damping forces are brought into play.

9.4.1. Dynamical Equation

Let the rotor position in electrical degrees at time t be

$$\theta = \omega_s t + \alpha \quad \cdot \quad \cdot \quad \cdot \quad \cdot \quad \cdot \quad \cdot \quad (9.9)$$

where $\omega_s = 2\pi f$, and α_1 is the angle of advance due to a steady load P_1 and corresponding torque T_1 (fig. 9.6).

Then $d\theta/dt = \omega_s + d\alpha/dt \quad \cdot \quad \cdot \quad \cdot \quad \cdot \quad \cdot \quad (9.10)$

and $d^2\theta/dt^2 = d^2\alpha/dt^2 \quad \cdot \quad \cdot \quad \cdot \quad \cdot \quad \cdot \quad (9.11)$

Now if the steam supply to the turbine is suddenly increased, the torque T_1 abruptly changing to T_2, the rotor will accelerate and α_1 will change to α_2, but this change of angle cannot take place instantaneously owing to the inertia of the rotor. During the time which elapses, work is done by the excess torque $T_d = T_2 - T$, and thus when the rotor reaches the angle α_2 the velocity $d\theta/dt$

will be greater than ω_s. The angle α thus continues to increase, T_d becoming negative and deceleration commences. α increases to a point α_3, and if by this time the velocity has been reduced again to ω_s this will be the limit of the swing. T_d is still operating, however, and the rotor returns to α_2 where the velocity now will be less than ω_s.

Deceleration continues back to α_1. Thus the oscillation continues between the limits of α_1 and α_3 unless the excess energy is removed by damping forces.

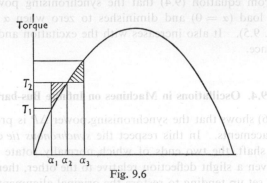

Fig. 9.6

The work done by the differential torque

$$W = \int T_d d\theta = \int_{t_1}^{t_2} T_d \omega_s dt + \int_{\alpha_1}^{\alpha_2} T_d d\alpha . \quad . \quad . \quad (9.12)$$

as α changes from α_1 to α_2 ($d\theta = \omega_s dt + d\alpha$).

Now

$$T_d = Mk^2 . d^2\theta_m/dt^2 = \{Mk^2/(p/2)\} . d^2\theta/dt^2 \quad . \quad . \quad (9.13)$$

(Mk^2 = moment of inertia of the rotor; $\theta_m = \theta/p/2$.)

$$\therefore \quad W = \int_{t_1}^{t_2} \frac{Mk^2}{p/2} \omega_s \frac{d^2\theta}{dt^2} dt + \int_{\alpha_1}^{\alpha_2} T_d d\alpha$$

$$= \left[\frac{Mk^2}{p/2} \omega_s \frac{d\theta}{dt} \right]_{t_1}^{t_2} + \int_{\alpha_1}^{\alpha_2} T_d d\alpha$$

$$= 0 + \int_{\alpha_1}^{\alpha_2} T_d d\alpha \quad . \quad . \quad . \quad . \quad . \quad (9.14)$$

if $d\theta/dt$ is sensibly constant (in equation (9.10) $d\alpha/dt$ is much less than ω_s).

Now in fig. 9.6 the value of $\int_{\alpha_1}^{\alpha_2} T_d d\alpha$ is the area of the cross-hatched portion between α_1 and α_2. This energy must be removed before the rotor returns to speed ω_s, thus

$$\int_{\alpha_1}^{\alpha_2} T_d d\alpha + \int_{\alpha_2}^{\alpha_3} T_d d\alpha = 0 . \quad . \quad . \quad . \quad . \quad (9.15)$$

This is known as the *equal-area criterion* and α_3 is determined by choosing the angle which makes the two cross-hatched areas equal.

Now although the amplitude of the swing is readily determined in the above manner, the periodic time of the oscillation is a much more difficult computation in a power-system analysis, and has usually to be carried out by a step-by-step method.

If, however, the swing is confined to a very small angle, we may proceed as follows.

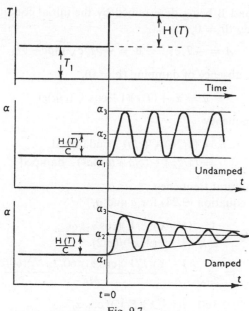

Fig. 9.7

The torque equation at instant t is given by

$$a\frac{d^2\alpha}{dt^2}+b\frac{d\alpha}{dt}+c'\sin\alpha = T_1+H(T) \qquad . \quad . \quad . \quad . \quad (9.16)$$

where $a.d^2\alpha/dt^2 = \{Mk^2/(p/2)\}.d^2\theta/dt^2$ is the inertia torque,

$b.d\alpha/dt$ is the damping torque (factors leading to the value of the co-efficient b will be discussed later),

$c'\sin\alpha$ is the load torque $= (V^2/X)(E/V)(\sin\alpha)/\omega_{s,m}$ from equations (9.3) and (9.8),

T_1 is the original steady-load torque, and $H(T)$ is the suddenly applied increase in torque (T_2-T_1) at time zero (fig. 9.7).

Now
$$T_1 = c'\sin\alpha_1 \qquad . \quad . \quad . \quad . \quad . \quad . \quad (9.17)$$

$$\therefore \; a\frac{d^2\alpha}{dt^2}+b\frac{d\alpha}{dt}+c'(\sin\alpha-\sin\alpha_1) = H(T) \quad . \quad . \quad . \quad (9.18)$$

and provided $\alpha-\alpha_1$ is sufficiently small,

$$a\frac{d^2\alpha}{dt^2}+b\frac{d\alpha}{dt}+c'\cos\alpha_1(\alpha-\alpha_1) = H(T) \quad . \quad . \quad . \quad (9.19)$$

or
$$a\frac{d^2\alpha}{dt^2}+b\frac{d\alpha}{dt}+c(\alpha-\alpha_1) = H(T) \quad . \quad . \quad . \quad (9.20)$$

where
$$c = (V^2/X)(E/V)(\cos\alpha_1)/\omega_{s,m}.$$

13—E.M.

The solution of a second-order differential equation of this type is very familiar, and when $b^2 < 4ac$, as is the case here, we have

$$\alpha = \alpha_1 + T/c + \{\exp(-bt/2a)\}\{A \cos \sqrt{(c/a - b^2/4a^2)}t + \\ B \sin \sqrt{(c/a - b^2/4a^2)}t\} \quad (9.21)$$

the constants A and B being determined by the initial conditions. As at time zero $\alpha = \alpha_1$ and $d\alpha/dt = 0$,

$$A = -T/c; \quad B = -bT/c\sqrt{(4ac - b^2)} \quad . \quad . \quad . \quad (9.22)$$

In the complete absence of damping ($b = 0$),

$$\alpha = \alpha_1 + (T/c)(1 - \cos \sqrt{(c/a)}t) \quad . \quad . \quad . \quad . \quad (9.23)$$

The oscillation frequency

$$f_0 = (1/2\pi) \sqrt{(c/a)} \quad \text{undamped} \quad . \quad . \quad . \quad . \quad (9.24)$$

or

$$= (1/2\pi) \sqrt{(c/a - b^2/4a^2)} \quad \text{damped} \quad . \quad . \quad . \quad (9.25)$$

is known as the natural frequency.

Substituting in equation (9.24) for c and a,

$$f_0 = \frac{1}{2\pi} \sqrt{\frac{(V^2/X)(E/V)(\cos \alpha_1)/\omega_{s,m}}{(Mk^2)/(p/2)}} \quad . \quad . \quad . \quad . \quad (9.26)$$

$$= \frac{1}{2\pi} \sqrt{\frac{(V^2/X)(E/V)(\cos \alpha_1)(60/2\pi N_s)(60f/N_s)}{Mk^2}}$$

$$= \frac{3 \cdot 81}{N_s} \sqrt{\frac{(V^2/X)(E/V)f \cos \alpha_1}{Mk^2}} \quad . \quad . \quad . \quad . \quad (9.27)$$

since $\omega_{s,m} = \omega_s/(p/2) = 2\pi N_s/60.$

and $p/2 = 60f/N_s.$

9.4.2. The Damping Coefficient

The m.m.f. wave due to stator current advances steadily at synchronous speed, consequently as α is changing at the rate $d\alpha/dt$ there will be relative movement between the poles and this wave.

There will thus be some movement of the flux relative to the poles since the flux axis depends on both the rotor and stator m.m.f. This flux swing affects principally the pole shoes, and if the latter are solid eddy currents will be set up in them. The eddy currents themselves and the torque reaction they set up are both proportional to the e.m.f. causing them which in turn depends upon $d\alpha/dt$. They are thus primarily responsible for the coefficient b in equation (9.16).

Cage windings are introduced to promote this effect. These consist of copper conductors in slots cut in the pole shoes connected by end rings as in the cage winding of an induction motor.

In the case of a round-rotor-type machine, the rotor is normally solid and eddy currents are set up near the surface. The presence of non-magnetic wedges covering the slots which are keyed to the end bells covering the rotor end windings also produce a cage-winding effect and increase the damping coefficient.

9.4.3. Forced Oscillations

When an alternator is driven by a reciprocating engine, or when a synchronous motor is driving an air compressor, the driving torque in the first case and the load torque in the second will not be uniform but will contain cyclical irregularity. This torque variation will not be truly sinusoidal but can be represented by a Fourier series with a prominent fundamental and a number of higher harmonics.

Now, when such a machine runs on infinite bus-bars, if the oscillatory torque or one of the harmonics coincides with the natural frequency of the machine, the effect of damping is reversed and oscillations may increase to such a magnitude that the machine falls from synchronism.

Even if the resonance condition is successfully avoided the amplitude of the cyclical oscillation is greater when the machine runs in parallel with others than when running alone.

The use of effective damping windings is therefore essential in the design of diesel-engine-driven alternators, and in modern machines these have been developed so that the use of extremely heavy and therefore costly flywheels to limit the amplitude of oscillation and also to reduce the natural frequency have been made unnecessary.

9.4.4. Amplitude of Forced Oscillation

Let the oscillatory torque be $T \sin \omega t$.   Then

$$a\frac{d^2\alpha}{dt^2}+b\frac{d\alpha}{dt}+c(\alpha-\alpha_1) = T \sin \omega t \quad . \quad . \quad . \quad (9.28)$$

which is a familiar equation similar in form to

$$L\frac{d^2q}{dt^2}+R\frac{dq}{dt}+(1/C)q = \sqrt{2} . V \sin \omega t \quad . \quad . \quad . \quad (9.29)$$

the equation for a series R, L, C circuit with an a.c. voltage source.   We are only interested in the steady-state solution, which is

$$\alpha = [T/\sqrt{\{(c-a\omega^2)^2+b^2\omega^2\}}] \sin [\omega t+\arctan \{b\omega/(c-a\omega^2)\}] \quad (9.30)$$

Now when the machine is running alone b and c in the above equation vanish, and the resulting oscillation

$$\alpha' = (T/a\omega^2) \sin \omega t \quad . \quad . \quad . \quad . \quad . \quad (9.31)$$

The per-unit increase in amplitude due to parallel running

$$\alpha/\alpha' = a\omega^2/\sqrt{\{(c-a\omega^2)^2+b^2\omega^2\}} . \quad . \quad . \quad . \quad . \quad (9.32)$$
$$= (\omega/\omega_0)^2/\sqrt{[\{1-(\omega/\omega_0)^2\}^2+\{(b/a\omega_0)(\omega/\omega_0)\}^2]}$$
$$= (\omega/\omega_0)^2/\sqrt{[\{1-(\omega/\omega_0)^2\}^2+\{2(b/b_0)(\omega/\omega_0)\}^2]} \quad . \quad . \quad (9.33)$$

where

$$b_0 = 2\sqrt{ac} \quad . \quad . \quad . \quad . \quad . \quad . \quad (9.34)$$

the critical damping coefficient, and

$$\omega_0 = \sqrt{(c/a)} \quad . \quad . \quad . \quad . \quad . \quad . \quad (9.24)$$

the undamped natural frequency.

In the undamped case ($b = 0$) equation (9.33) reduces to

$$\alpha/\alpha' = (\omega/\omega_0)^2/\{1-(\omega/\omega_0)^2\} \quad . \quad . \quad . \quad . \quad . \quad (9.35)$$

which rises to infinity when $\omega = \omega_0$. Equation (9.33) is plotted in fig. 9.8 to show the influence of the damping coefficient.

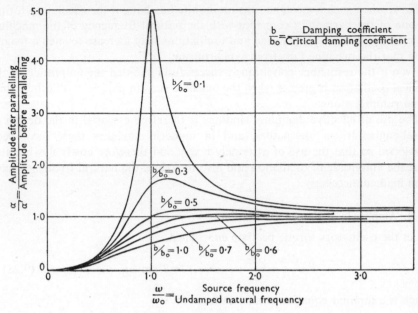

Fig. 9.8

9.5. Power/Angle Relation for a Salient-pole Machine

We now refer back to fig. 9.4, the operating chart for a round-rotor-type alternator when connected to infinite bus-bars and from which the power/angle equation (9.2) was derived. When resistance is neglected, the equation reduces to

$$P = (V^2/X_s)(E/V) \sin \alpha \quad . \quad . \quad . \quad . \quad . \quad (9.3)$$

corresponding to the vector diagram fig. 9.9, which shows that the power/angle relation is the simple sine curve of fig. 9.5. This curve has been derived in terms of the single synchronous reactance X_s of the round-rotor machine.

To apply this to the salient-pole type machine a slightly more complicated construction will be needed since the two reactances X_d and X_q will have to be incorporated as demanded by the two-axis theory applicable to this machine.

Considering once more fig. 7.18, the vector diagram of the salient-pole alternator, this has been redrawn in fig. 9.10 as a current diagram by dividing each voltage vector by X_d the direct-axis reactance.

Figs. 9.9 and 9.10 should be compared as these illustrate the differences between conditions in the two types of machine. In fig. 9.10 the vector **oa** is extended to the point **c** meeting the line **cf** which is parallel to **ae**. It will now be seen from the triangle **ofc** that

$$ac/oa = hf/oh \qquad \ldots \ldots \ldots \quad (9.36)$$

and therefore

$$ac = (V/X_d)\{(X_d - X_q)/X_q\} = V(1/X_q - 1/X_d) \quad \cdot \quad \ldots \quad (9.37)$$

The power corresponding to the current I

$$P = V \cdot oc$$
$$= V \cdot cf \cdot \sin \alpha \qquad \ldots \ldots \ldots \quad (9.38)$$

Now

$$cf = gf + cg$$
$$= ae + ac \cdot \cos \alpha$$
$$= E/X_d + V(1/X_q - 1/X_d) \cos \alpha \quad , \quad \ldots \ldots \quad (9.39)$$

whence $\quad P = V\{(E/X_d) + V(1/X_q - 1/X_d) \cos \alpha\} \sin \alpha$

$$= (V^2/X_d) [(E/V) \sin \alpha + \tfrac{1}{2}\{(X_d/X_q) - 1\} \sin 2\alpha] \quad \ldots \quad (9.40)$$

When this equation is compared with the corresponding equation (9.3) for the round-rotor machine it is noticed that a second term is introduced involving the angle 2α.

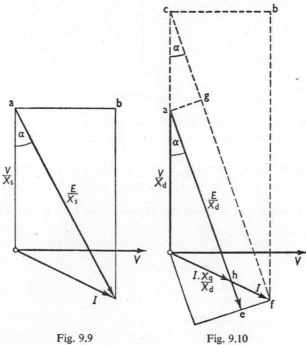

Fig. 9.9   Fig. 9.10

The first term gives rise to the simple sine curve for the power/angle relation the magnitude of which is proportional to the per-unit excitation E/V.

The second term, however, is independent of the excitation depending only upon the ratio X_d/X_q which is introduced by the saliency. The total power/angle relation is shown in the curves of fig. 9.11 which have been plotted for various values of excitation.

Comparing these with the curve for the round-rotor machine it is seen that all the curves rise more steeply when α is small indicating a greater value of the synchronising power coefficient ($dP/d\alpha$).

Indeed, even if excitation is removed, the machine exerts some synchronising torque contributed by the second term of the expression. This contribution is referred to as the *reluctance torque*. For this reason a salient-pole machine may

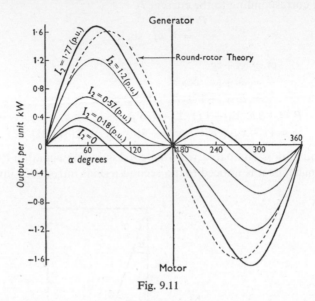

Fig. 9.11

remain in step under conditions of low load even in the event of a field fault. The transient stability is however considerably reduced under these circumstances.

Operating charts for salient-pole machines similar to that of fig. 9.2 for the round-rotor machine are to be found in a paper by Dr. J. H. Walker.*

* "Operating Characteristics of Salient-pole Machines", by J. H. Walker, *I.E.E. Proceedings*, **100**, Pt. II, No. 73.

CHAPTER 10

INDUCTOR ALTERNATOR AND
SYNCHRONOUS CONVERTER

10.1. The Inductor Alternator

10.1.1. High-frequency Machines

THE generation of frequencies of the order of 1000 c/s by means of alternators of conventional design involves both high speeds and very large numbers of poles. Since peripheral speeds are limited by mechanical stresses, the pole pitch becomes uneconomically small and indeed the field winding cannot be successfully accommodated.

The demand for frequencies from 1 to 10 kc/s which are required for use with induction furnaces and high-frequency heating equipment has led to a return to the inductor-type machine originally developed side by side with the conventional machine but found to be much less efficient at power frequencies.

The major advantage of the inductor alternator is that both armature and field windings can be stationary and the rotor consists merely of laminations notched with open slots, no rotor winding being used or slip rings necessary.

10.1.2. The Homopolar Inductor Alternator

The machine is usually symmetrical about the central field winding F (fig. 10.1), the stator on either side being slotted and the armature winding consisting of coils C wound around each tooth. The rotor has half as many slots as the

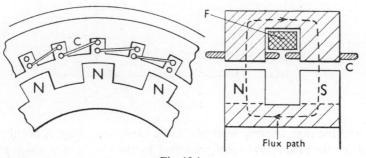

Fig. 10.1

stator, the rotor teeth being known as inductors. The flux produced by the excitation of the field follows the paths shown in the figure, cast-steel yokes connecting the two halves of the rotor and stator.

It will be seen that the polarity of the inductors are all the same on the one side of the machine and not alternate as in the conventional machine. Electromotive force is generated, however, in each armature turn, since the flux linking

199

with it will change from a maximum, as an inductor faces the tooth, to a minimum, as the pole passes by and a slot takes its place. Flux in the coil does not reverse as in the conventional machine and it is this fact that is responsible for most of the characteristic differences between the two types. It should be noted that the number of cycles per revolution is equal to the number of rotor projections and not half this number as with the normal machine, e.g. to obtain 10 kc at 3000 r.p.m. 200 rotor slots are needed. The e.m.f. wave-form of each conductor will be identical with the space distribution of flux density B, and this would appear in the first instance to be rectangular as the flux changes rapidly from the low value in the slot portion to the high value in the tooth. The effect of fringing at the edges of the rotor teeth modifies this considerably in practice, but the actual wave-form is far from sinusoidal. The coil voltage is the difference between the e.m.f.s in two conductors spaced by a stator tooth pitch, which eliminates even harmonics from the coil voltage but the odd harmonics remain.

Corresponding to given values of the gap length δ, the slot opening s and the tooth width t, the exact form of the flux distribution on no load can be obtained by flux plotting and the magnitudes of the harmonics can be calculated.

10.1.3. Magnetisation Curve

For simplicity we will assume that the flux wave-form is rectangular varying from B_t to B_s (fig. 10.2). The coil e.m.f. is due to the difference between these quantities $(B_t - B_s)$.

Now as the excitation F is increased, B_t will follow the normal type of magnetisation curve to be expected from a small gap with an associated iron circuit,

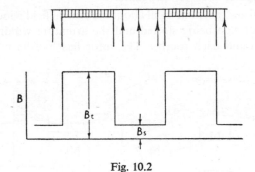

Fig. 10.2

but B_s will increase linearly over the same excitation range, since the m.m.f. required for the much larger gap presented by the slot is very much greater.

The difference curve thus shows the anticipated shape of the open-circuit voltage characteristic (fig. 10.3). The manner in which it droops at the higher values of excitation is a particular feature of the inductor-type machine.

10.1.4. The Heteropolar Inductor Alternator

The homopolar machine has several disadvantages. Its construction is expensive since it differs considerably from other standard types of electrical

machine. The heavy solid yokes and separate cores add particularly to their
cost. The central field coil magnetises the shaft and bearing troubles are
prevalent. Moreover, the rotor has an abnormally large moment of inertia
imposing heavy starting duty on the driving motor. A further disadvantage
is the large time constant of the field system since all the flux is linked with a

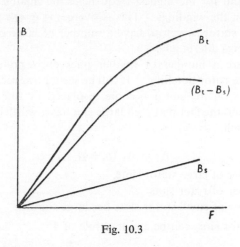

Fig. 10.3

single coil. This may be of the order of 5 to 20 seconds, causing difficulty in
maintaining constant voltage under fluctuating load conditions.

These disadvantages are overcome in the heteropolar machine. In this type
there is only one rotor system, the stator and rotor cores being very similar to
those used for cage-rotor induction motors.

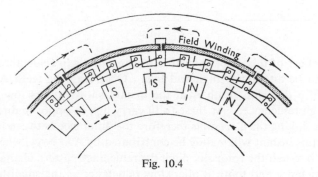

Fig. 10.4

The rotor is notched as for the homopolar machine and the H.F. winding is
also similar. The d.c. field winding, however, is split up into coils at the bottom of specially deep slots as shown in fig. 10.4. The d.c. flux paths are now
no longer axial but are circumferential as shown by the chain lines. As the
rotor teeth move around they change polarity in passing from one field coil to
the next, so that the connections of the H.F. coils are reversed in alternate pole
groups. One cycle of H.F. is still generated in each coil with the passage of
one rotor tooth.

The relatively small flux per pole reduces the depth of the stator and rotor cores and the moment of inertia of the rotor is quite normal.

10.1.5. Guy Notched Machines

The number of stator slots in the heteropolar machine is again twice the number of rotor slots, and for the highest frequencies the small slot pitch imposes a severe limitation on the windings.   This is overcome in the machine shown in fig. 10.5 where the stator is seen to have a number of large open slots carrying a.c. and d.c. windings alternately.

Between these are a number of smaller ones corresponding in pitch and dimensions with the rotor notching.   It will be seen, however, from the diagram that the small slots on the stator become displaced by one half slot pitch at each large slot, due to the fact that each large slot has a width equal to a multiple of the small slot pitch.

Thus

$$N_1 = N_2/(n_s + \tfrac{1}{2}) \quad . \quad . \quad . \quad . \quad . \quad . \quad (10.1)$$

where $N_1 =$ number of large stator slots,

$\quad\quad\; N_2 =$ number of rotor slots

and $\quad n_s =$ number of small stator slots per large tooth.

The number of stator slots can be any multiple of 4.

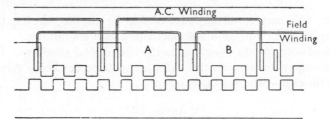

Fig. 10.5

Now the effect of this displacement is to cause the gap reluctance under the large teeth to be alternately high and low.   Observing the teeth A and B on either side of a d.c. slot, tooth A at the instant shown offers low reluctance, tooth B a high reluctance.   As these teeth carry flux in opposite directions and the total flux linking the a.c. coil is therefore the difference between the two, the total flux at this instant will mainly be contributed by A.   Now, when the rotor advances by one-half the rotor slot pitch the reluctance pattern changes, tooth A has high reluctance and tooth B offers low reluctance as the small teeth on the stator and rotor come into line.   Hence the flux linking with the a.c. coil changes from A to B.   The frequency of the alternating current thus depends solely on the speed and the number of rotor teeth, but the stator windings are confined to a smaller number of larger slots with a much more economical space factor.

10.2. The Synchronous Converter

Although mercury-arc rectifier installations are now the principal means of converting alternating to direct current—due chiefly to the better conversion efficiencies to be obtained with this type of equipment—the advantages are not so pronounced at the lower voltages required for electrolytic applications, and in a limited sphere synchronous converters, and particularly motor converters, are still economically competitive.

10.2.1. Motor-generator Sets

An obvious method of converting alternating to direct current is by means of a two-machine set in which an a.c. motor is used to drive a d.c. generator. Such a system is extremely flexible; the generator voltage can be controlled by field regulator and a completely variable output voltage arranged. Compounding windings may be used and the equipment is reversible if necessary, i.e. energy can be transferred from the d.c. side to the a.c. side. If the a.c. motor is a synchronous motor, power factor control on the a.c. side is possible. The efficiency of the system leaves much to be desired, since a double conversion of energy is entailed.

Under certain circumstances, with the synchronous motor-generator combination, the two machines can use a common field system, one armature with two windings being employed, one winding, the synchronous motor winding, being brought out to slip rings and the other winding being connected to the commutator.

The synchronous converter is a further simplification in which only one armature winding is used with a commutator and brushgear at one end and symmetrical tappings brought out to slip rings at the other, the one winding acting simultaneously as a synchronous motor and as a d.c. generator.

10.2.2. Comparison with the D.C. Generator

The synchronous converter is thus similar in construction to a d.c. generator, having revolving armature, commutator, brushgear, field poles and compoles. In addition damper windings are usually fitted in the pole faces as with synchronous motors. Now, since the direct current component in the armature conductors is a generating current, and the a.c. component flowing in the same conductors is a motoring one, a partial balance between the two is to be expected, thus reducing the armature heating for a given output (fig. 10.6). A synchronous converter can therefore be expected to be smaller than a d.c. generator of the same rating.

The combined armature reactions due to the a.c. and d.c. components of current also partially balance with the result that the converter has an adequate stability factor with a smaller gap resulting in fewer field ampere-turns and fewer compole turns.

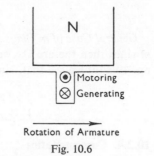

Fig. 10.6

In addition it is better able to carry momentary overloads. Commutation difficulties exist owing to the frequency being necessarily that of the a.c. side.

The armature is usually lap wound with equaliser connections governed by the usual winding rules, but, in addition, as the a.c. tappings must be symmetrical the number of coils per pole pair must be integral and a multiple of the number of rings.   Since both a.c. and d.c. voltages are developed in the same winding there is necessarily a relationship between them.

10.2.3. Voltage Ratios

In Chapter 4 we saw that the a.c. voltages developed in a closed armature winding form a vector polygon, the diagonal of which represents the voltage between the brushes on the commutator and also the maximum value of the a.c. voltage between tappings spaced by a pole pitch.

Thus in fig. 10.7 (a), which represents a two-ring or single-phase converter,

$$\frac{\text{maximum a.c. voltage}}{\text{d.c. voltage}} = \frac{\sqrt{2}.V_a}{V_d} = \frac{AB}{PQ} = 1$$

$$V_a/V_d = 1/\sqrt{2} = 0{\cdot}707 \quad . \quad . \quad . \quad . \quad (10.2)$$

In a three-phase winding the tappings have a pitch $2\pi/3$, and from the geometry of fig. 10.7 (b) we see

$$\sqrt{2}.V_a/V_d = AC/PQ = \sqrt{3}/2 \quad . \quad . \quad . \quad . \quad (10.3)$$

$$V_a/V_d = \sqrt{3}/2\sqrt{2} = 0{\cdot}612 \quad . \quad . \quad . \quad . \quad (10.4)$$

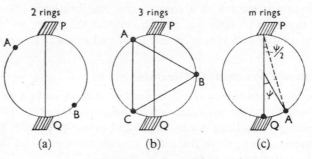

Fig. 10.7 (a), (b) and (c)

General Case of m Rings.   If Q and A are adjacent rings of a converter having m rings then the arc QA subtends an angle at the centre $\psi = 2\pi/m$, and from fig. 10.8 (c) we see that, since angle QAP is a right angle,

$$\sqrt{2}.V_a/V_d = QA/PQ = \sin(\psi/2) = \sin(\pi/m)$$

$$V_a/V_d = (1/\sqrt{2}) \sin(\pi/m) \quad . \quad . \quad . \quad . \quad . \quad (10.5)$$

10.2.4. Current Ratios

From the a.c. point of view, a converter with m rings is a mesh-connected system of m phases, and thus if the efficiency is η and the power factor $\cos\phi$, the output power

$$V_dI_d = mV_aI_a\eta \cos\phi \quad . \quad . \quad . \quad . \quad (10.6)$$

where I_d is the line current on the d.c. side and I_a is the a.c. phase current.   (The actual a.c. component of conductor current will be I_a divided by the number of parallel paths, $p/2$ for a lap winding.)

Thus

$$I_a/I_d = V_d/mV_a\eta \cos \phi$$
$$= \sqrt{2}/m \sin (\pi/m)\eta \cos \phi . \quad . \quad . \quad . \quad . \quad (10.7)$$

This phase current must not be confused with the line current or the current which is fed to the rings. The latter, I_l, is the difference between adjacent phase currents (fig. 10.8).

If A, B and C are adjacent tappings of an m-ring converter, the a.c. phase voltages V_{AB} and V_{BC} will be displaced by $2\pi/m$ and the currents in these two sections will be displaced by the same angle. The difference current, which is the current entering at the slip ring B, will be represented by the vector BD.

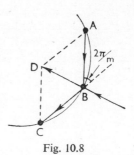

Fig. 10.8

Thus

$$I_l/I_a = BD/AB = 2 \sin (\pi/m) \quad . \quad . \quad . \quad . \quad . \quad (10.8)$$

and the ratio

$$I_l/I_d = 2 \sin (\pi/m) . \sqrt{2}/m \sin (\pi/m)\eta \cos \phi$$
$$= 2\sqrt{2}/m\eta \cos \phi \quad . \quad . \quad . \quad . \quad . \quad . \quad (10.9)$$

The following table gives the values of these ratios for converters assuming 100% efficiency and unity power factor:

Number of rings:						2	3	4	6	12
V_a/V_d	.	.	.	.	.	0·71	0·61	0·5	0·35	0·18
I_a/I_d .	.	.	.	.	.	0·71	0·54	0·5	0·47	0·45
I_l/I_d .	.	.	.	.	.	1·41	0·94	0·71	0·47	0·24

10.2.5. Wave-form of Current in Armature Conductors

The alternating component of the armature current I_a may be assumed to be sinusoidal and as the coils are in series it is the same value for all conductors of the same phase, that is, for all the conductors between the same tappings. It is related to the voltage between rings by the power factor of the system. This depends upon the value of the excitation in the usual manner of synchronous motors, since the machine behaves as such on the a.c. side. The d.c. component is in effect a square wave, the current remaining constant until the instant of commutation when reversal takes place. This wave differs for each armature coil since each commutates at a different time. It follows, therefore, that, although the d.c. and a.c. components are in opposition, the difference in wave-form leaves a residue, and, moreover, this residue differs from one conductor to the next.

Consider the case of a two-ring converter (fig. 10.9), an elementary two-pole machine.

Let I_d = d.c. line current. The conductor current = $I_a/2$, and

$$I_a = \sqrt{2}.I_d/2$$

and

$$[I_a]_{max} = \sqrt{2}.I_a = I_d.$$

In fig. 10.9 the current wave-form is built up for three coils: coil **a** at the centre of the phase, coil **c** next to the tapping point and coil **b** midway between **a** and **c**.

When the tapping points are in the position shown, the a.c. voltage is zero, and, assuming unity power factor, the alternating current component will be at

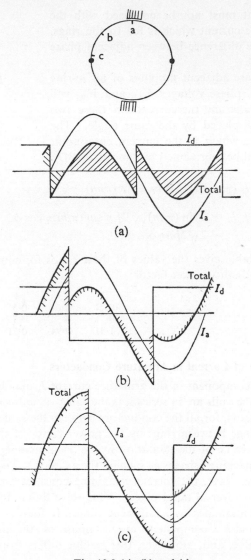

Fig. 10.9 (a), (b) and (c)

the commencement of a cycle.   At this instant coil **a** at the centre of the phase will be just about to commutate so that the d.c. component will be as shown by I_d in fig. 10.9 (a).

For conductor **b** the d.c. wave is displaced by $\pi/4$ and for conductor **c** by $\pi/2$.   The total current wave-form is obtained by addition of the two waves in each case, and these resultant wave-forms show considerable difference for the three cases. The r.m.s. value of the current is obviously much greater in conductor **c** than in conductor **a**, and the losses in the armature coils and consequent heating is thus irregular.

Assuming 100% efficiency and a power factor $\cos \phi$, the instantaneous current in the armature coil displaced by an angle β from the mid-point of the phase is given by

$$i = (I_d/2)\{1-(4/m)\ \mathrm{cosec}\ (\pi/m)\ \sec \phi \cos (\theta-\phi)\} \quad . \quad . \quad (10.10)$$

between the commutation limits

$$\theta = (\pi/2-\beta) \quad \text{and} \quad (-\pi/2-\beta)$$

where $\theta = \omega t$.

The conductor heating depends on the mean square of this current, that is on $(1/\pi)\int i^2 d\theta$ taken over these limits, namely

$$I^2 = (I_d^2/4)\{1-(16/\pi m)\ \mathrm{cosec}\ (\pi/m)\ \sec \phi \cos (\beta+\phi)+$$
$$(8/m^2)\ \mathrm{cosec}^2\ (\pi/m)\ \sec^2 \phi\} \quad (10.11)$$

which shows how rapidly the heating rises with the angle β.

Now in a machine having m phases the maximum value of β is π/m, so that increasing the number of phases has the effect of cutting out the worst of the heating conditions, and we may expect therefore a six-ring machine to have a higher rating than a three-ring machine of the same dimensions.

To obtain an average figure for the heating of all the conductors, equation (10.11) is integrated over the phase, i.e. from $\beta = +\pi/m$ to $\beta = -\pi/m$, giving

$$[I^2]_{\mathrm{mean}} = (I_d^2/4)\{1-(16/\pi^2)+(8/m^2)\ \mathrm{cosec}^2\ (\pi/m)\ \sec^2 \phi\} \quad . \quad (10.12)$$

Except for the fact that due allowance must be made for hot-spot temperatures, the ratio $I_d^2/[I^2]_{\mathrm{mean}}$ gives the relative ratings of converters with respect to d.c. generators of the same frame size. The following table is computed from equation (10.12):

Number of rings	Rating
0	1·0
2	0·85
3	1·33
6	1·93
12	2·19

This table shows the marked superiority of the six-ring machine compared with the three-ring machine, and although the twelve-ring machine is better still the increase is insufficient to justify the additional complexity.

10.2.6. Converter Connections

For a given d.c. output voltage, the input voltage at the rings is fixed by equation (10.5), and as this value is unlikely to coincide with the voltage of the a.c. mains, a transformer is an essential part of a converter installation. Fig. 10.10 (a) shows the connections of a three-ring rotary in which the delta/star three-phase transformer has its secondary winding connected to the rings. The potential of the neutral point of the secondary winding is maintained at the centre of the vector polygon of the conductor voltages and is therefore mid-way between the potentials of the positive and negative brushes.

This point may be used to connect a neutral line if a three-wire d.c. supply is required, and provided the out-of-balance between the loads on the two sides is not severe the voltages will remain balanced.

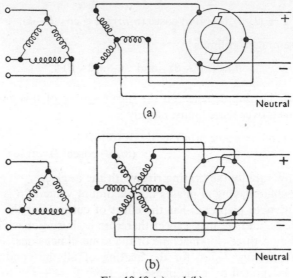

(a)

(b)

Fig. 10.10 (a) and (b)

In fig. 10.10 (b) a six-ring converter is shown, the transformer windings being connected to diametrically opposite rings. It is not essential for the centre tappings of the windings to be connected together, but if this is done a star point is formed enabling a three-wire d.c. supply to be provided.

10.2.7. Voltage Control

In contrast with the d.c. generator, the output voltage of a converter is not directly dependent on the field ampere-turns but is determined solely by the voltage applied to the rings (equation (10.5)). Variation of excitation by means of a field regulator alters the power factor on the a.c. side, over-excitation causing the voltage to lead in the way usual with synchronous motors. This fact may be used to provide some variation of output voltage.

If the transformer has a high leakage reactance, or additional series reactors are connected, when the converter takes a leading current the regulation drop in the transformer will be negative (Section 2.7), and the output voltage V_a applied to the rings will therefore be greater than the no-load voltage. This is shown in fig. 10.11.

Representing the transformer by an ideal ratio change with series reactance X_2', the equivalent reactance referred to the secondary, the output voltage

$$V_a = V_{bc} = V_{ab} - Ij X_2'$$
$$= (n_2/n_1)V_1 - Ij X_2' \quad . \quad . \quad . \quad . \quad . \quad (10.13)$$

This is shown in the vector diagram drawn with the current I leading the ring voltage V_a by angle ϕ. V_a is seen to be numerically greater than the no-load voltage $V_1 . n_2/n_1$.

Thus a variation of excitation which causes a change in ϕ adjusts the value of V_a and also the output voltage V_d.

Synchronous converters are frequently designed with a series compounding winding to give over-compounded characteristics similar to those of d.c. generators.

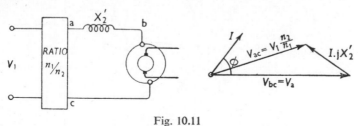

Fig. 10.11

10.2.8. Starting

Converters are usually started by the tap-starting method, in which the converter rings are first connected to a reduced voltage tapping on the transformer, the field winding being open-circuited.   The machine then starts as an induction motor with the pole-face damper windings acting as the secondary and accelerates to a speed just short of synchronism running with a small slip S.   The voltage at the brushes is then seen to rise and fall at frequency $f_2 = Sf_1$ (Section 6.5) and this can be observed by a centre-zero voltmeter connected on the d.c. side.   If the field circuit is closed at the instant when the voltage is zero and rising positively, then as the field current rises and the poles are magnetised synchronising forces are brought into play; and if sufficient torque is available in one-quarter of a cycle of slip frequency, the machine is enabled to rise in speed the last step to synchronism.

The transformer tapping is then changed quickly to the normal value after which the converter develops full voltage and is ready for paralleling on the d.c. side.

10.3. The Motor-converter

This equipment is a two-machine set comprising an induction motor mechanically coupled to a converter, at the same time the machines being electrically connected in cascade, that is, the secondary windings of the induction motor are connected to the tappings of the converter.   These connections are usually made by leads carried between the machines through the shaft which is hollow for the purpose (fig. 10.12).

The induction motor thus takes the place of the transformer normally used with a converter and its stator winding can usually be designed for direct connection to H.V. mains.   The motor supplies energy to the converter both mechanically and electrically thereby acting both as a motor and as a transformer, and since the converter is being driven it doubles the role of generator and converter.

14—E.M.

Its advantages over the transformer-converter installation are its easy starting and the fact that the converter operates at reduced frequency which considerably reduces the possibility of flash-over and enables the machine to be designed for higher voltages.   Wider voltage regulation is also possible.

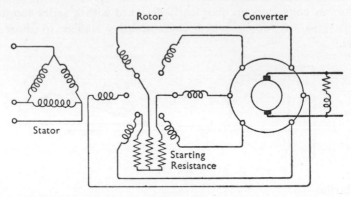

Fig. 10.12

10.3.1. Synchronous Speed of Motor-converter

Let p_1 be the number of poles of the induction motor, f_1 the supply frequency, p_2 the poles of the converter and N the speed of the set in revolutions per minute.

The synchronous speed of its induction motor running alone would be

$$N_1 = 120f_1/p_1 \quad \text{or} \quad f_1 = N_1p_1/120 \quad . \quad . \quad . \ (10.14)$$

The converter frequency

$$f_2 = Np_2/120 \quad . \quad . \quad . \quad . \quad . \ (10.15)$$

But the converter frequency is also the rotor frequency, i.e. the slip frequency of the induction motor when the latter runs at speed N.

Thus

$$f_2 = Sf_1$$
$$= f_1(N_1-N)/N_1 \quad . \quad . \quad . \quad . \ (10.16)$$

Hence
$$Np_2 = N_1p_1(N_1-N)/N_1$$
$$= p_1(N_1-N)$$

$$N(p_1+p_2) = N_1p_1$$

and
$$N = N_1p_1/(p_1+p_2)$$
$$= 120f_1/(p_1+p_2) \quad . \quad . \quad . \quad . \ (10.17)$$

10.3.2. Energy Ratios

For any induction motor,

mechanical power output/rotor input = rotor speed/synchronous speed

$$= N/N_1 \quad . \quad . \quad . \quad . \quad . \ (10.18)$$

Thus for the motor of the motor-converter assuming no losses,
power transmitted mechanically/total power $= N/N_1$

$$= p_1/(p_1+p_2) \quad . \quad . \quad . \quad (10.19)$$

and the corresponding ratio
power transmitted electrically/total power $= 1-p_1/(p_1+p_2)$

$$= p_2/(p_1+p_2) \quad . \quad . \quad . \quad . \quad (10.20)$$

10.3.3. Starting

Fig. 10.12 shows the connections of a motor-converter. Three rings are permanently connected to a starting resistance and the machine starts when the stator is connected to the mains. The machine is self-synchronising as synchronous speed is approached and the converter field builds up. The six rings are then short-circuited, forming the neutral of the d.c. system.

CHAPTER 11

D.C. MACHINES

11.1. Symbols

The symbols to be used in this chapter are as follows:

p = number of poles.
a = number of parallel paths in the armature winding.
Z = total number of armature conductors.
ϕ = flux per pole.
L_c = core length.
D_a = armature diameter.
$[B]_{mean}$ = average gap density over the pole pitch.
E = armature generated e.m.f.
I = armature current.
I_c = conductor current.
ψ = ratio pole arc/pole pitch.
ω = speed in radians per second.
N = speed in revolutions per minute.
F = force on armature conductor.
B_g = apparent gap density.
q = ampere-conductors per metre of armature circumference.
τ = pole pitch.

11.2. Relation between Rating and Dimensions

It is the purpose of this section to try to relate the rating of a d.c. machine to its main dimensions.

The many factors which affect a design cannot be introduced into one simple formula, nor must it be assumed that there is a unique solution leading to a machine of certain optimum dimensions which fulfils the requirements of a particular specification. The aim of the designer is, however, to comply with the specification relating to the performance required and to produce a machine having maximum reliability and efficiency together with minimum cost, which in general means minimum size. The result is that by and large the main dimensions of a satisfactory machine are fairly definitely related to its output.

11.2.1. Electric and Magnetic Loading

The average force on an armature conductor carrying a constant current I_c,

$$[F]_{mean} = [B]_{mean} L_c I_c \qquad \cdots \qquad (6.10)$$

212

The total work done in one revolution by an armature having Z conductors,

$$W = Z[F]_{mean} \pi D_a = [B]_{mean} L_c \pi D_a I_c Z \quad . \quad . \quad . \quad (11.1)$$

But

$$[B]_{mean} L_c \pi D_a = p\phi \quad . \quad . \quad . \quad . \quad . \quad (11.2)$$

Thus the total work per revolution

$$W = p\phi . I_c Z \quad . \quad . \quad . \quad . \quad . \quad (11.3)$$

where $p\phi$ is termed the *magnetic loading* and $I_c Z$ is the *electric loading*.

These two quantities are related to the amounts of iron and copper respectively in the machine and it is the product of the two, and not the individual values, that is of consequence.

11.2.2. Specific Magnetic Loading

The value $[B]_{mean}$ is known as the specific magnetic loading since

$$[B]_{mean} = \text{total magnetic loading/armature surface area} \quad (11.4)$$
$$= p\phi/p\tau L_c = \phi/\tau L_c \quad . \quad . \quad . \quad . \quad . \quad (11.5)$$

It is related to B_g, the apparent gap density, which is the value of the gap density under the pole neglecting slotting and assuming a rectangular flux distribution.

Thus

$$B_g = \text{flux per pole/area of pole shoe} \quad . \quad . \quad . \quad (11.6)$$
$$= \phi/\psi\tau L_c \quad . \quad . \quad . \quad . \quad . \quad . \quad (11.7)$$

and from equations (11.5) and (11.7),

$$[B]_{mean} = \psi B_g \quad . \quad . \quad . \quad . \quad . \quad (11.8)$$

11.2.3. Specific Electric Loading

This is defined by

$$q = \text{total electric loading/armature circumference} \quad . \quad . \quad (11.9)$$
$$= Z I_c / \pi D_a . \quad . \quad . \quad . \quad . \quad . \quad . \quad . \quad (11.10)$$

11.3. The Output Equation

In terms of B_g and q, we can relate the output of the machine to the main dimensions of the machine in the following way.

The power converted from mechanical energy to electrical energy in a generator (or vice versa in a motor),

$$P = EI \quad . \quad . \quad . \quad . \quad . \quad . \quad (11.11)$$

Therefore the work done per revolution

$$W = EI/(\omega_m/2\pi) = EI/(N/60) \quad . \quad . \quad . \quad (11.12)$$
$$= (p\phi)(I_c Z) \quad . \quad . \quad . \quad . \quad . \quad . \quad (11.3)$$

and by equations (11.7) and (11.10)

$$W = (p\psi\tau L_c B_g)(\pi D_a q)$$
$$= \pi^2 D_a{}^2 L_c B_g \psi q \quad . \quad . \quad . \quad . \quad . \quad . \quad (11.13)$$

Thus

$$D^2 L_c = (EI/N)(60/\pi^2)/B_g \psi q \quad . \quad . \quad . \quad . \quad (11.14)$$

which is known as the output equation for the machine.

It shows that the volume of the armature is mainly dependent on the ratio of the output to the speed (i.e. to the torque), if B_g and q may be treated as constants.

11.3.1. Limitations of B_g and q

The value of B_g is limited by the maximum permissible value of the flux density in the iron at the bottom of the tooth or the tooth-root density.

If λ = slot pitch,

    W_t = width of tooth at root,

and L_i = net length of iron in the core length L_c (fig. 11.1),

then the flux entering an armature tooth which is under the centre of the pole will be

$$\phi_2 = B_g \lambda L_c \quad . \quad . \quad . \quad . \quad . \quad . \quad (11.15)$$

and the apparent tooth-root density (assuming the tooth carries the whole of this flux),

$$B_{t.r.} = B_g . \lambda L_c / W_t L_i \quad . \quad . \quad . \quad . \quad (11.16)$$

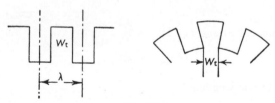

Fig. 11.1

This is the section of the magnetic circuit of the machine where the highest density occurs, and excessive tooth-root density results in high tooth losses and magnetic noise.   The value of $B_{t.r.}$ should not exceed $2 \cdot 15$ Wb/m^2 and by (11.16) the value of B_g must be proportionately less.   Due to taper of the teeth, which is more noticeable in smaller machines, the value of B_g varies with armature diameter to some extent.

Fig. 11.2 shows the approximate relationship between B_g and D_a for continuously rated d.c. generators of the open type.   Higher values of magnetic loading would lead to excessive iron loss, saturation, increased excitation and therefore excitation loss, increased pole-face losses and a reduction of efficiency.

The value of q, the specific electric loading, depends on many factors.   The limit set is chiefly due to heating, and so the effectiveness of the system of ventilation employed has a considerable influence which is difficult to assess and varies according to the type of enclosure and ventilation, number of air ducts, length of core, type of fan used and so on.

High values of q mean high values of current density in the conductors and increased copper losses unless deep slots are used, which is an impossibility in small machines and in any case impairs the ventilation.

With a non-interpole machine q is limited by commutation difficulties to be discussed later, and it must be noted that the armature reaction ampere-turns

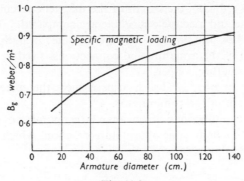

Fig. 11.2

per pole vary directly with q.   Fig. 11.3 shows the order of the values of q for different values of D_a.

The ratio $\psi = pole\ arc/pole\ pitch$ is usually about 0.65.   It is desirable that the pole arc should be as large as possible, but too high a value of ψ leads to increased pole leakage flux and reduced ventilation.

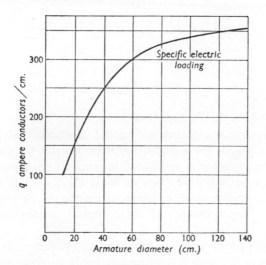

Fig. 11.3

11.3.2. Choice of Number of Poles

Having obtained from the output equation an approximate value of the product D^2L as the starting point in a design, before the individual values of D and L can be determined separately it is necessary to choose the number of poles p.

11.3.3. Advantages and Disadvantages of a Large Number of Poles

The advantages are:

(a) The flux per pole is reduced, also the thickness of the armature core and yoke, thus reducing the weight of the machine.

(b) The length of the magnetic circuit is less, resulting in a reduction of field ampere-turns.   The field spools can be accommodated on a shorter pole, thus still further reducing the length of the magnetic circuit.   (In fig. 11.4 a two-pole machine and a six-pole machine are compared.   The armature dia-meter, the total flux, and flux densities are the same in both cases.)

(c) The length of the armature end connections is reduced making a more efficient use of armature copper.

(d) A greater number of brush arms reduces the current per brush arm and also the length of the commutator.

(e) Too small a number of poles means a larger number of armature ampere-turns per pole and a high value of armature reaction, which requires a longer air-gap as will be shown later.

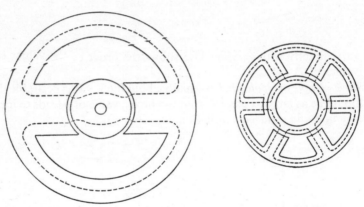

Fig. 11.4

On the other hand the disadvantages are:

(a) More commutator segments are needed or alternatively there must be more volts per segment for a given commutator diameter and thickness of segment.   A larger number of small-section armature conductors will also be necessary in the case of lap windings reducing the slot space factor.

(b) The brush arms are closer together, increasing the danger of flash-over.

(c) There is a larger number of small parts increasing machining and assembly costs.

(d) Frequency is proportional to p and the core loss depends on frequency.

(e) The armature diameter is increased, L_c being correspondingly less, and the limiting value of peripheral speed may be reached.   This is about 2000 m/min for machines of normal construction, special reinforcement being required to combat centrifugal force at higher speeds.

We thus find in general that the upper limit to the number of poles is imposed by frequency which is of the order 20–30 c/s for large machines and not exceeding 50 c/s for small ones. The lower limit is due to the current per brush arm, which should not exceed about 400 A or an excessively long commutator will be necessary.

These limits usually restrict the choice of p to about two alternatives.

11.3.4. Armature Proportions

The proportions of the armature can now be selected on the basis that the ratio L_c/τ is usually between 0·7 and 0·9. Thus

$$L_c \simeq 0·8\pi D_a/p \quad . \quad . \quad . \quad . \quad . \quad (11.17)$$

enabling the output equation to be solved for D_a.

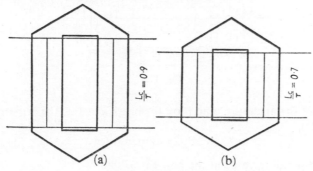

Fig. 11.5 (a) and (b)

The approximate shapes of the armature and field coils at the limiting values of this ratio are shown in fig. 11.5. Where mechanical conditions permit (i.e. if maximum peripheral speed does not impose an overriding limit) these proportions lead to a minimum value of total copper in the field and armature coils.

11.4. Armature Reaction

We have seen (Chapter 4) how the armature m.m.f. due to load current distorts the wave-form of gap flux, the rectangular shape at no-load becoming almost triangular at full load, the flux density under one pole tip being very much reduced and correspondingly increased under the other. Excessive distortion cannot be permitted particularly with non-compole machines where the fringe flux at the weaker tip is required to produce a commutating e.m.f. With modern compole machines the permitted distortion is greater and the flux may almost be reduced to zero or even reversed at this point. The limiting factor is now the increased flux density at the opposite tip causing saturation of the teeth and high tooth loss and eddy current loss in the conductors. The voltage distribution around the commutator, which has the same shape as the flux waveform, is also irregular and the high value of voltage between segments over a portion of the commutator tends to promote flash-over, particularly in a high-voltage machine where the average voltage per segment is necessarily high.

The flux distortion due to armature reaction may be considered as the superposition on the main field of a cross-magnetising flux set up by the armature m.m.f. alone. The path of this flux is shown in fig. 11.6. The length of the gap is an obvious factor controlling the value of this flux, and it is for this reason that the gap length cannot be reduced to a very small value sufficient only for mechanical clearance as with the induction motor.

Unless the gap is to be excessively long, a limit must be placed on the total armature ampere-turns, and for this reason the pole-pitch even of a large machine seldom exceeds 45 cm.

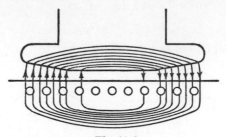

Fig. 11.6

The value of the armature m.m.f. on the brush axis (i.e. the armature ampere-turns per pole),

$$F_a = ZI_c/2p \text{ ampere-turns} \quad . \quad . \quad . \quad . \quad (11.18)$$

and the corresponding value at the pole tip will be

$$\psi F_a = \psi . ZI_c/2p \quad . \quad . \quad . \quad . \quad . \quad (11.19)$$

Now if $F_{(g+t)}$ is the field m.m.f. required to drive the flux across gap and teeth at no load (the height of the rectangle fig. 4.30 (a)), then the total m.m.f. at the pole tip on load will be

$$F_{(g+t)} \pm \psi F_a.$$

If the flux density at the weaker tip is to be greater than zero,

$$F_{(g+t)} - \psi F_a > 0.$$

Thus

$$F_{(g+t)}/F_a > \psi \simeq 0.65 \quad . \quad . \quad . \quad . \quad (11.20)$$

In special cases of compole machines where speed is varied by field weakening and the air gap is tapered, this ratio may be reduced to a limit of 0·25. This ratio is known as the *stability factor* from which the gap ampere-turns, and ultimately the gap length, can be decided.

For a non-compole machine a much higher stability factor (1·2) is required.

11.4.1. Compensating Windings

Machines which are subject to abrupt changes of load, such as motors driving rolling mills and haulage equipment, also the generators supplying them, are liable to "flash-over". The sudden changes of load produce sudden changes in the cross-flux of armature reaction which may induce in the armature coils momentary voltages much greater than the normal "volts per segment". Such voltages may be sufficient to maintain ionisation initiated by sparking at the brushes, and so to produce an arc between segments which is rapidly carried over the surface of the commutator forming a complete short circuit from brush to brush. This arc is known as "flash-over" and produces severe burning of the commutator and brushgear, causing much damage.

To minimise the possibility of flash-over, arc shields are frequently fitted to the brushgear to break up the ionised paths should they occur, and the cross flux is minimised by means of a *compensating winding*. The armature m.m.f. is balanced by that of a winding connected in series with the armature and distributed in slots over the surface of the poles (fig. 11.7). The specific electric loading q_c of the compensating winding must be the same as that of the armature and, as the conductors are restricted to the pole faces, the ampere-turns per pole

$$F_c = \psi F_a \quad . \quad . \quad . \quad . \quad . \quad . \quad (11.21)$$

The pole-face winding produces a trapezoidal m.m.f. pattern (fig. 4.29) and the armature a triangular wave (fig. 4.28) of equal slope. The m.m.f.s thus balance over the pole face and no distortion of flux takes place.

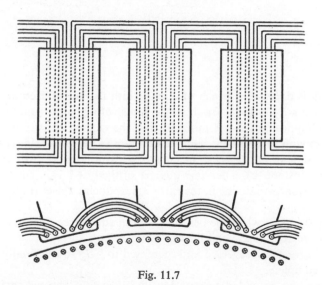

Fig. 11.7

Alternatively, the inductance of the two windings together is much less than that of the armature alone and consequently the effect of a sudden change of armature current is much less severe.

It is not necessary, nor is it desirable, to arrange the pole slotting to have the same pitch as the armature slots, but the ampere conductors per centimetre must be the same.

11.5. Commutation

The direction of the currents in the armature conductors of a d.c. generator with a lap-wound armature is shown in fig. 11.8. The coils on the left carry current in the anti-clockwise direction, whilst on the other side of the diagram the current is clockwise. Thus as an individual coil passes through the neutral axis the current must be reversed. This change occurs whilst the coil (shown in thicker outline in the figure) is short-circuited by the brush, and the process is known as commutation.

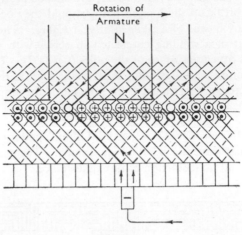

Fig. 11.8

In fig. 11.9 is depicted a brush of equal width to that of a commutator segment, and successive instants are shown as a pair of segments x and y pass under the brush. Supposing for the moment that the current density in the area of brush contact with the segment remains constant (a very desirable feature), then when the brush is in position (a) the current $2I_c$ will flow into the segment x.

At the later instant (b), when one-quarter of the brush is in contact with segment y, the current will divide in the ratio 3:1, reducing the current in the coil A to $I_c/2$.

Now in position (c) when the brush makes an equal area of contact with both segments the current in the coil falls to zero.

In (d) the current has reversed and increased to $-I_c/2$; and finally at (e) commutation is complete.

We thus see that, provided current density is constant, the current in the short-circuited coil changes linearly with time, an ideal condition known as *straight-line commutation*. The rate of change of current is constant and

$$di/dt = 2I_c/t_c \qquad \qquad . \quad . \quad . \quad . \quad . \quad (11.22)$$

These ideal conditions would be brought about automatically if the armature coil had neither resistance nor inductance, and if brush contact resistance was proportional to area. In practice all armature coils possess inductance (equation (5.53)) due principally to the slot portion where the coil is almost embedded in iron, and consequently the rapid change of current can only be produced by the application of a suitable voltage,

$$v = L.di/dt \qquad . \quad . \quad . \quad . \quad . \quad . \quad (11.23)$$

where L is the inductance of the coil and di/dt the rate of change of current.

The effective value of L may be increased by mutual inductance with other coils also undergoing commutation at another brush.

The average value of this voltage with straight-line commutation,

$$v = 2L . I_c/t_c \qquad . \qquad . \qquad . \qquad . \qquad . \qquad . \qquad (11.24)$$

is known as the *reactance voltage*, which is seen to be proportional to the load current.

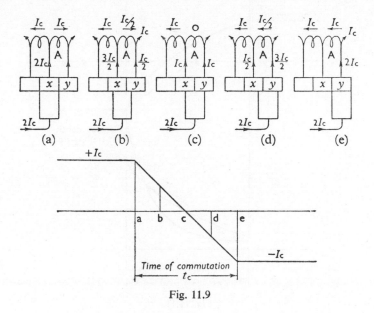

Fig. 11.9

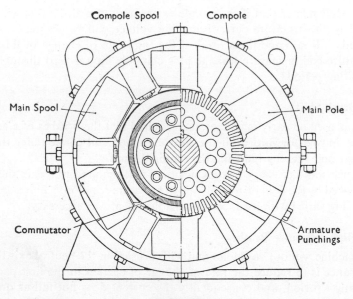

Fig. 11.10

11.5.1. Compoles

The reversing voltage is most conveniently produced by compoles, which are intermediate poles (fig. 11.10) situated on the neutral axis and excited by a series winding. The compole produces a narrow band of flux cut by the conductors of the coil undergoing commutation, thus generating the required voltage.

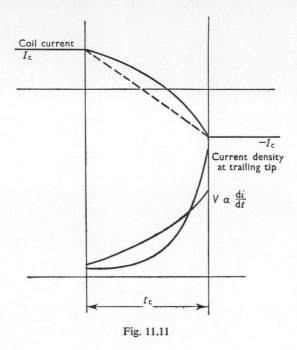

Fig. 11.11

It will be shown later that if the compoles are unsaturated the flux will be proportional to the armature current and the voltage will be correct at all loads and speeds. Ideal conditions result if the total rate of change of flux linking the armature coil (armature leakage plus compole flux) is zero throughout the commutating period.

11.5.2. Brush Shift

This was used on early machines and required that the brushes of a generator should be moved forward until the short-circuited coil came under the fringe of the next pole thereby inducing the required e.m.f.

The brush shift necessary was greater than that required to regain the neutral axis displaced by the field distortion due to armature reaction. Since the correct brush setting varied with load, continual adjustment was necessary.

11.5.3. High-resistance Brushes

In a machine without compoles and with brushes in the neutral axis the effect of inductance is to reduce the rate of change of current in the first part of the commutation period, and consequently the current does not fall as quickly as it should in the rapidly reducing area of segment (shown at x, fig. 11.9 (d)) in

contact with the trailing brush tip.   The current density under the brush is no
longer uniform, increasing from the leading to the trailing tip.   The resistance
drop in the contact also increases, and a differential
voltage is produced between the segments which
will act as a commutating voltage.

The manner in which the current changes
together with the corresponding density at the
trailing tip is shown in fig. 11.11 for a coil which
has inductance.   The differential voltage responsible for di/dt is also shown.   An indication of
this voltage can be obtained with the aid of a
voltmeter, one terminal of which is connected to
the brush lead and the other to a pointed graphite

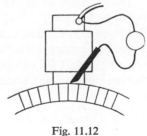

Fig. 11.12

electrode, in contact with the commutator, which can be moved over the
commutation arc (fig. 11.12).

11.5.4. Sparking on Load

The relationship between current density and voltage drop across the contact
between carbon brush and copper commutator segment is by no means linear,
and moreover there is a considerable temperature variation.   Fig. 11.13 shows
the type of curve relating current density and voltage-drop across a carbon copper
contact for steady current values.   Although the conditions are not the same,
it indicates that a differential voltage of more than one or two volts cannot be

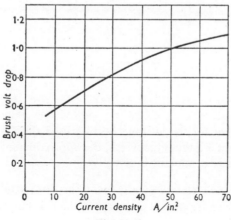

Fig. 11.13

produced even if the current density rises to ten or more times the average figure.
Such high densities cause local heating of the trailing tip sufficient to produce
thermo-electric emission, with the result that the commutation time is prolonged
by a spark between the tip and the segment leaving it and thereby to some
extent relieving the current density.

The critical density at which sparking commences, which for a given machine
varies with the load, is not definite, due to the very considerable temperature

variation.   A machine may thus take a momentary overload without sparking, but if the overload is prolonged sparking will commence and may continue even if the load is considerably reduced.

The condition of the commutator surface, presence of oil or dust or insufficient brush pressure are all contributory causes of sparking.

Although resistance commutation alone is restricted to very small machines a modern compole machine relies partly on resistance commutation to give some latitude if the compole flux does not produce exactly the voltage required for straight-line commutation at all load values.

11.5.5. Calculation of Reactance Voltage

In determining reactance voltage the inductance of the armature coils must first be found by the methods described in Section 5.4, finding first the permeance of the slot portion and then the overhang.   The accuracy required hardly justifies such detailed treatment, and the results may be obtained more simply as follows.

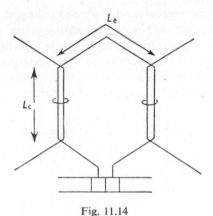

Fig. 11.14

Hobart showed that for the average slotting used on a d.c. machine, where the slot depth is about $3 \cdot 5$ times the width, the approximate value of the leakage flux due to one ampere conductor is given by:

10 maxwells per inch length of conductor in the slot portion (4×10^{-6} Wb/m).

2 maxwells per inch length of conductor in the overhang ($0 \cdot 8 \times 10^{-6}$ Wb/m).

The flux linking a coil of t turns with dimensions shown in fig. 11.14 due to a current of one ampere

$$= 2(4L_c + 0 \cdot 8L_e)t \times 10^{-6} \quad . \quad . \quad . \quad . \quad . \quad (11.25)$$

Now, at the same time, commutation will also be taking place in the other coils shown in the figure and, as these lie in the same slots, there will be mutual inductance between them, and this has the effect of approximately doubling the flux linkages in the slot portion.

This applies in the case of full-pitch coils only.

The total flux per ampere per coil

$$= 1{\cdot}6t(10L_c+L_e)\times 10^{-6} \quad . \quad . \quad . \quad . \quad . \quad (11.26)$$

Inductance (flux links/ampere)

$$L = 1{\cdot}6t^2(10L_c+L_e)\times 10^{-6} \quad . \quad . \quad . \quad . \quad (11.27)$$

and the reactance voltage will then be obtained from equation (11.23).

11.5.6. Effect of Brush Width

In fig. 11.15 (a) is shown a slot having 3 coils, and it is assumed that a narrow brush is used equal in width to one segment. Commutation is completed in one coil before commencing in the next and the time of commutation is t_c. Comparing this with fig. 11.15 (b), where a wider brush is used covering three

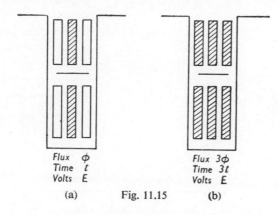

Flux ϕ
Time t
Volts E

(a)   Fig. 11.15   (b)

Flux 3ϕ
Time $3t$
Volts E

segments, we note that the flux linking with each is increased, but so also is the time of commutation. The reactance voltage per coil is thus the same in the two cases. From this we infer that there is no advantage to be gained by using a narrow brush, but it should be wide enough to short-circuit all the coils of one slot.

11.5.7. Compole Density

The value of the average flux density in the gap under the compoles which is necessary for straight-line commutation is derived in the following way.

Let B_{cp} = flux density under the compole,

$\quad L_{cp}$ = axial length of the compole,

$\quad U/2$ = number of coils per slot,

$\quad\quad t$ = turns per coil,

$\quad Ut$ = conductors per slot,

$\quad b_w$ = brush width,

$\quad C_w$ = segment width,

$\quad v_c$ = commutator peripheral speed (m/sec),

$\quad v_a$ = armature peripheral speed,

and $\quad D_c$ = commutator diameter.

15—E.M.

The distance travelled by the commutator during the time required for the commutation of current in all the conductors of a given slot is shown in fig. 11.16 and will be equal to

$$(U/2-1)C_w+b_w \qquad \ldots \ldots \ldots \quad (11.28)$$

Thus the time of commutation

$$t_c = \{(U/2-1)C_w+b_w\}/v_c \qquad \ldots \ldots \quad (11.29)$$

and since the current change is $2I_c$ the rate of change of current during straight-line commutation is

$$di/dt = 2I_c/t_c = v_c2I_c/\{(U/2-1)C_w+b_w\} \qquad \ldots \quad (11.30)$$

The inductance of the group of $U/2$ coils treated as a single coil with $Ut/2$ turns is obtained from equation (11.27)

$$L = 1 \cdot 6(U^2t^2/4)(10L_c+L_e)\times 10^{-6} \qquad \ldots \ldots \quad (11.31)$$

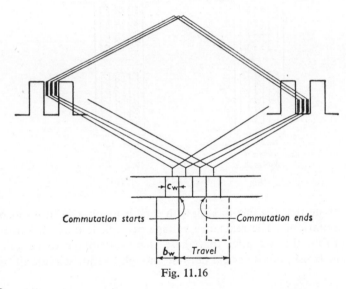

Fig. 11.16

Thus

$$L \cdot di/dt = \{0 \cdot 8U^2t^2(10L_c+L_e)I_cv_c\times 10^{-6}\}/\{(U/2-1)C_w+b_w\} \quad (11.32)$$

This voltage must be produced by the conductors cutting the compole flux for which

$$Blv = B_{cp}L_{cp}Utv_a \qquad \ldots \ldots \ldots \quad (11.33)$$

assuming that there is a compole in each interpolar space.

Equating expressions (11.33) and (11.32):

$$B_{cp} = 0 \cdot 8U^2t^2(10L_c+L_e)I_c(v_c/v_a)/[L_{cp}Ut\{(U/2-1)C_w+b_w\}\times 10^6]$$
$$= 0 \cdot 8\times 10^{-6}Ut(10L_c+L_e)I_c(D_c/D_a)/L_{cp}\{(U/2-1)C_w+b_w\} \quad (11.34)$$

The compole length is usually about 80% of the core length to give adequate ventilation, and the width is such as to ensure that the slot remains under the pole during the whole of the commutation period. This demands a width about $1 \cdot 6$ times the slot pitch.

The gap length is about twice that of the main poles to avoid excessive pulsation as the armature slots pass underneath.

Equation 11.34 is independent of speed, and hence, provided B_{cp} is at all times proportioned to I_c, straight-line commutation will be ensured.

11.5.8. Compole Ampere-turns

The proximity of the compole and the main pole results in leakage flux which is difficult to avoid (fig. 11.10) and tends to saturate the compole at its root.

Introducing a gap at the root by arranging brass shims will reduce the leakage flux, and to avoid saturation the compoles are frequently tapered.

The m.m.f. of the compole winding must be sufficient to oppose the armature m.m.f. which is directed along the compole axis and to provide the m.m.f. for the compole gap.

Thus

$$F_{cp} = F_a + F_{cp.g.} \quad \cdot \quad \cdot \quad \cdot \quad \cdot \quad \cdot \quad (11.35)$$

and since from equations (5.6a) and (5.12)

$$F_{cp.g.} = (10^7/4\pi)B_{cp}k_{cp}\delta_{cp} \quad \cdot \quad \cdot \quad \cdot \quad \cdot \quad (11.36)$$

$$F_{cp} = In_{cp} = ZI_c/2p + (10^7/4\pi)B_{cp}k_{cp}\delta \quad \cdot \quad \cdot \quad \cdot \quad (11.37)$$

from which n_{cp}, the number of compole turns, can be determined.

11.6. Speed/Torque Characteristics

The mechanical characteristics of any motor are most comprehensively described by plotting its speed/torque characteristic, that is, a graph relating the speed of the machine to the torque produced, each point on the curve corresponding to a different value of load current. Important information can be

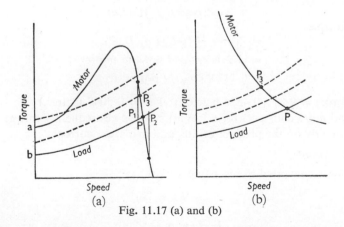

Fig. 11.17 (a) and (b)

obtained by plotting on the same graph the speed/torque characteristic of the load to be driven by the machine.

For example, in fig. 11.17 (a) the characteristic curve of the load is a rising one, torque increasing slightly at the higher values of speed. The curve for an

induction motor is also drawn on the same axes. The combination shows clearly
that the normal running speed will correspond to the point P. Should the speed
change momentarily to P_1 or P_2, considerable difference torque is set up tending
to cause a return to the point P. Such a combination of motor and load leads
to stable running without the tendency for speed to fluctuate. The torque available at starting to accelerate the machine is the ordinate **ab**, which is comparatively small, indeed, if the load curve is increased by a small amount to the
dotted line (say by increased viscosity of lubricating oil on a cold morning) the
margin is considerably reduced and the machine will be very sluggish in picking
up speed, although the final speed P_3 will be very close to P.

A further rise in the load curve would render the machine incapable of starting
unless some form of slipping-clutch mechanism were employed.

In fig. 11.17 (b) a d.c. series motor characteristic is shown with the same loads.
There is now ample starting torque, but the speed variation due to small changes
in load is comparatively large.

11.6.1. Torque Equation

In all motors (a.c. machines included) torque is produced by the interaction
of the main field and the current in armature conductors at right angles to it.

The average force on each armature conductor is given by

$$F = [B]_{mean}L_cI_c \quad . \quad . \quad . \quad . \quad . \quad (6.10)$$

where $[B]_{mean}$ is the average gap density over the pole pitch, and thus

$$[B]_{mean} = p\phi/\pi D_aL_c \quad . \quad . \quad . \quad . \quad . \quad (11.5)$$

also

$$I_c = I/a.$$

The total force on the Z conductors of the armature

$$= Z(p\phi/\pi D_aL_c)L_c(I/a) \quad . \quad . \quad . \quad . \quad (11.38)$$

and the torque

$$T = Z(p\phi/\pi D_aL_c)L_c(I/a)(D_a/2)$$
$$= (1/2\pi)(Zp/a)\phi I \text{ newton metres} \quad . \quad . \quad . \quad (11.39)$$
$$= 0 \cdot 1173(Zp/a)\phi I \text{ pound-feet} \quad . \quad . \quad . \quad (11.40)$$

(1 Lb. (force) $= 9 \cdot 81 \times 0 \cdot 4536$ newtons; 1 ft $= 0 \cdot 3048$ metres.)

Z, p and a are constants for a given machine, consequently torque is seen to
depend directly on the product of flux and armature current.

Alternative proof:

The power converted to mechanical work

$$= EI = T\omega \quad . \quad . \quad . \quad . \quad . \quad (11.41)$$

Now

$$E = (p/a)(\phi NZ/60) \quad . \quad . \quad . \quad . \quad . \quad (4.13)$$

and

$$\omega = 2\pi N/60$$

$$\therefore (p/a)(\phi NZ/60)I = T2\pi(N/60)$$
$$T = (1/2\pi)(Zp/a)\phi I \quad . \quad . \quad . \quad . \quad (11.39)$$

This value of torque is known as the gross torque of the machine.   It is a little greater than the torque available at the shaft of the machine (the output torque) the difference being the torque due to the mechanical losses (friction and windage) and also the armature core loss and pole-face loss.   It is important to note that all these losses convert mechanical energy to heat.   Copper loss in the armature on the other hand is an electrical loss whereby electrical energy is converted directly to heat.   Copper loss reduces the value of the generated e.m.f. and with it the speed of the motor.

11.6.2. Speed Equation

Rewriting equation (4.13):

$$N = (a/p)(60/Z)(E/\phi) \quad . \quad . \quad . \quad . \quad (11.42)$$

The speed of any d.c. machine is thus directly proportional to its generated e.m.f. and inversely proportional to the flux.

11.6.3. Speed/Torque Characteristics of D.C. Motors

It will be convenient when plotting speed/torque characteristics to use per-unit values.   This involves expressing each value of T, I, E and ϕ as a fraction of its corresponding value at full load.

From equation (11.40)

$$T/T_{f.l.} = (\phi/\phi_{f.l.})(I/I_{f.l.})$$

or

$$T_{p.u.} = \phi_{p.u.}I_{p.u.} \quad . \quad . \quad . \quad . \quad . \quad . \quad (11.43)$$

and equation (11.42) shows

$$E_{p.u.} = \phi_{p.u.}N_{p.u.} \quad . \quad . \quad . \quad . \quad . \quad (11.44)$$

In all cases the terminal voltage is greater than the generated voltage in the armature by the resistance drop in the complete armature circuit (including compoles, compensating winding and series winding).

$$V = E + IR_a \quad . \quad . \quad . \quad . \quad . \quad . \quad . \quad (11.45)$$

Thus

$$E/E_{f.l.} = (V - IR_a)/(V - I_{f.l.}R_a)$$
$$= (1 - IR_a/V)/(1 - I_{f.l.}R_a/V)$$

or

$$E_{p.u.} = (1 - I_{p.u.}r_{p.u.})/(1 - r_{p.u.}) \quad . \quad . \quad . \quad (11.46)$$

where $r_{p.u.} = I_{f.l.}R_a/V$.

Combining with equation (11.44),

$$N_{p.u.} = (1 - I_{p.u.}\, r_{p.u.})/\{\phi_{p.u.}(1 - r_{p.u.})\} \quad . \quad . \quad . \quad (11.47)$$

D.C. Shunt Motor.   Ignoring possible saturation of the pole tips and armature teeth, when the brushes are in the neutral axis the effect of armature reaction (Section 4.5.2) is entirely cross-magnetising and can therefore be neglected.*

* In practice, except for small machines with relatively large IR drop, the effect of armature reaction cannot be ignored.   The saturation of the pole tips and armature teeth in the field distorted by armature reaction reduces the total flux on overload and produces a rising speed characteristic leading to instability.

A small series winding, known as a stabilising winding, is often fitted to counteract this effect and to ensure a drooping characteristic.

Since the field current is constant, the flux per pole ϕ is independent of the load current I. That is,

$$\phi_{p.u.} = 1,$$

the speed and torque equations reduce to

$$N_{p.u.} = (1 - I_{p.u.}r_{p.u.})/(1 - r_{p.u.}) \quad . \quad . \quad . \quad . \quad (11.48)$$

and

$$T_{p.u.} = I_{p.u.} . \quad . \quad . \quad . \quad . \quad . \quad (11.49)$$

The family of curves (fig. 11.18) derived from these equations show the slight fall in speed from no load to full load (0·05 p.u.) normally to be expected. More drooping characteristics result if resistance is added in series with the armature increasing the value of $r_{p.u.}$. The introduction of resistance in the field circuit, thereby reducing $\phi_{p.u.}$, is seen to elevate the characteristic.

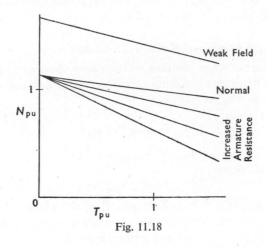

Fig. 11.18

The possibility of producing higher speeds (within limits) by field weakening without introducing serious loss of efficiency is a particular advantage of the d.c. shunt motor, but a machine to be used in this way must be designed so as to be stable in the weakest field condition (Section 11.4).

D.C. Series Motor. In this case flux is no longer independent of load current. Field current and armature current are now the same (or I_f is a constant fraction of I, if a diverter resistance is incorporated in parallel with the series winding). The flux ϕ is therefore related to I by the magnetisation curve.

Thus

$$\phi_{p.u.} = f(I_{p.u.}) \quad . \quad . \quad . \quad . \quad . \quad (11.50)$$

For many simple approximations, when saturation can be neglected and the magnetisation curve is reduced to the air-gap line,

$$\phi_{p.u.} \simeq I_{p.u.} \quad . \quad . \quad . \quad . \quad . \quad (11.51)$$

and torque and speed are obtained from equations (11.43) and (11.47).

Such approximations cannot be justified at the higher values of current when saturation is inevitable. The magnetisation curve is essentially a complex one and cannot be reduced to a simple formula though it may be determined experimentally quite simply. It is usually determined by driving the machine at a constant speed (N') on open circuit, supplying the field current I from a separate source, and measuring the open-circuit terminal voltage (E'). This gives the curve of fig. 11.19.

E' is then plotted in per-unit values when

$$\phi_{\text{p.u.}} = E'_{\text{p.u.}} \quad . \quad . \quad . \quad . \quad . \quad . \quad (11.52)$$

Equations (11.43) and (11.47) become

$$T_{\text{p.u.}} = E'_{\text{p.u.}}I_{\text{p.u.}} \quad . \quad . \quad . \quad . \quad . \quad (11.53)$$

and

$$N_{\text{p.u.}} = (1-I_{\text{p.u.}}r_{\text{p.u.}})/\{E'_{\text{p u.}}(1-r_{\text{p.u.}})\} \quad . \quad . \quad . \quad (11.54)$$

from which the speed/torque curve can be plotted.

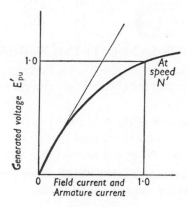

Fig. 11.19

Alternatively the actual values of torque and speed can be found as follows.

At a point P on the magnetisation curve let the field current be I, the generated voltage E' and the speed at which the machine was tested N'. This means that when the machine runs as a series motor with the same load current (and field current) I, if the applied voltage is sufficient for the generated e.m.f. to have the same value E', then the speed will be again N'.

The power converted to mechanical work

$$= E'I/746 \text{ (horse-power)}$$
$$= 2\pi N'T/33\,000.$$

Thus

$$T = 7 \cdot 05 \ (E'/N')I(\text{ft lb}) \quad . \quad . \quad . \quad . \quad . \quad (11.55)$$

Now for any other terminal voltage V with the same load current I the flux will be unchanged. Thus

$$N/E = N'/E'$$

and the speed N corresponding to terminal voltage V is given by

$$N = (N'/E')E$$
$$= (N'/E')(V-IR_a) . \quad . \quad . \quad . \quad . \quad (11.56)$$

The ratio N'/E' must be obtained from the magnetisation curve corresponding to I, and so from equations (11.55) and (11.56) T and N can be plotted against I.

EXAMPLE

The following figures refer to the magnetisation curve of a d.c. series motor running on open circuit at 640 r.p.m. The total resistance of the machine is 0·78 Ω. Plot the speed/torque curve of the motor when operating on a 550-V supply.

Current (amp.):	.	.	.	.	20	40	60	80	100
Generated e.m.f.:	.	.	.	.	215	380	485	550	590
N' .	.	.	.	.	.	640	640	640	640	640
E' .	.	.	.	.	.	215	380	485	550	590
IR drop .	.	.	.	.	15·6	31·2	46·8	62·4	78
$V-IR$.	.	.	.	.	534·4	518·8	503·2	487·6	472
Speed $N = (V-IR)N'/E'$ (r.p.m.)	.	1590	873	665	567	513
Torque $= 7·05E'I/N'$ (ft lb)	.	.	47·4	167	321	485	650

11.6.4. Speed Control of Series Motor by Field Weakening

Higher speeds may be obtained from a series motor by the process of field weakening. This means that the effective field current is reduced in relationship to the armature current by

(a) tapping only a portion of the field turns;

(b) series parallel connection of the field spools; or

(c) connecting a diverter resistance across the field terminals.

The first method is used extensively with d.c. series motors on electric locomotives to obtain high running speeds on level tracks.

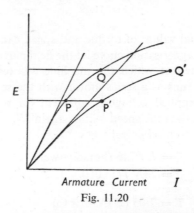

Armature Current   *I*

Fig. 11.20

To determine the torque/speed curve corresponding to the field-weakened condition, the original magnetisation curve must be modified. In fig. 11.20, if the curve OPQ is the normal magnetisation curve of the machine, then, if the field is weakened by using say the 50% field tapping, the flux ϕ corresponding to the point P will be generated with the same ampere-turns as before, but this will require twice the load current. The point P thus becomes P', Q becomes Q', and so on.

From the new magnetisation curve the torque/speed relation is deduced by the method of Section 11.6.3.

If the original magnetisation curve is not given explicitly and only the full field torque/speed curve is available, an approximation to it can be obtained by plotting $1/N$ (varying as ϕ) against $T \times N$ (varying as I).

EXAMPLE

A d.c. series crane motor gives the following speed/torque curve. Find the corresponding approximate characteristic if the field turns are reduced to a 50% tap.

If this motor was originally driving a load at 600 r.p.m., what will be the new speed assuming that the load characteristic is: (a) constant torque; (b) torque proportional to speed; (c) torque proportional to speed²?

Torque (lb ft)	.	.	.	22	41	100	200	350	750
Speed (r.p.m.)	.	.	.	1600	1200	800	600	500	400

Using the end column as the datum for per-unit values:

$I_{p.u.} = T_{p.u.}N_{p.u.}$	.	.	.	0·117	0·167	0·267	0·4	0·583	1·0
$\phi_{p.u.} = 1/N_{p.u.}$	.	.	.	0·25	0·33	0·5	0·67	0·8	1·0

These are plotted in magnetisation curve (a). Curve (b) is derived by doubling the values of $I_{p.u.}$

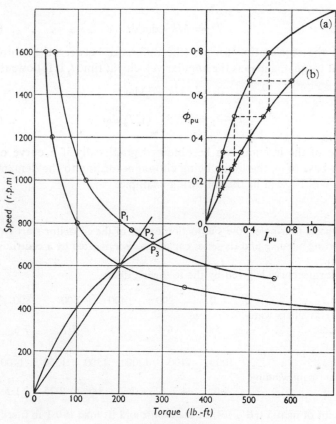

Fig. 11.21

New flux values from this curve corresponding to the same armature currents are:

$\phi'_{p.u.}$ . . .	0·12		0·16	0·28	0·40	0·52	0·74
$\therefore T'$ (lb ft) proportional to flux	$\left(22 \times \dfrac{0·12}{0·25}\right) = 10·6$		20	56	120	228	555
N' (r.p.m.) inversely proportional to flux .	$\left(1600 \times \dfrac{0·25}{0·12}\right) = 3300$		2480	1600	1000	700	540

The characteristics are plotted on the graph (fig. 11.21) together with the three load characteristics. The new speeds are given by points: P_1, constant torque (810 r.p.m.); P_2, torque varies as speed (740 r.p.m.); P_3, torque varies as speed² (710 r.p.m.).

11.7. Starting Time

From graphs such as shown in fig. 11.17 giving the torque/speed relationships of a motor and its load, the time required to reach a given speed from starting can be computed provided the total moment of inertia (Mk^2) of the system is known.

Since

$$T_a = Mk^2 . d\omega/dt \quad . \quad . \quad . \quad . \quad . \quad . \quad (11.57)$$

where T_a is the accelerating torque (the difference between the motor torque and the load torque), and ω is the angular velocity at time t, it follows that

$$dt = (Mk^2/T_a)d\omega$$

and

$$t_2 - t_1 = Mk^2 \int_{\omega_1}^{\omega_2} (1/T_a)d\omega \quad . \quad . \quad . \quad . \quad . \quad (11.58)$$

The value of the integral can be obtained graphically if a curve of $1/T_a$ is plotted to a base of ω, the limits being chosen according to the demands of the question as will be seen in the following example.

EXAMPLE

A single-phase, four-pole, 50-c/s induction motor of the capacitor-start type has the auxiliary starting winding and its series capacitor disconnected by a centrifugal switch at 1000 r.p.m.

Its speed-torque curve is given by the following data:

Speed (r.p.m.) . . .	0	200	400	600	800	1000
Torque (lb ft) (auxiliary winding connected). . .	5·0	6·4	7·5	7·7	7·6	6·5

Speed (r.p.m.) . . .	1000	1100	1200	1300	1350	1400	1500
Torque (lb ft) (main winding only)	5·0	4·7	4·1	3·0	2·25	1·5	0

The moment of inertia (($W/g)k^2$) of the motor and its load is 0·1 lb ft/sec², and the load torque is constant at 2·0 lb ft.

Determine: (a) the total time taken by the machine during starting to reach 1350 r.p.m.; (b) the time during which the auxiliary winding is in circuit.

Starting winding only:

Speed (r.p.m.)	0	200	400	600	800	1000
Accelerating torque (motor torque −2·0)	3	4·5	5·3	5·7	5·6	4·5
1/T	0·33	0·23	0·19	0·18	0·18	0·22

Mean value of $1/T = 0·21$.
Time with starting winding connected

$$= 0·21 \times 0·1 \times 1000 \times 2\pi/60.$$
$$= 2·2 \text{ sec.}$$

With main winding only:

Speed (r.p.m.)	1000	1100	1200	1300	1350
Accelerating torque	3·0	2·7	2·1	1·0	0·25
1/T	0·33	0·37	0·48	1·0	4·0

Mean valve of $1/T$ (from curve by counting squares) = 0·7.
Time with main winding only

$$= 0·7 \times 0·1 \times 350 \times 2\pi/60.$$
$$= 2·6 \text{ sec.}$$
$$\text{Total time} = 4·8 \text{ sec.}$$

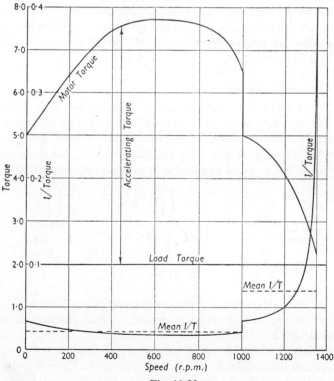

Fig. 11.22

11.8. Rotating Amplifiers

Every normal d.c. generator driven at constant speed is in a sense a power amplifier in so far as the power output of the machine is dependent upon the power input to the field windings. Control of the output power can therefore be achieved by varying the much smaller power supplied to the field, a factor of great convenience made use of with exciters for alternators, synchronous motors and Ward-Leonard generators. A power gain from 20:1 to 100:1 is obtained according to the size of the machine. If two stages are used with a very small pilot exciter supplying the field of the main exciter (fig. 11.23), the overall gain

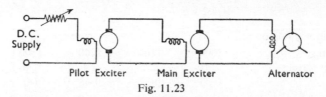

Fig. 11.23

is the product of the two, and the regulating equipment in the field circuit of the pilot exciter has only to deal with a very small power, possibly less than one watt. With normal machines the response to control is very sluggish, due mainly to the inductance of the field windings, and although this system is used in certain applications it is not suitable for use with automatic control circuits of the closed-loop type. The possibility of combining the two machines in one and so retaining the high gain, at the same time considerably decreasing the time lags, has led to the development of special types of machine now classified as rotating amplifiers.

11.8.1. The Cross-field Principle

These machines make use of the cross-field principle which is illustrated by fig. 11.24. The first diagram is of a conventional two-pole d.c. machine with armature and brushgear. Flux ϕ in the horizontal axis will generate voltage between brushes placed at **a** and **b** on the commutator, but there will be no voltage between brushes placed at **c** and **d** at no load (Section 4.1.3).

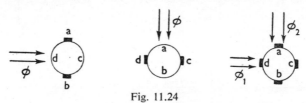

Fig. 11.24

The flux axis and voltage axis are thus at right angles. Now flux in the axis **ab** in the second diagram will similarly produce voltage between **c** and **d** but none between **a** and **b**. Consequently, combining the two together as in the third diagram, flux ϕ_1 along the main axis is responsible for $V_{ab} = V_1$, and ϕ_2 along the cross-axis determines $V_{cd} = V_2$ and neither the fluxes nor the voltages will interfere with each other. Thus one single armature winding can be used as two separate machines provided that armature reaction is negligible or full compensation is arranged.

Although the currents are superimposed in the same armature conductors they still can be considered to have a separate existence. The m.m.f. of the one current (its armature reaction), however, lies along the axis of the flux which generates the other. This leads to an interconnection between the two systems which is exploited to great advantage in the machines which are to be described.

11.8.2. The "Magnavolt"

The first machine to be described is known in this country as the "magnavolt" and consists of a combination of a two-pole exciter and a four-pole machine superimposed in the same magnet system. The two armature windings (fig. 11.25) are wound in the same slots with their commutators at opposite ends. The magnet system has four salient poles with two sets of windings, one of which produces a four-pole field and the other magnetises adjacent poles with the same polarity and thus makes a two-pole system although each pole is divided in the centre. The control winding is the field of the two-pole machine or the

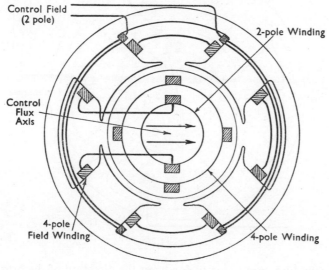

Fig. 11.25

exciter, and the output of this armature is taken to the four-pole field winding. The output from the four-pole armature winding is collected by four brush arms in the usual way.

Although the two fluxes, the control field (two-pole) and the main flux (four-pole) are superimposed, no voltage is produced between the four-pole brushes by the two-pole flux and vice versa.

(Electromotive force is generated in opposite directions in each armature turn of the two-pole winding by the four-pole flux, and the two-pole flux acts in the cross-field direction with respect to the four-pole winding.)

The machine thus behaves as the two entirely separate machines of fig. 11.23. The time constants of the field circuits are reduced to a minimum by using as small a number of turns on each of the field windings as possible and by laminating the whole of the magnetic circuit.

11.8.3. The "Amplidyne" or "Metadyne"

The second type of machine uses the cross-field principle and a single two-pole armature winding. The poles, however, are divided and give the appearance of a four-pole field though actually the poles are in pairs with the same polarity. (Since the poles are divided in this way the machine is sometimes termed a split-field machine.) Compoles may be arranged in all the interpolar spaces. Control windings are arranged as shown in fig. 11.26 and produce a small control flux ϕ_1 in the horizontal axis developing a voltage between the brushes **a** and **b**. These brushes are short-circuited and a current I_1 flows between them (the control flux being very small, the control winding needs few ampere-turns).

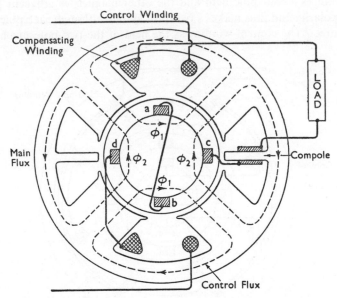

Fig. 11.26

Now the armature m.m.f. due to I_1 acts in the direction of the brush axis **ab**, and it is this m.m.f. which is responsible for the main flux ϕ_2 in the vertical axis. The voltage due to this flux is developed between the output brushes **c** and **d**. Thus the amplidyne is a two-stage amplifier like the magnavolt, but unlike the latter the excitation of the second stage is obtained directly from the armature m.m.f. of the first stage instead of by a separate winding. In the figure the separate flux paths are shown. Although the fluxes are superimposed in the poles and parts of the armature and yoke, in the absence of saturation they are mutually independent.

When the amplidyne is loaded and current I_2 flows, the armature m.m.f. due to I_2 acts along the control axis and directly opposes the m.m.f. of the control winding. It is essential, therefore, for this m.m.f. to be neutralised if the machine is to operate as a high-gain amplifier. A series compensating winding is therefore used, which has been shown for clarity in the figure as a single coil.

It is usually distributed in slots over the poles' faces matching the armature distribution and having a similar triangular m.m.f. wave-form. With full compensation, gains of the order of 20 000:1 are possible and the power supplied to the control winding may be less than one watt even in a 10–20-kW rated machine which means that the amplidyne can be fed directly from an electronic amplifier in an automatic control scheme. The control winding does not take up much space, and frequently several windings are fitted as a convenient method of summation of inputs from various sources.

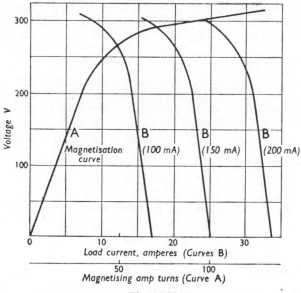

Fig. 11.27

The fully compensated machine has a constant-voltage characteristic drooping with load due to IR drop in the manner of a normal generator. When only partial compensation is employed the load curve droops sharply and becomes an almost constant-current characteristic over the operating portion.

Compoles are fitted at the brush axes to assist commutation, but it is not usual to fit them in the cross-axis, except in the largest machines, owing to the small value of I_1, the exciting current.

Laminated construction is used throughout the magnetic circuit.

The derivation of the output characteristics of an undercompensated metadyne will be seen from the following example (fig. 11.27).

EXAMPLE

The open-circuit magnetisation curve of a metadyne at normal speed is given by:

Generated voltage	.	.	10	60	110	160	210	260	290	310
Control winding ampere-turns			1·5	8·5	15·5	22·5	30	45	69	100

The control winding has 1700 turns, and the armature and compensating windings differ by an effective 10 turns per pole under-compensated. The total armature circuit resistance is 0·38 Ω. Plot the output characteristics corresponding to control currents of: (a) 200 mA, (b) 150 mA, (c) 100 mA.

Control current 200 mA:

(1) Generated voltage E .	10	60	110	160	210	260	290	310
(2) Nett ampere-turns required to produce E .	1·5	8·5	15·5	22·5	30	45	69	100
(3) Control field ampere-turns: (1700×0.2) .	340	340	340	340	340	340	340	340
(4) Ampere-turns uncompensated: (3)−(2) .	338·5	331·5	324·5	317·5	310	295	271	240
(5) Line current: (4)÷10 .	33·9	33·2	32·5	31·8	31·0	29·5	27·1	24·0
(6) IR drop: (5)×0·38. .	13	13	13	13	12	12	11	10
(7) Output volts: (1)−(6) .	−3	47	97	147	198	248	279	300

Control current 150 mA:

(3) (1700×0.15). . .	255	255	255	255	255	255	255	255
(4)	253·5	246·5	239·5	231·5	225	210	186	155
(5)	25·4	24·6	24	23·2	22·5	21·0	18·6	15·5
(6)	10	10	10	9	9	8	7	6
(7)	0	50	100	151	201	252	283	304

Control current 100 mA:

(3) (1700×0.1) . . .	170	170	170	170	170	170	170	170
(4)	168·5	161·5	154·5	147·5	140	125	101	70
(5)	16·9	16·2	15·5	14·8	14·0	12·5	10·1	7·0
(6)	6	6	6	6	6	5	4	3
(7)	4	54	104	154	204	255	289	307

11.8.4. The "Magnicon"

This machine also uses the cross-field principle, and once again the main excitation is produced by the armature m.m.f. of the short-circuited first stage. In the case of the amplidyne, the poles were seen to be split so as to provide an interpolar space where commutation could take place assisted by compoles if necessary.

With the magnicon, the same result is achieved by using a winding having coils of only 50% pitch instead of the nearly 100% pitch coils of the normal d.c. machine (the armature has thus the appearance of a four-pole winding). The shorter coil span spaces the commutation axes to 45° on either side of the main poles instead of the usual 90°, and thus separate poles can be used for the main flux and for the cross-flux. The magnicon can therefore be described as a split-armature machine in contrast with the amplidyne which is a split-pole machine. It is shown in diagrammatic form in fig. 11.28. The control winding once again determines the control flux ϕ_1 and the voltage in the axis **ab**, the brushes of which are short-circuited. The armature m.m.f., which this time has a trapezoidal distribution due to the short pitch coils, provides the main flux ϕ_2 and the output voltage between brushes **cd**.

Comparing figs. 11.26 and 11.28, both ϕ_1 and ϕ_2 are seen to traverse the same poles in the amplidyne but are separated in the magnicon.

The control poles of the latter can thus be smaller than the main poles; indeed they can be further subdivided into saturated and non-saturated teeth, an ingenious modification with advantage for combining the reference and feed-back currents in a control scheme.

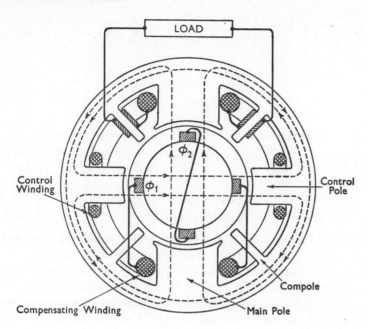

Fig. 11.28

11.8.5. Automatic Regulators.   Basic Principles of the Closed-loop System

The object of an automatic regulating system is usually the control of some particular output quantity, maintaining it constant at a value equal to or very nearly equal to a prescribed reference standard. For example, automatic temperature control of a kiln or an oven requires the maintenance of the temperature at a set figure in spite of changes taking place in external conditions. Similarly, a voltage regulator for a generator should keep the voltage within prescribed limits in spite of load or speed changes. For reeling operations it may be necessary to keep constant the tension in the material or the torque of a motor. Another example is position control equipment, which requires that the angular position of an output shaft, possibly driving a heavy load as in gun-laying equipment, should follow precisely and rapidly the position of a similar input shaft some distance away without at the same time loading the latter.

All such mechanisms demand accuracy, rapidity of response, and complete stability, factors which invariably conflict with one another.

The fundamental principle of the closed-loop system can be seen from fig. 11.29, which shows an elementary voltage regulator for a generator. It

16—E.M.

requires first a constant reference voltage which is provided by a potential divider connected across constant-voltage mains and is known as the reference θ_i.

It is required that the generator voltage (the output voltage θ_o) should be maintained as nearly as possible equal to the reference, changing only if θ_i is altered.

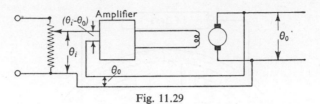

Fig. 11.29

The field of the generator is fed from a high-gain power amplifier, the input to which is obtained by connecting the output voltage and the reference voltage in opposition and is thus $\theta_i - \theta_o$. If the overall gain of the amplifier and generator is K, then

$$K(\theta_i - \theta_o) = \theta_o$$

and
$$\theta_o = \{K/(1+K)\}\theta_i \quad . \quad . \quad . \quad . \quad . \quad (11.59)$$

From this it would appear that if K is large θ_o will be practically equal to θ_i, and indeed quite a large variation of K will not materially affect the result.

The way in which the output may be matched to the reference when a rotating amplifier is used is shown in fig. 11.30. The amplidyne has two control windings, one connected to the reference source and one to the output, the coils being in opposition so that the total control m.m.f. is due to the difference between the two currents and thus to the difference between θ_i and θ_o. Equation (11.59) is an equation relating only to steady-state conditions and does not give information as to the result of sudden changes.

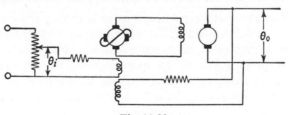

Fig. 11.30

If θ_o falls momentarily, say due to the sudden application of load, the input to the amplifier increases enormously and so does the control current. There will be time lags due to the inductances of the various parts of the system, principally the field circuits. However, the generator field current will be momentarily increased tending to restore θ_o rapidly to its original value, and when this is achieved the input to the amplifier will fall again to the original small difference or error figure.

For a comprehensive treatment of closed-loop systems, reference should be made to Volume V of this series.

CHAPTER 12

POLYPHASE COMMUTATOR MACHINES

12.1. Variable-speed Drive

MOST industrial apparatus to be driven by individual electric motors requires only single-speed machines.

Usually a slight variation of speed between no load and full load is permissible, and in these cases the induction motor, cage or wound rotor, with less than 5% slip on full load, is the ideal machine.

There exist, however, many drives requiring a motor whose speed must be varied over a wide range according to the setting of some control device. For example, such provision has to be made in the case of many types of conveyor, with high-speed lifts, fans and pumps, and in the drives for cement kilns, pulverised fuel plants, stokers, calenders, printing presses and many textile machines. It will be appreciated that motors suitable for these purposes are necessarily more complicated, and therefore more expensive, than single-speed machines.

In this chapter will be explained the fundamental principle of machines, which, though operating directly from three-phase a.c. mains, are available for wide-range speed control.

12.1.1. Comparison with the D.C. Shunt Motor

The speed of a d.c. shunt motor can be controlled by adding resistance in the armature circuit. Fig. 12.1 shows the armature of a d.c. machine connected across the mains. By adding resistance in series, the voltage available across the armature is reduced and speed also falls in practically the same ratio.

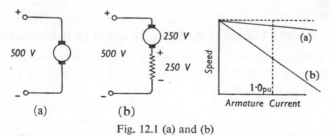

Fig. 12.1 (a) and (b)

This method of varying the speed of a motor, although simple, has two disadvantages:

(a) energy is lost in the series resistance—amounting to half the total power supplied in the case when speed is reduced to 50% of normal value, and

(b) the speed/load characteristic of the machine droops, the change in speed at no load being very small.

Unless the load is constant in practice, this arrangement leads to considerable fluctuations of speed.

Now suppose that the resistance is replaced by a booster-generator producing the same voltage drop (fig. 12.2). The main motor operates under the same conditions as before running at reduced speed. The booster will be acting as a motor—since current is flowing in at its positive terminal—driving the coupled machine as a generator.

Thus the energy, which was dissipated in the case of the resistance, is now returned to the line via the motor-generator set.

The speed of the main motor is controlled by varying the voltage drop across the booster, that is, by varying the field of the latter, and as this voltage drop is

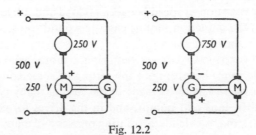

Fig. 12.2

reasonably independent of the load current, the speed of the main motor will be reduced at no load as well as at full load.

A further advantage lies in the possibility of reversing the voltage at the terminals of the booster (by reversing the field).

The voltage across the main motor is now greater than that of the mains and the speed is raised above normal. In these circumstances energy is being supplied to the main motor partly direct from the mains and partly via the auxiliary set.

It will be seen that to achieve a 3:1 speed variation of the main motor, an auxiliary set is required, each machine of which is half the rating of the main motor.

12.1.2. Injection of a Voltage in the Rotor Circuit of an Induction Motor

We have already seen in Chapter 6 that by adding resistance in series with the secondary winding of an induction motor, speed is reduced in a very similar manner to that of the d.c. machine above.

Fig. 12.3 (a) shows the secondary circuit of a wound-rotor machine running on full load with a slip S. $E_{2,s}$ is the induced secondary e.m.f.; R_2 and X_2 being the secondary resistance and leakage reactance respectively.

If as in fig. 12.3 (b) extra resistance R_2' is added, the sequence of events will be as follows. Since impedance has been increased, current is reduced and also torque. Assuming that the load torque remains constant the speed therefore falls and slip increases.

$E_{2,s}$ thus increases and the fall of speed is arrested when current and torque are restored to their original values. The machine thus runs on load at a reduced speed. Note that the voltage drop across R_2' has to be balanced by an increase of $E_{2,s}$. As in the case of the d.c. machine, although R_2' causes a reduction of speed on load its effect at no load is small, and again the energy losses on load are prohibitive, except for cases when slow running is only required for very short periods.

If now as in fig. 12.3 (c) the resistance R_2' is replaced by an alternating voltage source E_k producing the same voltage drop as would take place across R_2' speed will be reduced to the same figure.

Variation of the value of E_k thus varies the slip of the induction motor.

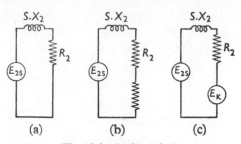

Fig. 12.3 (a), (b) and (c)

It will be observed that the voltage source E_k must have:

(a) correct frequency, i.e. rotor frequency $f_2 = sf_1$ at all times and for all values of s;

(b) correct phase relationship to $E_{2,s}$ (if E_k is in phase opposition to $E_{2,s}$, speed falls below normal; if E_k is advanced 180°, speed rises); and

(c) must be capable of being varied by some form of controller which then becomes the speed control device.

These conditions are not easy to fulfil, particularly the frequency condition, and the next section will show how a commutator winding may be used for this purpose.

12.1.3. Frequency-changer Action of a Commutator

It is necessary now to revise fundamental ideas of a commutator winding and to extend the simple conception of Chapter 4.

Consider in the first place a simple two-pole lap or wave-wound armature of a normal d.c. machine as shown in fig. 12.4.

As the armature rotates, alternating e.m.f. is set up in each armature coil, each e.m.f. being displaced from that of the next coil by an angle dependent on the slot pitch. Thus the voltages in a winding which has all coils connected in series form the vector polygon of fig. 12.5. When there are many slots this polygon approximates to a circle.

We have already seen that the voltage between diametral fixed tappings p and q would produce an alternating voltage represented by the vector V_{pq}, and that maximum instantaneous value of this voltage occurs when the tappings are in the position **ab**. Thus sliding tappings, fixed in space but always making contact with the armature at the points **a**, **b** (i.e. brushes on a commutator), have always $[V_{pq}]_{max}$ between them.

Between these brushes the armature can be represented as two batteries connected in parallel as shown in fig. 12.6.   Although individual coils move forward, this voltage diagram remains fixed in space.

This, of course, is the normal d.c. generator.

Now consider a d.c. generator of normal design with brushes mounted on a brush rocker so as to permit adjustment when setting the brush axis in the magnetic neutral of the machine.   Suppose this brush rocker to be rotated slowly, the brushes moving from the axis **ac** to **bd** then to **ca** and so on

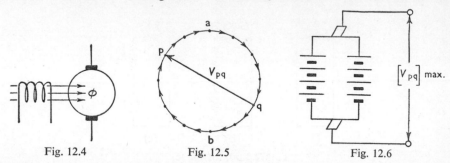

Fig. 12.4   Fig. 12.5   Fig. 12.6

(fig. 12.7).   The voltage at the brushes will be normal for the machine when they are in the position **ac**, and the magnitude will depend as usual on the value of the flux and the speed of rotation.

This voltage will fall to zero as the brushes move to the position **bd**.   As the brushgear makes one revolution, one cycle of low-frequency alternating voltage will be developed between the brushes.

Thus, when both brushgear and armature rotate relative to the field, the commutator is seen to be a frequency changer.   The d.c. machine (and the synchronous converter) are really special cases of the more general principle.

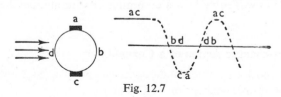

Fig. 12.7

Since the production of alternating current at the brushgear of a commutator is somewhat unfamiliar at this stage it is advisable to formulate rules whereby the value of the brushgear voltage and frequency can be recognised.

FREQUENCY CHANGER PRINCIPLE OF COMMUTATOR AND BRUSHGEAR

FREQUENCY of a.c. voltage at the brushes.	depends on relative motion between—	BRUSHES/FIELD
MAGNITUDE of a.c. voltage at the brushes.	depends on relative motion between—	CONDUCTORS/FIELD

12.2. The Scherbius Generator

In fig. 12.8 a machine is arranged with a brush rocker fixed to the base-plate but with the magnet-frame mounted in a cradle so as to rotate slowly.

Again it will be observed that alternating voltage of low frequency will be produced at the brushes. The direction of rotation of the armature should

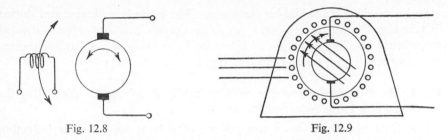

Fig. 12.8　　　　　　　　　　　　Fig. 12.9

preferably be in the opposite direction to that of the field since the magnitude of the voltage depends on the relative motion between them.

This physically rotating field system is next replaced by a stator with a distributed winding fed with low-frequency polyphase alternating current (fig. 12.9).

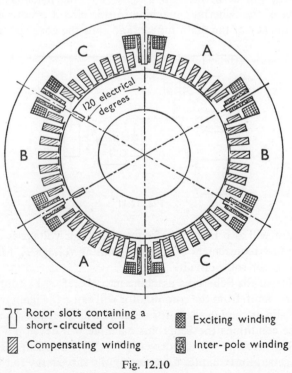

Fig. 12.10

These stator currents set up rotating field passing the brushes at the same frequency. Applying the commutator principles we see that the voltage picked off the commutator by fixed brushes will be at the same frequency as that at which the field rotates, i.e. the stator supply frequency.

The magnitude of this voltage depends on the flux and the speed of rotation of the armature relative to the flux.

Three brushes spaced at 120° enable three-phase voltage to be tapped from the commutator and the phase of this voltage can be varied by rocking the brushgear.

Such a machine is a Scherbius generator. The stator is laminated and slotted to take the distributed winding. For large outputs the windings are divided at the brush axes and compoles added as for a d.c. machine. Distributed compensating windings are also employed (fig. 12.10).

12.2.1. The Scherbius Generator used as a Slip Regulator for controlling the Speed of a Large Induction Motor

Fig. 12.11 shows the main connections of a large wound-rotor induction motor. For clarity only one phase of the three-phase supply is shown. The usual rotor starting resistance is cut out as the machine is started in the normal way. The auxiliary set consists of an induction motor driving a Scherbius generator of the type described above.

Now, when the rings of the induction motor are short-circuited, the current flowing in them will be at the slip frequency of the machine. Inserting the stator winding of the Scherbius machine in this circuit produces rotating field at the slip frequency of the main motor, and thus the corresponding voltage at

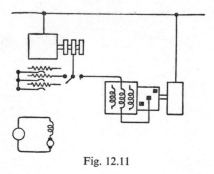

Fig. 12.11

the commutator will also be at this frequency. This voltage is thus in accordance with the first requirement of a slip regulating voltage E_k for injecting into the induction motor rotor circuit.

The armature of the Scherbius machine may therefore be connected in series and the injected e.m.f. from the commutator will cause the main induction motor to increase in slip as though the rotor resistance had been re-inserted.

Under these conditions the Scherbius machine will develop a driving torque and its coupled machine will be driven above synchronism thereby acting as an induction generator (Chapter 6) returning the slip energy to the line.

Since the voltage at the commutator of the Scherbius machine depends on the flux which in turn depends on the stator current, i.e. the rotor current of the main induction motor, it will increase as the load on the latter is increased.

Slip thus increases with load and the overall speed/load characteristic droops in a manner somewhat akin to that of a d.c. series motor.

This type of characteristic may be of use in certain types of haulage equipment.

12.2.2. The Shunt-type Scherbius Regulator

Alternatively the Scherbius machine may be shunt connected (fig. 12.12) with an auto-transformer between field and armature.

With the latter on maximum tapping it will be seen that the stator windings of the Scherbius machine are once again connected across the rings of the main induction motor and will carry slip-frequency current. The commutator voltage is also at the same frequency and also connected across the same terminals.

As with the d.c. shunt generator the terminal voltage depends on satisfying simultaneously the relationships between field voltage and field current, which depends on field resistance, and that between armature voltage and field current determined by the magnetisation curve of the machine.

The voltage which is built up across the brushes is primarily independent of the current flowing in the armature and hence the voltage injected—the slip-regulating voltage—will be constant. Adjustment of the auto-transformer tapping varies this voltage and thus acts as the speed controller.

This equipment is a single-range equipment only, that is, the main induction motor only runs at sub-synchronous speeds. To obtain speeds above synchronism an additional pilot exciter is required as shown in fig. 12.13.

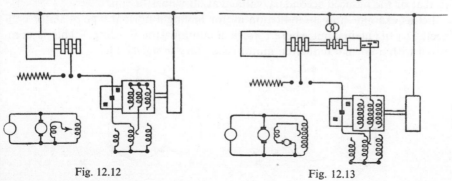

Fig. 12.12   Fig. 12.13

12.2.3. The Pilot Exciter

This pilot exciter is yet another type of commutator machine, the operation of which can be appreciated if the commutator principles of Section 12.1.3 are thoroughly understood.

It consists of an armature with commutator winding, fixed brushes and, in addition, with three-phase symmetrical tappings brought out to slip rings. There is no winding on the stator of the machine. The rings are connected to the mains, usually via a step-down transformer, and the exciter is chain driven from the shaft of the main induction motor.

Mains frequency current applied to the rings sets up rotating field *relative to the conductors* at mains frequency. But, since the armature is driven in the *opposite direction* at the rotor speed of the induction motor, the field rotates at *slip frequency* in space.

The frequency at the brushes (field/brushes) is thus slip frequency and is suitable for exciting the Scherbius machine.

The phase of this voltage is arranged to coincide with the secondary voltage of the main induction motor and thus raises the speed above synchronism.

As the auto-transformer is tapped up the Scherbius machine builds up in the direction of the prior excitation supplied by the exciter, the speed range of the main motor thus being extended in the hypersynchronous direction.

When driving the main motor above synchronism the Scherbius machine acts as a generator supplying additional energy.

Double-range Scherbius equipments of this type have been installed for regulating the speed of induction motors exceeding 1000 h.p. for duties such as circulating water pumps, sewage pumps, mine ventilating fans and recipro-cating compressors.

Modified schemes operating on the same principles are used with flywheel motor generator sets supplying the power for mine winding equipment using the Ward-Leonard control system with load equalisation.

12.3. The Shunt Motor or Stator-fed A.C. Commutator Motor

The difficulty of applying a slip-regulating voltage to an induction motor is chiefly that of finding a suitable source whose frequency always remains equal to that of the induced secondary voltage at all values of slip.

Let us examine now an induction motor having a normal type of stator con-nected to the mains, but whose rotor is a commutator winding. This is com-pared with a normal induction motor secondary in fig. 12.14.

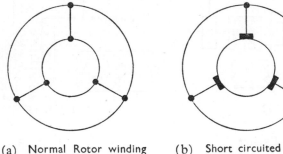

(a) Normal Rotor winding   (b) Short circuited
     short circuited   commutator winding

Fig. 12.14

The rings of the latter are short-circuited in the normal way, and in the case of the former three brushes set on the commutator at 120° are short-circuited externally to the machine. It will be seen that the short circuit is just as effective in the two cases and the operation of the two machines will be identical.

However, the current in the brush leads of the slip-ring machine is obviously of slip frequency, but applying the commutator principles to the other machine, the current in the brush leads is seen to be at mains frequency.

Mains-frequency voltage, of correct phase, injected in these leads will produce slip-regulating action and a variable-speed motor is thus produced.

A double-wound induction regulator connected as shown in fig. 12.15 is used to supply this voltage.

12.3.1. Double-wound Induction Regulator

The principle of the induction regulator has been discussed in Chapter 6. It is seen there that the voltage in the secondary of a polyphase regulator does not vary in magnitude but only in phase as the rotor of the regulator is rotated throughout its range.

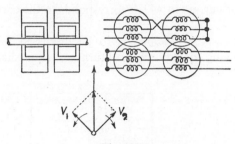

Fig. 12.15

Such a regulator would be useless for the purpose now required.

But, if two of these regulators are mounted on the same shaft and rotate together, having the connections to their primaries reversed to give opposite phase sequence, then, as the voltage of the first unit is advanced, that of the second unit will be retarded by the same angle.   The total voltage output of the two units in series is thus seen to be the vector sum of V_1 and V_2 (fig. 12.15).

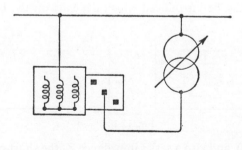

Fig. 12.16

This voltage does not vary in phase but is decreased from a maximum value to zero with 90° phase shift of the regulator.   A further 90° causes the voltage to increase again in antiphase.

This variation is ideal for the purpose and produces a double-range speed control of the motor.

12.3.2. Current Locus Curves of the Shunt Motor

In order to understand fully the behaviour of a shunt motor under various conditions of load it is important to know how the input current varies in both magnitude and phase angle.

As with the induction motor, a plot of the current vector shows that the extremity of the vector has a circular locus, but whereas there is just one circle—the familiar circle diagram—for the simple induction motor, a whole family of circles are obtained for the shunt motor, one circle for each regulator position.

12.3.3. Equivalent Circuit of the Shunt Motor

Following the procedure of Chapter 6 relating to the induction motor, it is convenient to set up an equivalent electrical circuit consisting of resistance and reactance elements, the current in which corresponds to the current in the actual machine.

For simplicity a two-pole machine is to be discussed with primary and secondary windings having equal numbers of turns and equal distribution factors.

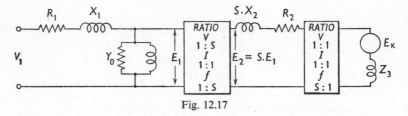

Fig. 12.17

The so-called "exact" equivalent circuit is shown in fig. 12.17.

This will be seen to correspond to the equivalent circuit of the induction motor (fig. 6.15 (b)), but in addition the commutator frequency changer is connected in the secondary circuit.

The induction regulator is represented by a voltage E_k which, is equal to V_1 multiplied by a ratio corresponding to its setting (this ratio is usually complex, i.e. a phase angle may be introduced which depends on the brush setting and

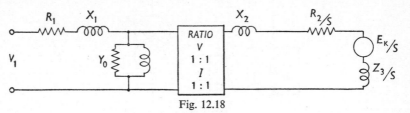

Fig. 12.18

the type of regulator), and also a series impedance Z_3 the short-circuit impedance of the regulator.

Since the commutator is only a frequency changer, current and voltage magnitude being equal on either side of it, it does not enter into the calculation.

The first stage of simplification is to divide all voltages and impedances in the secondary circuit by S.

This does not alter current values and permits the circuit to be further simplified as shown in fig. 12.18.

The solution of this network by analytical methods enables the complete performance of the machine to be determined and its efficiency, power factor, output, etc., to be found.

This is the method usually adopted by designers.

12.3.4. The "Approximate" Equivalent Circuit

To obtain a simpler picture of the machine's performance a number of approximations will now be made. It is not to be assumed that the items neglected are always negligible in practice.

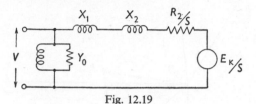

Fig. 12.19

Firstly, the voltage drop in the primary impedance due to magnetising current is ignored, i.e. the magnetising admittance is considered connected across the supply terminals. Secondly, R_1 and Z_3 are omitted. The equivalent circuit is reduced to fig. 12.19.

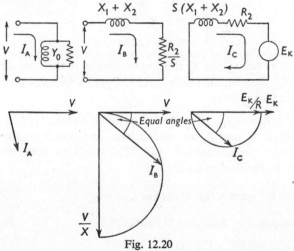

Fig. 12.20

The current in this circuit can now be found by applying the theorem of superposition, when the total current will be seen to be the vector sum of three currents (fig. 12.20).

$$I = I_A + I_B + I_C \quad . \quad . \quad . \quad . \quad . \quad (12.1)$$

I_A is the current in the magnetising admittance;
I_B is the current in the main circuit due to V and with E_k removed; and
I_C is the current in the main circuit due to E_k and with V removed.

These circuits are shown in fig. 12.20. Note that in the case of the third circuit, voltage and impedance have both been multiplied by S.

The current I_A is independent of S. I_B on the other hand is the current in a circuit of constant reactance and variable resistance. The locus of the current vector in this circuit is circular (as described in Appendix A). I_B increases from zero and moves round the circle as S increases. The current I_C flows in a constant-reactance variable-resistance circuit and again the locus will be circular, but this time the form will be as shown in fig. 12.20. I_C has a maximum value when S is equal to zero, decreasing to zero when S approaches infinity.

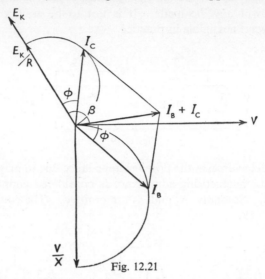

Fig. 12.21

In both circuits for I_B and I_C the phase angle ϕ is the same, being equal to $\arctan S(X_1 + X_2)/R_2$, with the result that, as S varies, the vectors I_B and I_C move around their circles together.

Addition of I_A, I_B and I_C. To obtain the total current I_A, I_B and I_C must be added vectorially. I_B and I_C are added first, and it will be shown that their resultant has also a circular locus.* Fig. 12.21 shows the general case when the voltage vectors are inclined at an angle β.

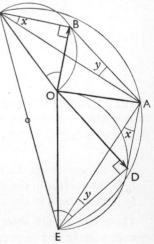

* To prove that the point A (fig. 12.22) has a circular locus:

OBAD is a parallelogram. Triangles CBO and ODE are similar.

$$\therefore \quad OB/DE = CB/OD$$

and $$AD/DE = CB/BA.$$

Now $$\angle OBA = \angle ODA$$

and $$\therefore \quad \angle CBA = \angle ADE$$

and thus triangles CBA and ADE are similar.

In triangle ADE

$$\angle ADO + 90° + x + y = 180°$$
$$\therefore \quad \angle ADO = 90° - (x+y).$$
$$\angle BAD = 180° - ADO$$
$$= 90° + (x+y).$$
$$\therefore \quad \angle CAE = 90°$$

and the locus of A is a circle with centre at the middle of the line CE.

Fig. 12.22

Complete Locus of I.   Figs. 12.23 and 12.24 show the complete current locus developed for a machine in which the ratio reactance to resistance is 4:1.   The locus is to be drawn for one particular setting of the regulator, i.e. one particular value of E_k, and it is assumed that E_k is in phase with V.

The locus of I_B is first obtained by inversion, commencing with the reactance jX and values of R/S as S varies.   The diameter of the current circle will be V/X and the value of I_B corresponding to increments of S will be obtained by projection (fig. 12.23).

To this locus, the circle corresponding to I_C is added (diameter E_k/R).   Bisecting **ab** gives the centre of the locus of I_B+I_C and this circle is next drawn (fig. 12.23).

Since in this case I_B and I_C are in phase it is only necessary to extend the vector I_B to meet the outer circle to obtain the resultant vector.   Projecting backward

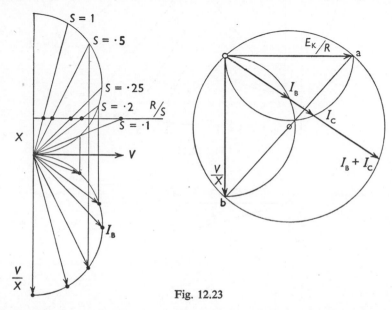

Fig. 12.23

from the point O by a line representing the current I_A gives the origin of the total current I.

The final diagram, fig. 12.24, shows the value of I corresponding to various values of slip.

Examining these points around the final locus it will be observed that for the value of E_k chosen and with E_k in phase with V the machine runs on no load $(I_B+I_C = 0)$ at a slip of about -0.2, that is 20% above synchronous speed.   As the machine is loaded the vector I advances around the circle with an increase of slip, the working range possibly extending as far as $S = -0.1$.

An increase of the regulator setting means an increase in the value E_k/R, and so for each value of E_k another circle can be drawn giving the family of curves of fig. 12.25.

To obtain speeds below synchronism E_k is opposed to V and the corresponding family of curves is shown in fig. 12.26.

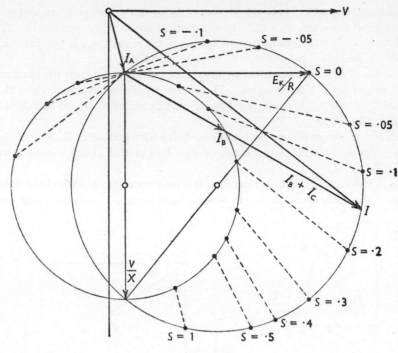

Fig. 12.24

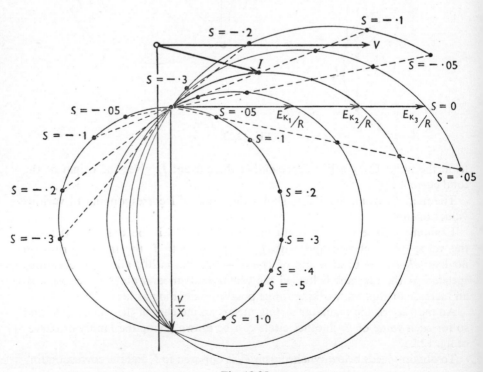

Fig. 12.25

12.3.5. Power-factor Improvement

It will be observed from all the foregoing curves that the power factor over the working range is poor, particularly in the case of the sub-synchronous values.

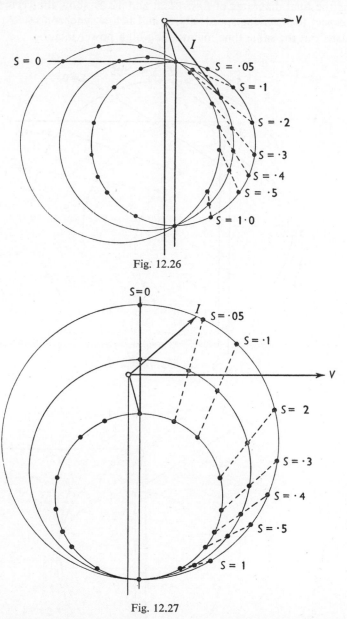

Fig. 12.26

Fig. 12.27

If, however, E_k is injected at right angles to V, the circle diagrams become those of fig. 12.27 from which it will be seen that although there is little change in speed, the power factor becomes leading at light load and with the correct amount of E_k, a full-load power factor of unity can easily be achieved.

17—E.M.

It thus becomes advisable to introduce a quadrature component of E_k—obtained from a quadrature booster transformer—in addition to the values of E_k which by themselves gave us the curves of figs. 12.25 and 12.26.

Thus the final diagrams of figs. 12.28 and 12.29 show the vector E_k inclined with respect to V, giving speeds above and below synchronism as the regulator is adjusted, at the same time maintaining high power factors.

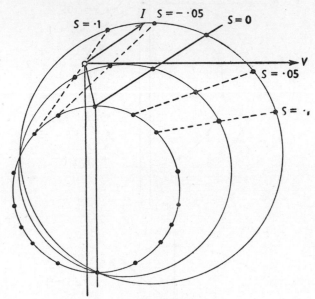

Fig. 12.28

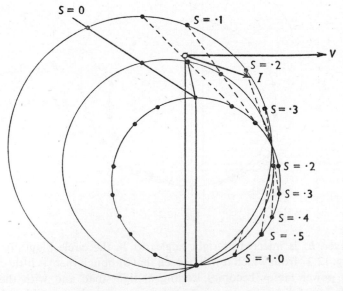

Fig. 12.29

12.4. The Schrage Motor

The second basic type of polyphase commutator motor is the Schrage motor. It also can be considered as an induction motor with a built-in slip-regulator.

Since the supply is taken direct to slip rings on the rotor, this machine is commonly known as the "rotor-fed"-type commutator motor.

Its principle of operation is shown in the following manner.

Fig. 12.30 represents an induction motor with a frequency-changer-type commutator machine directly coupled to it. The second machine is the pilot-exciter

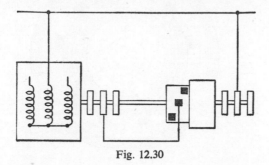

Fig. 12.30

used in the double-range Scherbius system. The supply is connected to both the induction motor stator and to the rings of the frequency changer.

Once again, rotating field is set up in the commutator winding passing the conductors at synchronous speed, but as the whole armature is rotated in the opposite direction by the induction motor, it only passes the brushes at slip frequency.

The frequency of the voltage picked off the brushes is thus slip frequency and

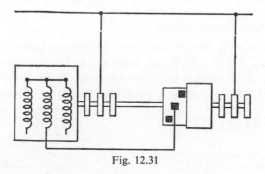

Fig. 12.31

this voltage is thus a suitable slip regulating voltage to be fed back to the rings of the motor.

In the next diagram, fig. 12.31, the induction motor is shown inverted, that is, the supply is applied to the rings and the stator forms the secondary. The slip regulator is now connected to the stator.

This interchange of windings makes no difference whatsoever to the performance of the motor, though it is unusual for a simple induction motor to be connected this way (except for some fractional h.p. single-phase machines).

Its field will now be rotating relative to the rotor conductors at synchronous speed, in fact exactly as in the commutator machine. The two rotors may thus be combined in one, the primary winding and the commutator winding (known as the regulator winding) being separate windings but wound in the same slots.

It now remains to find some suitable manner of varying the slip-regulating voltage picked off the commutator to be applied to the induction motor secondary (now on the stator).

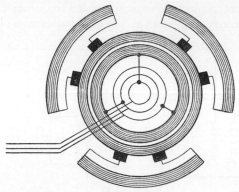

Fig. 12.32

Brushes are arranged on the commutator in pairs, alternate brushes being secured to two separate brush rockers. The rockers are rotated in opposite directions, usually by a rack-and-pinion mechanism.

As a pair of brushes separate, the number of segments between them increases and so does the voltage. Each secondary phase winding is connected across a pair of brushes, the brush pairs being symmetrically disposed around the commutator at 120 electrical degrees to each other (fig. 12.32).

12.4.1. Double-range Speed Control

It will be readily seen that speeds above as well as below synchronism can easily be obtained. When the brush pairs are in line on the commutator the machine behaves as a normal induction motor. Parting the brushes in one direction reduces speed; reversing the brush movement and parting in the

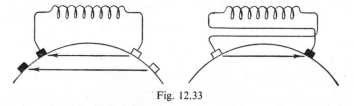

Fig. 12.33

opposite direction (fig. 12.33) reverses the direction of the regulating voltage and thus increases speed. The maximum voltage to be obtained from the commutator occurs when the brushes are separated by a pole pitch, which therefore determines maximum and minimum speeds. If this voltage is equal to $E_{2,0}$, the secondary induced voltage at standstill, the machine is capable of a speed variation from zero to approximately twice synchronous speed. It is unusual for such a large speed range to be demanded, a speed range of 3 : 1 being sufficient for most applications.

The number of turns and relative size of the regulating winding is dependent on the speed regulation required. The winding is usually wave wound, though many special connections have been developed especially for larger machines to improve commutation conditions.

Since the brushes are movable, compoles are not a practical proposition. With small machines employing wave windings the brush pairs may not be obviously opposite each other but may be separated by two pole pitches.

On large machines it is quite common for the number of phases of the secondary and regulating windings to be greater than that of the primary.

12.4.2. Power-factor Improvement

A phase shift of the injected voltage to bring about power-factor improvement can easily be obtained with the Schrage motor. It will be seen from fig. 12.34 that if one set of brushes is advanced more rapidly than the other is retarded, the necessary quadrature component is added to the voltage. This differential

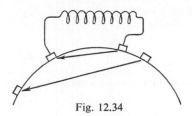

Fig. 12.34

movement is usually arranged by coupling the racks driving the brush rockers to the handwheel with gears having differing ratios.

It is not possible to maintain unity power factor at all loads and speeds with simple mechanism, but in practice a satisfactory compromise can be made.

The brush movement is controlled by handwheel for manually operated regulation of speed, but the use of a geared pilot motor enables remote and automatic control schemes to be developed.

12.4.3. Starting

Provided the speed range is 3 : 1 or more, Schrage motors may be started with brushes in the lowest speed position by direct-on contactor starters. Interlocks are usually arranged to prevent the contactor being closed on the line when the brushes are in any other position.

12.4.4. The Equivalent Circuit of the Schrage Motor

The derivation of the performance diagrams of a Schrage motor is more complicated than that of the shunt machine largely owing to the effect of magnetic linkages between the regulator and primary windings.

In the following analysis once again simplifying assumptions are made transforming an "exact" equivalent circuit into one yielding much simpler results. It must not be assumed that the quantities neglected are so small as to have no significance in an actual design.

Again, equal numbers of turns in all windings have been assumed.

The magnetic linkages between the various windings of the Schrage motor on load are depicted in fig. 12.35. The primary winding lies in the bottom of the rotor slots with the regulating winding above it.

The most important flux is the mutual flux ϕ linking all three windings. This flux gives rise to the induced secondary e.m.f. E_2. Leakage fluxes also exist: ϕ_1, ϕ_2 and ϕ_3 responsible for the corresponding leakage reactances X_1, X_2 and X_3.

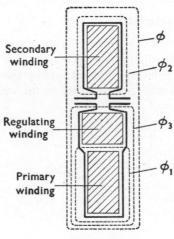

Fig. 12.35

The total flux linking the regulating winding is $\phi+\phi_3$ thus inducing the voltage E_t at the commutator. The voltage between pairs of brushes is

$$E_k = E_t\gamma \qquad \qquad (12.2)$$

where γ is a complex ratio $\gamma = \gamma e^{j\psi}$, γ being dependent on the separation of the brushes and ψ being introduced by the position of the brush axis relative to the axis of the secondary winding.

The commutator thus acts as a phase-shifting transformer in addition to a frequency changer, and the current in the regulating winding will consequently be $I_2\bar{\gamma}$, where $\bar{\gamma}$ is the conjugate of γ.*

To obtain the primary current the machine is regarded as a three-winding transformer, whence

$$I_1 = I_0+I_2+I_2\bar{\gamma} \qquad \qquad (12.3)$$

---

* Equating the input and output volt-amperes of the equivalent phase-shifting transformer
$$\bar{V}_1I_1 = \bar{V}_2I_2.$$
Thus
$$I_1/I_2 = \bar{V}_2/\bar{V}_1 = \bar{\gamma}.$$

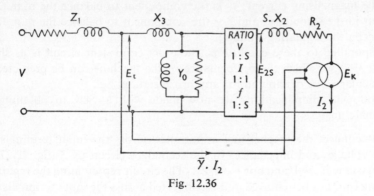

Fig. 12.36

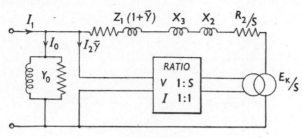

Fig. 12.37

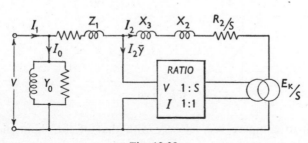

Fig. 12.38

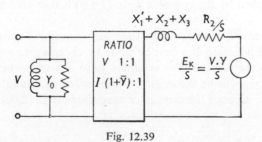

Fig. 12.39

I_0 is the magnetising current; I_2 is the component to balance the m.m.f. due to current in the secondary; and $I_2\gamma$ the component to balance the m.m.f. due to current in the regulating winding.

Corresponding to these conditions, the exact equivalent circuit is as shown in fig. 12.36 from which the performance of the machine can be predicted for any particular value of slip and for any brush setting.

The following simplifications are now made with a view to obtaining an approximate analysis:

1. Reconnect the magnetising admittance across the input terminals and divide voltages and impedances in the secondary circuit by S (fig. 12.37).

2. Assume $E_t = V$ and not $V - I_1Z_1$. The circuit representing the regulating winding can thus be removed and reconnected across the input terminals. In order, however, that the voltage drop across Z_1 should remain the same in fig. 12.38, Z_1 becomes $Z_1(1+\gamma)$ the components of which are R_1' and X_1'.

3. Neglecting primary resistance R_1' the circuit finally simplifies to that of fig. 12.39.

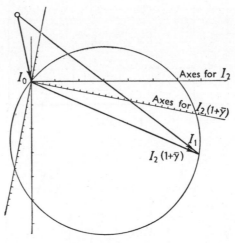

Fig. 12.40

This is seen to compare very closely with that of the shunt machine and families of circle diagrams of a similar character are to be expected by way of solution.

The difference lies in the fact that the current in the main part of the circuit I_2 has to be multiplied by the complex ratio $(1+\gamma)$ before the magnetising current I_0 is added.

If the current vector I_2 is obtained by the method outlined above for the shunt machine, this multiplication can best be done by choosing new axes and a new scale according to the value of the complex ratio $(1+\gamma)$. The angle between the new and old axes will be the angle corresponding to this ratio and the new scale will take into account the change of magnitude (fig. 12.40).

CHAPTER 13

MERCURY-ARC RECTIFIERS

13.1. Fundamental Principles

THE principle of operation of the mercury-arc rectifier is best seen by examining the ignitron or single-anode type.

In its simplest, and smallest, form this comprises an evacuated glass vessel with a pool of mercury at the bottom which forms the cathode, and a graphite anode at the top. Dipping into the mercury is a pointed electrode made of semi-conducting material (boron carbide) known as the igniter (fig. 13.1). A short-duration current pulse is applied to the igniter causing the surface of the mercury at this point to be heated to a temperature sufficient to emit electrons. Now, if at the same time the anode is maintained at a high potential relative to the cathode these primary electrons will be attracted to it, and having acquired sufficient energy they will ionise by collision the mercury vapour in the inter-electrode space.

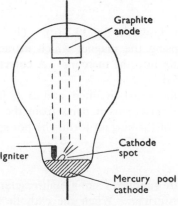

Fig. 13.1

Current flow between the electrodes then consists of the movement of electrons in the direction cathode to anode, together with the corresponding movement of positive ions in the opposite direction, this mechanism being known as arc conduction. Now, the positive ions arriving at the cathode surface bombard it, and, provided the current is sufficient (more than about 2 A), this energy is enough to maintain the cathode spot and with it the supply of primary electrons. The arc is thus self-supporting after the igniter pulse has ceased, and will continue until the anode voltage falls below 10 V, the ionisation potential of mercury. So copious is the supply of electrons from a cathode pool that currents up to 3000 A are possible in the largest sizes of steel-tank rectifiers.

The tube is essentially a rectifier or unidirectional device, since, when the anode potential is negative, electrons will not be attracted to it and current ceases to flow.   The voltage drop across the arc when conducting is only of the order of 15–25 V, but the tube will withstand an inverse voltage of several thousand volts.

The characteristic feature of a single anode rectifier or ignitron is that it must be ignited or "fired" at each operation, but with the multi-anode type, which uses a common cathode and several anodes, the cathode spot is first formed by a process known as ignition, and then maintained by the excitation circuit.

13.2. The Three-anode Glass-bulb Rectifier

Glass-bulb rectifiers are widely employed, particularly in this country, for installations ranging between a few tens of kilowatts to a few thousand kilowatts, but for higher powers and higher voltages steel-tank rectifiers are more suited. Each bulb has an inverted pear shape with the mercury pool at the bottom, the top portion forming a large dome providing a radiating surface for condensing the mercury vapour and dissipating the heat generated.   The main anodes are sealed into L-shaped side arms, and smaller arms are also attached carrying auxiliary anodes.

13.2.1. Ignition

The ignition circuit is shown in fig. 13.2 (a).   The supply is taken from a small transformer energising the magnet which attracts the flexible ignition electrode, causing it to dip into the mercury.   A current of about 5 A, limited by the reactor, is produced.

The electromagnet is now short-circuited, and as its flux decays the electrode is released, breaking the current as it parts from the mercury surface.   The process of the extinction of the current forms the hot-spot momentarily.

13.2.2. Excitation

The auxiliary anodes are supplied from a high-reactance centre-tapped winding on the ignition transformer.   When the cathode spot is formed by the igniter, an arc is struck between the cathode and the anode which is positive at that instant.   As the cycle proceeds and the voltage of this anode falls, the effect of the reactance of the circuit not only limits the current but delays its collapse until the other anode has become positive.   The arc is then transferred to the other excitation anode, and so the cathode spot and the ionisation of the tube are maintained.   The rectified current in the excitation circuit flows through the operating coil of a small relay thus opening the ignition circuit.

13.2.3. Main Anode Connections

Assuming for the moment that the rectifier is supplied from a star-connected transformer the connections of the main anodes will be as shown in fig. 13.3.

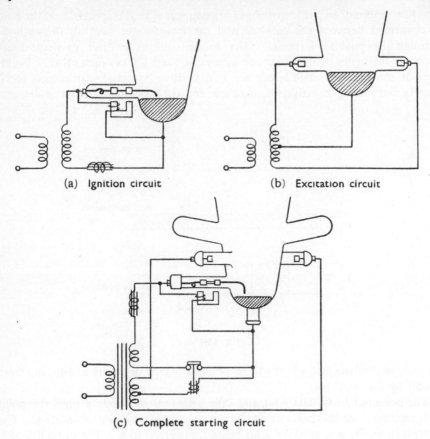

(a) Ignition circuit   (b) Excitation circuit

(c) Complete starting circuit

Fig. 13.2 (a), (b) and (c)

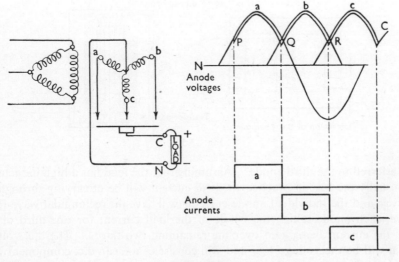

Fig. 13.3

The line terminals of the transformer are connected to the anodes, and the load is connected between the cathode and the transformer neutral, the cathode forming the positive terminal. The anode voltages relative to neutral are shown in the figure by the three sine waves displaced 120° to each other. Beginning at the point P when anode **a** is at a positive potential with respect to N, **b** and **c** both being negative, the load current will flow through this anode, and

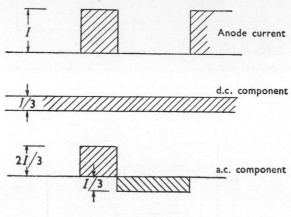

Fig. 13.4

the potential of the cathode C will be practically that of anode **a**, differing from it only by the arc drop.

The potential of C thus rises and falls with that of anode **a** until the point Q is reached. At this point anode **b** rises above the potential of anode **a**. The current in anode **a** ceases, the load being transferred to **b**. The potential of C now follows that of **b** until commutation again takes place at R where the load

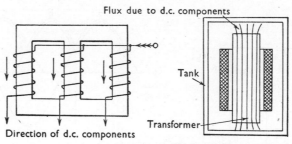

Fig. 13.5

is transferred to the third anode. Assuming that the load has a high inductance as is usually the case in practice, the load current will be unvarying throughout the cycle and the individual anode currents will have the rectangular wave-form shown, each anode taking the whole of the load current for one-third of the cycle, the current being zero over the remaining two-thirds. The d.c. voltage output will be the voltage V_{CN} and will consist of a mean d.c. component with a ripple at three times mains frequency.

The anode currents shown as unidirectional pulses may be resolved into d.c. and a.c. components (fig. 13.4). The primary phase-current wave-form will be that of the a.c. component only, since in a perfect transformer $i_1 N_1 = i_2 N_2$, the d.c. component being confined to the secondary winding. The three d.c. components in the three phases act side by side down the legs of the transformer (fig. 13.5) and tend to produce an unvarying flux passing through the core and the tank. Such d.c. magnetisation must be avoided since it leads to saturation of the core and high values of magnetising current and harmonics; consequently zigzag secondary windings are always used in preference to star connected ones.

Each phase now consists of two winding sections in series, wound in opposite direction on two legs. Since the d.c. component carried by each winding section is the same, the total d.c. ampere-turns on each leg is zero. Fig. 13.6 also shows the wave-form of the phase and line currents of the transformer. Equal numbers of turns on the primary and the total secondary winding on each leg have been assumed. Each primary phase current is equal to the difference between two anode currents and each line current is the difference between two phase currents.

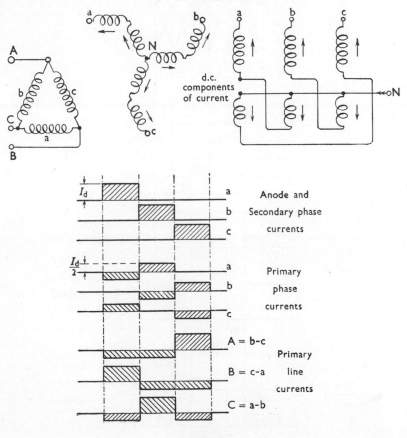

Fig. 13.6

13.3. The Six-anode Rectifier

13.3.1. Six-phase Star

If the transformer is arranged to give a six-phase supply by connecting the centre taps of the secondary windings to form the neutral, and a rectifier having six anodes is used, the corresponding diagrams of the voltage and current waveforms will be those of fig. 13.7. As the arc now passes from one anode to the

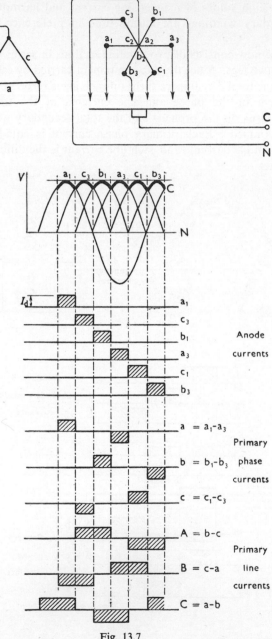

Fig. 13.7

next, six times per cycle, the ripple frequency will be six times the mains frequency and its amplitude will be reduced. The mean d.c. voltage on light load will be more nearly equal to the peak value of the voltage of each secondary winding section. The wave-forms of the primary currents are now symmetrical, but each secondary winding only carries current for one-sixth of a cycle which means that the winding has a poor utilisation factor (see Section 13.6.2).

There is no d.c. magnetisation of the core.

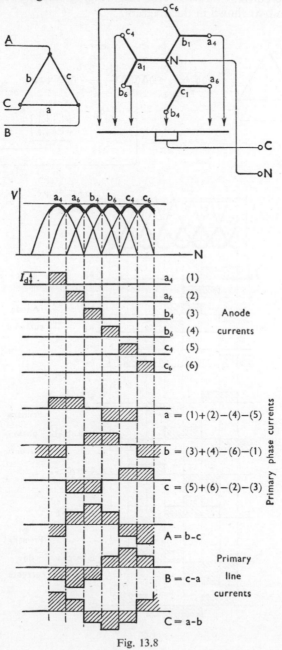

Fig. 13.8

13.3.2. Six-phase Fork

A better winding arrangement giving the same d.c. voltage wave-form with improved a.c. wave-form is the fork connection used for high-voltage rectifiers.

Each secondary phase has now three winding sections, three star groups being formed and interconnected to form the neutral according to fig. 13.8. Each block of anode current now flows in two winding sections resulting in phase currents built up as shown in the diagram.

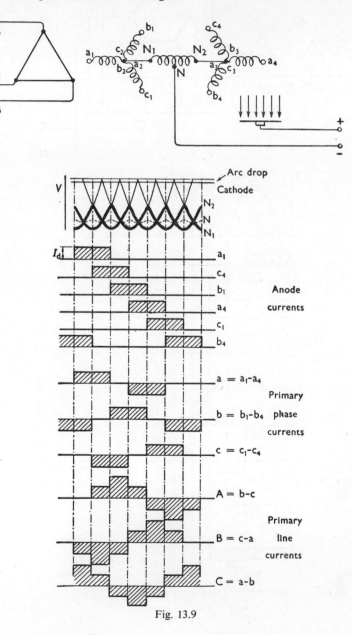

Fig. 13.9

13.3.3. Double Three-phase

A winding connection giving a still better utilisation factor, and consequently the most usual arrangement for six-anode rectifiers, is the double-three-phase connection. The secondary windings are now in two half-sections and these are connected in two separate star banks with neutrals N_1 and N_2 (fig. 13.9). Between these two points a reactor is placed known as the *interphase reactor*. The centre tapping of this is the neutral connection.

At very small values of load current for which the voltage drop in the reactor can be ignored, the three points N_1, N_2 and N are at the same potential and the rectifier operates as the six-phase installation described above. Now, as the arc commutates from a_1 to c_4, then to b_1, etc., the current flows in opposite directions in the reactor with each change; in other words, alternating current of triple mains frequency is produced here. When the load current exceeds the magnetising current of the reactor (a value known as the *transition point*) the voltage developed across N_1N_2 enables the current to be prolonged in a_1 until commutation to b_1 occurs, and similarly the arc persists at anode c_4 until it transfers to a_4.

The two three-phase banks thus operate independently. There are always two anodes in parallel each carrying half the output current. The voltages of the two neutrals N_1 and N_2 are shown in fig. 13.9 each having a triple-frequency ripple. The voltage drop across the reactor is the difference between these two curves, and the potential of the mid-point N is thus half-way between them, so the ripple at this point is seen to be smaller and to correspond to that of a six-phase rectifier. The double-three-phase connection therefore has the advantages of six-phase

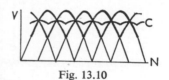

Fig. 13.10

working from the point of view of ripple, yet the currents are prolonged in the transformer giving a more effective utilisation of the windings and an improved a.c. wave-form.

The initial fall of voltage which takes place at the transition point, due to the change of wave-form from that of the envelope of N_1N_2, to that of N, is a characteristic feature of this connection.

Although the voltage wave-form diagram in fig. 13.9 is the only correct way of showing the relative potentials between the cathode and the neutrals N_1, N and N_2, this diagram is usually redrawn as in fig. 13.10 so as to compare readily with the wave-forms of the previous cases for three-phase and six-phase working.

13.4. Twelve-phase Connections

The double-three-phase system described above can be extended to quadruple three-phase working. One twelve-anode tank is used or, alternatively, twelve single-anode rectifiers, or two six-anode rectifiers, or four three-anode rectifiers can be banked.

A twelve-phase supply is obtained from two transformers. Each transformer provides two three-phase star-connected systems, a phase difference of 30° being

18—E.M.

obtained between them by arranging a star-connected primary winding on the one transformer and a delta-connected winding on the other. The vector diagram of the transformers is shown in fig. 13.11 from which it is seen that the anode voltages follow each other in sequence at 30° intervals.

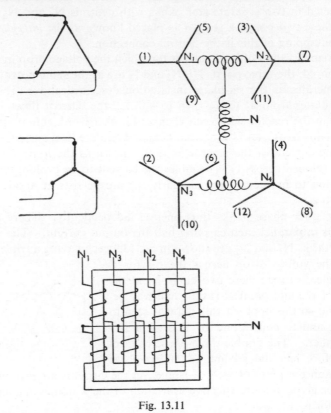

Fig. 13.11

Interphase reactors connect N_1N_2 and N_3N_4 to make two double-three-phase banks. A third interphase reactor connects the two systems and provides the main neutral.

The output voltage has a 12 times normal frequency ripple and the current divides equally between the four banks.

Alternatively, in place of the three interphase reactors, a four-phase reactor wound on a four-limb core can be used.

13.5. Steel-tank Rectifiers

Current ratings of single glass-bulb rectifiers do not exceed about 400 A. The need for larger ratings and also for more robust construction led to the development of steel-tank installations. A water-cooled multi-anode steel-tank rectifier of early design consisted of a large cylindrical tank with an insulated cathode pool at the bottom and having a flat circular top plate, bolted on, carrying the anodes. Considerable manufacturing skill was necessary to

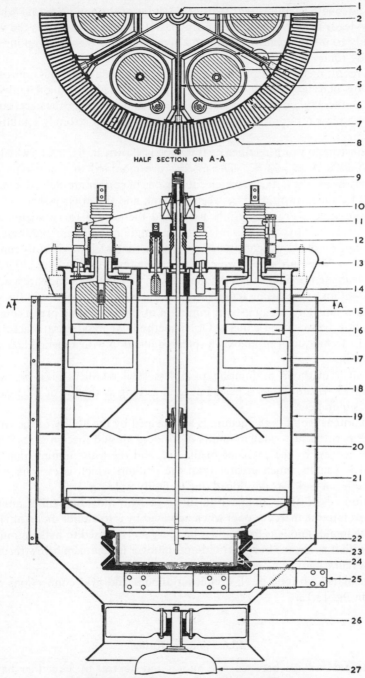

HALF SECTION ON A-A

A←↑ ↑→A

Fig. 13.12.—Pumpless rectifier without anode arms
Overall diameter of largest size, 30 in.

1, 10, 22. Ignition anode.	11. Anode seal.
2, 14. Excitation anode.	12. Vacuum valve.
3, 16. Control grid.	13. Air deflector.
4, 15. Main anode.	17. Deionizing baffle.
5, 18. Sector-shaped anode shield.	23. Vitreous-enamelled cathode seal.
6, 19. Cylindrical vacuum tank.	24. Cathode protective cylinder.
7, 20. Copper fins.	25. Cathode lead.
8, 21. Cylindrical air guide.	26. Fan.
9. Grid seal.	27. Fan motor.

provide adequate vacuum-tight seals at the joint of the top plate and where the insulated leads to the anodes were brought out, and in spite of this the vacuum could only be maintained by continuous pumping with mercury-vapour pumps backed by rotary pumps.

More recent methods of producing satisfactory anode seals, and improvement in welding and fabrication techniques, have enabled sealed off tanks to be developed, thereby reducing considerably the auxiliary apparatus necessary, and so the pumpless air-cooled multi-anode rectifier is now strongly established in this country.

The construction of a rectifier of this type is shown in fig. 13.12 which has a rating of 1200 A at 650 V. The anodes are mounted in sector-type shields completely inside the tank, on which cooling fins of copper are welded, and which is cooled by air blast directed between the tank and the outer jacket.

Graphite anodes are universally used, and these need to be adequately insulated from the tank at the same time maintaining vacuum tightness. The type of anode seal shown consists of a multiple sandwich of vitreous enamelled steel cones. These are given two coatings of enamel, the outer coating having a lower fusing temperature than the inner layer. When the cones are assembled and brought up to the fusing temperature of the outer layer, the mass fuses solid, making a completely vacuum-tight joint and at the same time preserving layers of insulation between the cones. Other methods of making satisfactory seals include the technique of producing a soldered junction with a metal glaze surface on porcelain.

With such methods of jointing, pumpless steel rectifiers may be expected to retain their vacuum over a period at least as long as the life of the associated electrical equipment.

The maintenance of high vacuum is also helped by the ability of the structure to absorb permanently small amounts of residual air and foreign gases when the latter are ionised by the presence of the arc, and the total amount that can be absorbed is usually much greater than the amount which is ever likely to be present unless a leak has developed due to faulty welding.

Initiation of the arc is obtained in this type by a movable igniter anode rod which dips into the mercury pool when actuated by a solenoid. In an alternative design the igniter anode is fixed and a mercury jet is caused to make momentary contact with it by means of a solenoid-and-plunger mechanism below the surface of the mercury pool.

The insulated cathode pool, excitation anodes and grid connections can all be seen in fig. 13.12.

13.6. Voltage Ratios

Let the a.c. voltage between one anode and neutral of a rectifier having p anodes be given by

$$v_{aN} = \sqrt{2} \cdot V_a \cos \theta$$

where V_a is the r.m.s. a.c. voltage. This anode is conducting for a time $2\pi/p$, and the wave-form repeats for the other anodes (fig. 13.13). The mean value of the d.c. output voltage V_d is thus obtained by taking the average of v_{aN} over the period from $-\pi/p$ to $+\pi/p$.

Thus

$$V_d = (p/2\pi)\int_{-\pi/p}^{\pi/p} \sqrt{2}.V_a \cos\theta d\theta \quad . \quad . \quad . \quad . \quad (13.1)$$

$$= \sqrt{2}(p/\pi)\sin(\pi/p)V_a \quad . \quad . \quad . \quad . \quad (13.2)$$

This value neglects the arc drop which must be subtracted from V_d to obtain the actual terminal voltage.

The following table shows the ratio V_d/V_a for commonly used values of p. When double or quadruple three-phase connection is used the output voltage is that of one of the three-phase banks which are in parallel (i.e. $p = 3$).

p	3	6	12	24
V_d/V_a	1·16	1·35	1·40	1·41

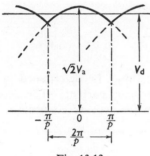

Fig. 13.13

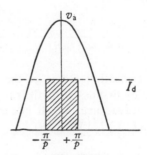

Fig. 13.14

13.6.1. Current Ratios

The anode current wave-form depends upon the load. In general, with an inductive load, it will consist of rectangular blocks as we have seen in previous diagrams (also fig. 13.14) (these must be modified later to take overlap into account).

The mean value of the anode current

$$I_{mean} = (1/2\pi)\int_{-\pi/p}^{\pi/p} I_d d\theta = I_d/p \quad . \quad . \quad . \quad . \quad (13.3)$$

and the r.m.s. value,

$$I_a = \sqrt{\left\{(1/2\pi)\int_{-\pi/p}^{\pi/p} I_d^2 d\theta\right\}} = I_d/\sqrt{p} \quad . \quad . \quad . \quad (13.4)$$

13.6.2. Utilisation Factor

The wave-forms of current and voltage on the a.c. side are not alike, and this gives rise to a difference between the volt-ampere rating of the transformer winding and its power output. The transformer thus operates with a power factor or utilisation factor less than unity:

$$\text{utilisation factor} = \text{watts/volt-amperes} \quad . \quad . \quad . \quad (13.5)$$

The term utilisation factor is used to avoid confusion with the accepted use of the term power factor which has come to be associated with the effect of the displacement of current and voltage waves.

The volt-ampere rating of the secondary winding (star-connected) supplying a p-anode rectifier is

$$S = pV_a I_a \qquad \cdots \qquad \cdots \qquad (13.6)$$

and the power (including loss in the arc)

$$P = V_d I_d \qquad \cdots \qquad \cdots \qquad (13.7)$$

Thus the utilisation factor

$$
\begin{aligned}
P/S &= (1/p)(V_d/V_a)(I_d/I_a) \\
&= (1/p)\{\sqrt{2}.(p/\pi)\sin(\pi/p)\}\sqrt{p} \\
&= \{\sqrt{(2p)}/\pi\}\sin(\pi/p) \qquad \cdots \qquad \cdots \qquad (13.8)
\end{aligned}
$$

The following table shows that the three-anode rectifier has the best utilisation factor and hence demonstrates the advantage of double and quadruple three-phase working.

p	2	3	4	6	12
Utilisation factor .	0·636	0·675	0·636	0·551	0·399

The utilisation factor of the primary winding may be determined in like manner by first assessing the r.m.s. value of the primary current. This depends on the wave-form, which in turn depends upon the type of connection used (figs. 13.6, 13.7, 13.8, 13.9).

13.6.3. Rating of Inter-phase Reactor

The voltage across the interphase reactor employed in the double-three-phase circuit is $V_{N_1 N_2}$ in fig. 13.9.

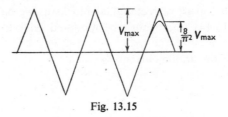

Fig. 13.15

The wave-form of this voltage is seen to be approximately triangular at triple mains frequency. The maximum value occurs when $V_{N_1 C}$ is also a maximum. At that instant $V_{N_2 C}$ being displaced $60°$ is at half maximum value. Thus

$$[V_{N_1 N_2}]_{max} = \sqrt{2}.V_a/2 \qquad \cdots \qquad \cdots \qquad (13.9)$$

The reactor is designed on the basis of the fundamental component of this voltage. From harmonic analysis of a triangular wave we find (fig. 13.15)

$$\text{amplitude of fundamental} = (8/\pi^2)(\text{height of triangle})$$

Thus the r.m.s. voltage rating of the reactor is

$$(1/\sqrt{2})(8/\pi^2)(\sqrt{2}.V_a/2) = 0\cdot405V_a \qquad . \quad . \quad . \quad (13.10)$$

The reactor current

$$= I_d/2 \qquad . \quad . \quad . \quad . \quad . \quad . \quad (13.11)$$

and the volt-ampere rating of the reactor

$$= 0\cdot405(V_d/1\cdot16)(I_d/2)$$
$$= 0\cdot174V_dI_d \qquad . \quad . \quad . \quad . \quad . \quad . \quad (13.12)$$

13.7. Overlap

So far it has been assumed that the transfer of current from one anode to the next is instantaneous at the moment of commutation. This cannot be true owing to the limiting effect of the inductance of the anode circuit, principally the leakage reactance of the transformer. There exists a period when the two anodes operate in parallel, current falling in the one and rising in the other. This period is known as the period of *overlap*. In fig. 13.16 (a) are shown two adjacent anodes of a p-phase rectifier with the corresponding transformer windings of voltage V_{aN} and V_{bN}.

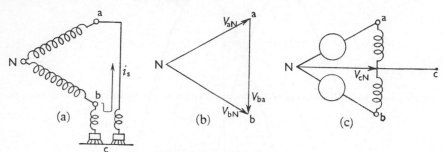

Fig. 13.16 (a), (b) and (c)

When commutation starts, the current i_a in anode **a** is I_d, and i_b is equal to zero. At this moment the difference between the two phase voltages is zero, but as v_{ba} increases, circulating current i_s is set up limited by the inductance of the circuit ($2L$). This current reduces i_a and increases i_b. By the time i_s has grown to the value I_d commutation is complete, i_a having fallen to zero.

From the vector diagram (fig. 13.16 (b)),

$$V_{ba} = 2V_{aN}\sin(\pi/p) \qquad . \quad . \quad . \quad . \quad (13.13)$$

and the instantaneous value

$$v_{ba} = \sqrt{2}.2V_{aN}\sin(\pi/p)\sin\omega t \quad . \quad . \quad . \quad (13.14)$$

commutation commencing at the time $t = 0$.

Now v_{ba} is the voltage applied to the reactance $2X$, i.e. inductance $2L$.

Thus

$$v_{ba} = 2L.di_s/dt \qquad . \quad . \quad . \quad . \quad . \quad (13.15)$$
$$di_s/dt = (\sqrt{2}.V_a/L)\sin(\pi/p)\sin\omega t \qquad . \quad . \quad (13.16)$$

and

$$i_s = (\sqrt{2}.V_a/L)\{\sin(\pi/p)\}(-\cos\omega t)/\omega + C \qquad . \quad . \quad (13.17)$$

When $t = 0$, $v = 0$ and $i_s = 0$.

$$0 = -(\sqrt{2} . V_a/\omega L) \sin (\pi/p) + C$$
$$\therefore \; C = (\sqrt{2} . V_a/X) \sin (\pi/p)$$

and

$$i_s = (\sqrt{2} . V_a/X)\{\sin (\pi/p)\}(1 - \cos \theta) \quad . \quad . \quad . \quad (13.18)$$

where $\theta = \omega t$.

It should be noted that this current is an asymmetrical short-circuit current, the wave-form being shown in fig. 13.17.

When $i_s = I_d$, $\theta = u$ and commutation is complete; thus

$$I_d = (\sqrt{2} . V_a/X)\{\sin (\pi/p)\}(1 - \cos u) \quad . \quad . \quad . \quad (13.19)$$

where u is termed the *angle of overlap*.

The wave-front of I_b is thus a portion of i_s, and the wave-tail of I_a is the same curve reversed. The duration of overlap and the angle u can be calculated from equation (13.19), and they will be seen to vary with the value of the load current I_d.

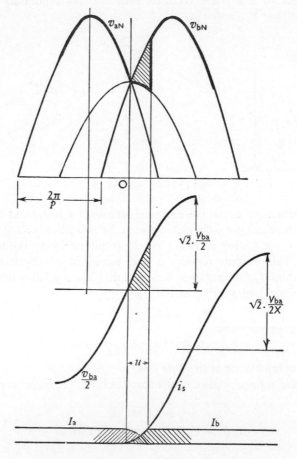

Fig. 13.17

13.7.1. Voltage Drop due to Overlap

During overlap the reactances act as a potential divider between the points **a** and **b** (fig. 13.16 (c)) with the cathode connected at the mid-point. The cathode potential during this period is the intermediate value

$$v_{cN} = (v_{aN} + v_{bN})/2 \quad . \quad . \quad . \quad . \quad (13.20)$$

At the end of overlap the voltage of C rises abruptly to that of **b** as the connection to anode **a** is broken. The output voltage thus includes the step shown in fig. 13.17.

This diagram has been built up in the following manner. First the anode voltages v_a and v_b are drawn, also the current I_d. The difference voltage v_{ba} is now established, and the circulating current i_s is found. This determines the wave-front of I_b and the duration of overlap. The average voltage v_{cN} from equation (13.20) is next plotted and the final output voltage wave can be found.

The shaded area under the voltage curve represents a reduction in voltage occurring p times per cycle.

The reduction of V_d, therefore, due to overlap is

$$\Delta V_d = (p/2\pi)(\text{shaded area of fig. 13.17}) . \quad . \quad . \quad (13.21)$$

The instantaneous depression of cathode potential is the p.d. across one reactance which from equation (13.14) is equal to

$$\sqrt{2} . V_a \sin (\pi/p) . \sin \theta \quad . \quad . \quad . \quad . \quad (13.22)$$

Thus

$$\Delta V_d = (p/2\pi) \int_0^u \sqrt{2} . V_a \sin (\pi/p) \sin \theta d\theta$$
$$= (p/2\pi)\sqrt{2} . V_a \{\sin (\pi/p)\}(1 - \cos u) \quad . \quad . \quad (13.23)$$

But from equation (13.19),

$$I_d X = \sqrt{2} . V_a \{\sin (\pi/p)\}(1 - \cos u)$$

Thus

$$\Delta V_d = (1/2\pi)p I_d X \quad . \quad . \quad . \quad . \quad (13.24)$$

The drop in voltage due to overlap is thus directly proportional to load current. On this account the voltage regulation curve of a rectifier is a straight line with a small slope. The slope is proportional to p and to X, which again shows the advantages of three-phase operation.

The equation for the terminal voltage on load can be derived from equations (13.2) and (13.23):

$$V_d' = V_d - \Delta V_d$$
$$= \sqrt{2} . V_a [(p/\pi)\{\sin (\pi/p)\} - (p/2\pi)\{\sin (\pi/p)\}(1 - \cos u)]$$
$$= \sqrt{2} . V_a (p/2\pi)\{\sin (\pi/p)\}(1 + \cos u) \quad . \quad . \quad . \quad . \quad (13.25)$$

13.8. Backfire

Should under any circumstances a cathode spot develop on an anode, an arc will immediately be struck to the other anodes that are more positive constituting a complete short circuit of the transformer with currents which may be as much as 50 to 100 times the r.m.s. value of the full-load anode current.   This is known as a backfire.   The exact process by which such a spot is formed is not completely understood, but to reduce the possibility of backfire it is important that the anode surfaces shall be uncontaminated and all occluded gas driven off during the baking-out process whilst the rectifier is under the pumps.   High vacuum must be maintained and the mercury pressure held below about 100 microns by adequate cooling of the condensing surface.   The anodes are also shielded by de-ionising grids.   These take the form of gratings in front of the anodes together with metal shields surrounding them.   If these grids are maintained at a sufficient negative potential with respect to the cathode, primary electrons are unable to pass and the spaces between anodes and grids cannot be ionised.   Under these circumstances the anode current cannot flow.   In order for an anode to fire it is necessary to apply to the grid a positive voltage impulse at the correct instant in a similar manner in which an impulse must be applied to the igniter of an ignitron tube.   The application of the positive voltage need be only momentary, since, when an anode has fired, positive ions are present around the anode for the remainder of the time that it is conducting, and these ions will be attracted to the negative grid forming a positive "blanket" over its surface and neutralising the effect of its negative potential.

Grid Control.   A rectifier operated with grids in this manner is said to be grid controlled.   The grid impulses are produced by magnetic means in special circuits devised for the purpose.   On the occurrence of a backfire a high-speed relay is arranged to remove the grid impulses leaving the grid with a strong negative bias.   This prevents other anodes contributing to the backfire, which will cease when the high-speed breakers operate on the d.c. side.   Glass-bulb rectifiers not fitted with grids rely on H.R.C. fuses in series with the anodes for protection if backfire occurs.

13.9. Voltage Control

By retarding the instant of application of the grid impulses, the output d.c. voltage can be reduced.   Fig. 13.18 shows the wave-forms of a grid-controlled rectifier.   In this the grid impulse to grid 2 is applied at the instant when anode 2 rises in potential to equal anode 1.   Commutation thus takes place in the normal way, and after the period of overlap the arc is fully transferred to anode 2.   The impulse to grid 3 is applied in a similar way, and so on for the other grids, the spacing between the impulses being $2\pi/p$.

The output voltage wave-form is shown, and the mean value is V_d.

In fig. 13.19 the grid impulses have all been delayed by an angle α.   The arc persists with anode 1, even though anode 2 is more positive, until the arrival of the pulse to grid 2, when the voltage rises abruptly to the mid-point between the potential of the two anodes.   After the period of overlap, commutation is complete and the voltage rises to that of anode 2.

Delaying commutation in this manner reduces the mean d.c. voltage and so a variation in the angle α affords a method of voltage control of the rectifier.   This is accomplished at the expense of an increase in the amplitude of the ripple and

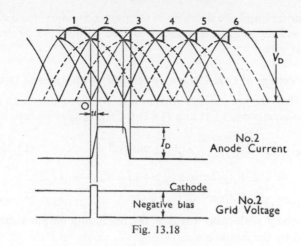

Fig. 13.18

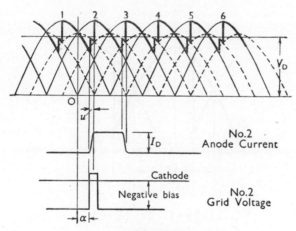

Fig. 13.19

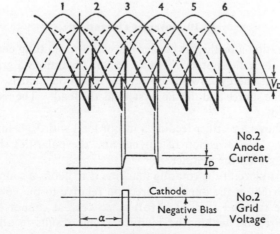

Fig. 13.20

the harmonic content, and of a decrease in the power-factor on the a.c. side. If α is increased to $\pi/2$ the voltage is reduced to zero. In fig. 13.20 the angle α is just short of this value.

13.9.1. Output Voltage of Grid Controlled Rectifier with Angle of Delay α

Ignoring overlap, the arc persists with anode 1 from $(-\pi/p+\alpha)$ to $(\pi/p+\alpha)$ (fig. 13.21); thus equations (13.1) and (13.2) for the output voltage become

$$V_d' = (p/2\pi)\int_{(-\pi/p+\alpha)}^{(\pi/p+\alpha)} \sqrt{2}.V_a \cos\theta d\theta \quad . \quad . \quad . \quad . \quad (13.26)$$

$$= \sqrt{2}.V_a(p/2\pi)\{\sin(\pi/p+\alpha)-\sin(-\pi/p+\alpha)\}$$

$$= \sqrt{2}.V_a(p/\pi)\{\sin(\pi/p)\}\cos\alpha \quad . \quad . \quad . \quad . \quad . \quad (13.27)$$

The output voltage with delay α is thus the maximum output voltage without delay multiplied by the factor $\cos\alpha$.

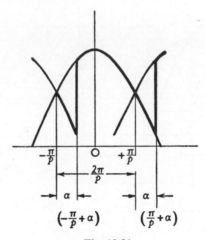

Fig. 13.21

13.10. Inverter Operation

In normal operation a rectifier is concerned with transmitting energy from an a.c. power system to a d.c. system. Under certain conditions a grid-controlled rectifier may permit energy flow in the reverse direction, that is, with the d.c. system acting as the source and the a.c. system as the load. The rectifier is then said to be inverted.

Fig. 13.22 (a) shows a rectifier feeding a motor load with V_d being the voltage across the motor. The direction of current and the polarities show that the motor acts as a load on the rectifier.

Now, in the first place, if the rotating machine is to act as a source and therefore to supply current in the opposite direction relative to the voltage, its connections must be reversed (fig. 13.22 (b)) since current cannot possibly flow in the reverse direction within the rectifier. This results in all the anodes being positive with respect to the cathode except for a very short portion of the cycle. It is essential therefore that they should be held off by grid bias for most of the time and should only be fired at the appropriate moment by the correct application of grid pulses.

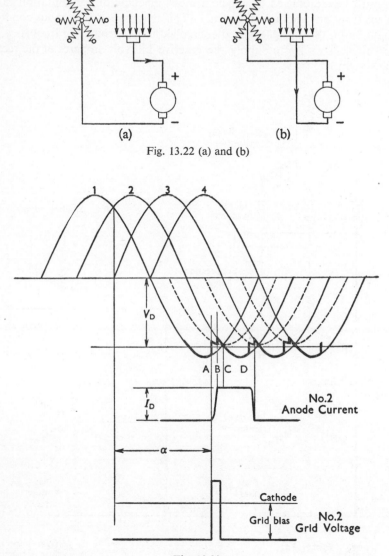

Fig. 13.22 (a) and (b)

Fig. 13.23

In fig. 13.23 we commence with anode 1 conducting, and at the point A a pulse is applied to grid 2 causing anode 2 to fire. Commutation will be complete by B when the arc will have transferred to anode 2. In the same way transfer to 3 takes place if anode 3 is fired by a grid pulse at the point D. The current in anode 2 flows as shown in the figure, and it occurs when the voltage of this phase is in the negative half-cycle. The transformer currents are thus displaced by almost 180° from those shown in fig. 13.7 for normal operation and thus indicate clearly that power flow is in the reverse direction.

It is important to appreciate that an inverted rectifier can only supply energy to an existing polyphase system to which it is connected. The sequence of the phases must be established by a synchronous machine, or commutation cannot take place from one anode to the next. (This may be a synchronous condenser running light on the a.c. side, speed controlled to determine the frequency, and having sufficient rating to supply the reactive kilovolt-amperes of the rectifier and the system.)

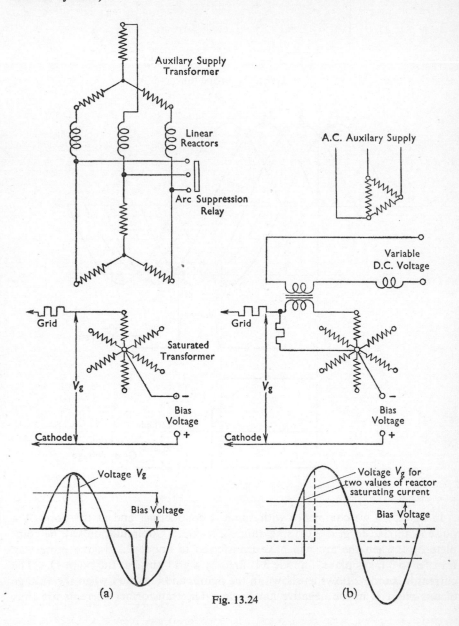

Fig. 13.24

It is also required that the grid pulses should be sufficiently short. It is essential for the grid of anode 1 to regain control before the point C (fig. 13.23), or back-commutation would take place at this point.

The use of a rectifier operating as an inverter is of importance in traction substations during periods of regenerative braking of the trains and also when similar conditions apply in speed-control schemes of large rectifier-fed d.c. machines for rolling mills, mine haulage, etc.

The inverter will also play an important part in the development of high-voltage d.c. transmission systems.

13.11. Basic Circuits used for Grid Excitation

Modern methods of producing voltages with steep wave-front suitable for exciting the grids are usually variants of the schemes shown in fig. 13.24.

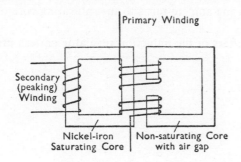

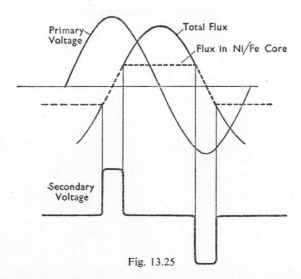

Fig. 13.25

The circuit of fig. 13.24 (a) employs a peaking transformer fed from the auxiliary supply transformer through linear reactors. The peaking transformer has two cores (fig. 13.25): one a closed core of nickel-iron which saturates readily, and the other a normal silicon-iron core with an air-gap. The secondary winding links only with the nickel-iron core.

The primary voltage is sinusoidal and the flux also. The latter divides between the cores, being wholly carried by the nickel-iron core at low densities until it saturates sharply, when the remainder flows through the gapped core. The secondary flux is thus almost trapezoidal and the e.m.f. wave $(d\phi/dt)$ is almost a pair of rectangular pulses as shown.

In fig. 13.24 (b) a potential divider is formed by a linear resistor and a saturable reactor. The voltage applied to the grid remains small until the current in the divider chain saturates the reactor, and the voltage drop across it diminishes almost to zero.

The grid voltage wave-form has thus the steep wave-front shown in fig. 13.24 (b), and the position of this can be varied by varying the current in the d.c. biasing winding of the reactor, thus affording voltage control of the rectifier.

Limited phase shift can also be obtained with the circuit of fig. 13.24 (a) by adding d.c. pre-magnetising ampere-turns to the saturating core of the peaking transformer.

Mechanical phase shifters of the induction regulator pattern are also used.

CHAPTER 14

APPENDIX

14.1. Admittance, Current and Power Charts

IF the admittance

$$Y = g+jb \qquad . \quad . \quad . \quad . \quad . \quad (14.1)$$

is known for a simple circuit, then with an applied voltage V the current will be

$$I = VY \qquad . \quad . \quad . \quad . \quad . \quad . \quad (14.2)$$

and multiplying by the conjugate of the voltage we have the vector power

$$S = P+jQ = \bar{V}I = \bar{V}VY \qquad . \quad . \quad . \quad . \quad (14.3)$$

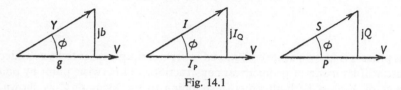

Fig. 14.1

Fig. 14.1 shows these vectors when the voltage vector is horizontal and it will be appreciated that they are all inclined to the horizontal by the same angle. Consequently, one diagram might be used for Y, I and S, with different scales showing admittance current and power (fig. 14.2).

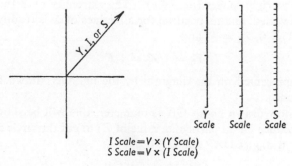

I Scale $=V \times$ (Y Scale)
S Scale $=V \times$ (I Scale)

Fig. 14.2

In a circuit which has only one constant-voltage source, if conditions cause the admittance vector to vary, current and power will vary in like manner.

Thus the locus of the admittance vector determines the locus of the current and power vectors.

19—E.M.   289

The variation of Y in turn depends on the variation of the impedance Z since

$$Y = 1/Z \quad . \quad . \quad . \quad . \quad . \quad . \quad . \quad . \quad (14.4)$$

and if
$$Z = Z \exp j\phi \quad . \quad . \quad . \quad . \quad . \quad . \quad (14.5)$$

then
$$Y = (1/Z) \exp (-j\phi) \quad . \quad . \quad . \quad (14.6)$$

in other words Y is a vector whose magnitude Y is the reciprocal of Z and whose phase is the conjugate angle $(-\phi)$. To trace the effect of changes in Z, it is first necessary to find the corresponding changes of Y.

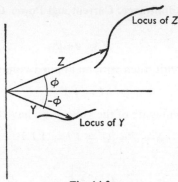

Fig. 14.3

This process is known as inversion, and in certain simple cases to be considered later use will be made of geometrical construction. Otherwise, point by point, the locus of Y must be built up corresponding to the locus of Z as shown in fig. 14.3.

14.1.1. Constant Resistance with Variable Reactance in Series

Consider a resistance R in series with a variable reactance X across constant-voltage mains. First choosing an impedance scale the resistance R is plotted, followed by jX at right angles (fig. 14.4). The extremity of Z thus moves up this line as X is varied, and its position for all values of X is readily seen.

Now, when $X = 0$, $Z_0 = R$, and

$$Y_0 = 1/Z_0 = 1/R \quad . \quad . \quad . \quad . \quad (14.7)$$

This may be represented on the diagram by the line OB, drawn to a suitable scale of admittance.

If a circle is now drawn about OB as diameter, this will be shown to be the locus of Y. Produce OP (a particular value of Z) to cut the circle at P'.

From similar triangles OAP and OP'B,

$$OP/OA = OB/OP'$$

that is
$$OP.OP' = OA.OB \quad . \quad . \quad . \quad . \quad (14.8)$$

Hence, if OP is measured to the impedance scale. and OP' to the admittance scale,

$$OP' = (1/OP).OA.OB = (1/Z)RY_0$$
$$= (1/Z)R(1/R)$$
$$= 1/Z \quad . \quad . \quad . \quad . \quad . \quad (14.9)$$

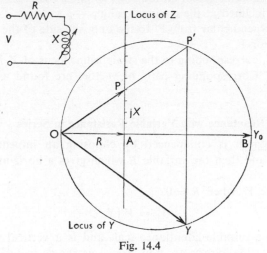

Fig. 14.4

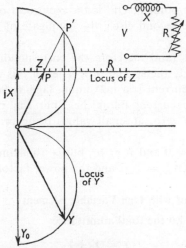

Fig. 14.5

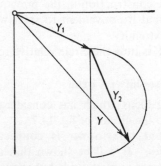

Fig. 14.6

OP′ is not the admittance vector although its length is correct. The admittance vector Y will be inclined at the conjugate angle $-\phi$.

Dropping a perpendicular from P′ to the opposite side of the circle gives the correct position for Y.

The locus at Y, corresponding to the straight-line locus of Z, is thus the circle of diameter Y_0. Corresponding pairs of vectors are found as demonstrated above.

14.1.2. Constant Reactance with Variable Resistance in Series

Again the diagram is commenced by choosing an impedance scale and plotting first jX and then the variable R which gives a horizontal line for the locus of Z.

The admittance Y_0 when $R = 0$,

$$Y_0 = V/jX \quad . \quad . \quad . \quad . \quad . \quad . \quad (14.10)$$

is then drawn to a suitable admittance scale and is a vertical vector pointing downwards. Two semicircles are now drawn as shown in fig. 14.5 with diameter Y_0, the lower one being the locus of Y. Corresponding to a particular impedance Z giving the point P, OP′ is the reciprocal of Z, and by projecting downwards to meet the second circle the conjugate of OP′ is found which is therefore the vector Y.

The admittance locus (and therefore the corresponding current and power loci) demonstrates clearly the special properties of this circuit.

When R is zero the current is a maximum, lagging 90° behind the voltage. As R is increased, the current diminishes, but the phase angle decreases. Eventually I shrinks to zero, at small values being practically in phase with the voltage.

$P = 0$ both when $R = 0$ and $R = \infty$, but is a maximum at an intermediate point. This occurs when $g = Y_0/2$ and the power factor is 0·707.

14.1.3. A Parallel Circuit with One Variable Element

In the circuit of fig. 14.6 the total admittance

$$Y = Y_1 + Y_2 \quad . \quad . \quad . \quad . \quad . \quad . \quad (14.11)$$

The component Y_1 is a constant vector, but Y_2 is constrained to a given locus according to the construction in the previous case. In the process of adding the vectors we find it convenient to start with the constant vector Y_1 and to place Y_2 on its extremity.

The locus of Y is thus the circle relative to the pole o.

14.1.4. R-C Phase-shifter Circuit

An interesting locus which has considerable use in control circuits is that corresponding to the circuit of fig. 14.7.

A centre-tapped transformer is connected to a variable resistance and capacitor in series. It will be shown that as the resistance is varied, the p.d. V_{cd} remains constant in magnitude but varies in phase almost through 180°.

The construction to find Y_{acb} is that of 14.1.2, giving the circular locus of the figure.

Now the voltage drop across the capacitor,

$$V_{cb} = I_{cb}/j\omega C = V_{ab}Y_{acb}/j\omega C$$
$$= Y_{acb}(V_{ab}/j\omega C) \quad . \quad . \quad . \quad . \quad . \quad . \quad (14.12)$$

The locus of V_{cb} is thus similar to that of Y_{acb}, a semicircle. It is operated upon by $1/j$ and multiplied by $V_{ab}/\omega C$. Since, obviously, when $R = 0$, $V_{cb} = V_{ab}$, the diameter of this circle is V_{ab} and it lies 90° behind the admittance locus.

The position of the centre tap is half-way along the vector V_{ab} and hence the vector V_{cd} is seen to be the radius of the circle swinging around as the point c moves along its locus.

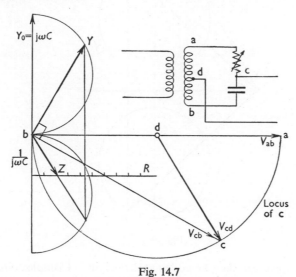

Fig. 14.7

14.1.5. To show that if the Locus of Z is a Circle then the Locus of Y is another Circle

If the locus of an impedance Z is given by the circle PTP′ of fig. 14.8, consider two values of Z, OP and OQ. Produce these lines until they meet the circle again at P′ and Q′.

By similar triangles OPQ′ and OQP′

$$OP/OQ' = OQ/OP'.$$

Thus

$$OP.OP' = OQ.OQ' \quad . \quad . \quad . \quad . \quad . \quad (14.13)$$

and as P moves around the circle P will become coincident with P′ at T.

Thus

$$OP.OP' = OT^2 \quad . \quad . \quad . \quad . \quad . \quad . \quad (14.14)$$

OP′ is thus to some scale the reciprocal of OP, and therefore if the image circle is drawn in the plane of OV, dropping a perpendicular from P′ to its image at R, OR is the admittance vector Y.

The admittance scale must be such that

$$(OP \times \text{impedance scale}) \times (OP' \times \text{admittance scale}) = 1$$

also

$$(OT \times \text{impedance scale}) \times (OT \times \text{admittance scale}) = 1$$

Thus

$$\text{admittance scale} = 1/(OT^2 \times \text{impedance scale}) \quad . \quad . \quad (14.15)$$

The construction described above is useful if the admittance of 14.1.3 has to be converted back to impedance.

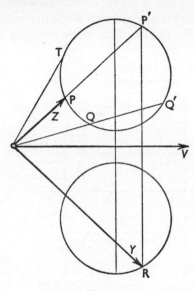

Fig. 14.8

A series impedance can then be added at the origin.   Complex circuits can be built up in this manner converting from Z to Y in order to add admittances of parallel branches and from Y to Z for impedances of series elements.

14.1.6. A Variable Impedance Z Preceded by a Four-terminal Network with Constant Applied Voltage

For the four-terminal network shown in fig. 14.9

$$V_1 = AV_2 + BI_2 \quad . \quad . \quad . \quad . \quad . \quad (14.16)$$

and

$$I_1 = CV_2 + DI_2 \quad . \quad . \quad . \quad . \quad . \quad (14.17)$$

where A, B, C and D are complex constants and

$$AD - BC \equiv 1 . \quad . \quad . \quad . \quad . \quad . \quad (14.18)$$

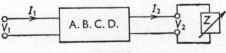

Fig. 14.9

For the load

$$V_2 = I_2 Z \quad \cdots \cdots \cdots \quad (14.19)$$

From equation (14.16)

$$V_1 = A\{V_2 + (B/A)I_2\}$$

$$= AI_2(Z + B/A) \quad \cdots \cdots \quad (14.20)$$

and

$$V_2 = (V_1 - BI_2)/A \quad \cdots \cdots \quad (14.21)$$

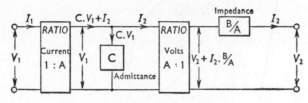

Fig. 14.10

Therefore from equation (14.17)

$$I_1 = (C/A)(V_1 - BI_2) + DI_2$$

$$= (CV_1 - BCI_2 + ADI_2)/A$$

$$= (CV_1 + I_2)/A \quad \cdots \cdots \cdots \quad (14.22)$$

From equations (14.22) and (14.20)

$$I_1 = V_1[(C/A) + (1/A^2)\{1/(Z + B/A)\}] \quad \cdots \quad (14.23)$$

The four-terminal network can therefore be represented by an equivalent circuit, either fig. 14.10 from equations (14.20) and (14.22), or fig. 14.11 from equation (14.23).

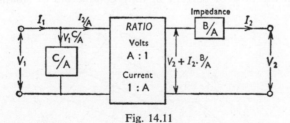

Fig. 14.11

Now, if the locus of Z is known (particularly if it is a straight line or a circle), the locus of the input admittance given by equation (14.23) can be obtained by the following procedure:

(a) add to Z the impedance B/A by off-setting at the origin;
(b) invert to find $1/(Z + B/A)$;
(c) multiply by $1/A^2$ by choosing new axes and a new admittance scale (the unit vector on the admittance axis must be multiplied by A^2);
(d) add C/A at the origin.

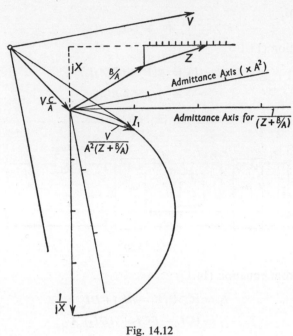

Fig. 14.12

14.2. Field Plotting

14.2.1. Current Flow in Conductors

A study of current flow in irregularly shaped conductors leads to interesting conclusions that can equally well be applied to similar problems relating to electric and magnetic fields. In most applications, an electrical engineer is concerned with the flow of current in long conductors of small and uniform

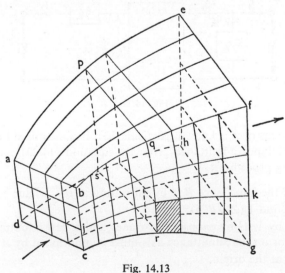

Fig. 14.13

cross-section, where the direction of current is obvious and current density is uniform, but this is a special case of a much more general problem.

Flow Lines. In any passive homogeneous conductor, current flows from high potential to low potential, and the path taken by a particular slow-moving point charge is known as a *flow line*. Thus in fig. 14.13, which represents an irregular conductor in which flow is taking place between the surfaces **abcd** and **efgh**, a number of flow lines such as **jk** are shown. Successive points along a flow line are at successively lower potentials, hence, if x is a distance measured along a flow line,

$$dV/dx = \text{space rate of fall of potential}$$
$$= \text{voltage gradient}$$
$$= E \quad . \quad . \quad . \quad . \quad . \quad . \quad . \quad . \quad . \quad . \quad . \quad (14.24)$$

14.2.2. Equipotential Surface

An equipotential surface is, by definition, a surface on which all points are at the same potential. Then as no p.d. exists between any two points on such a surface there can never be current flow between them. Flow lines can only exist therefore *normal to equipotential surfaces*. This is known as the *orthogonal law*. In fig. 14.13 a family of equipotential surfaces such as **pqrs** can be drawn, and we therefore see that the flow pattern is determined by the necessity for the flow lines and equipotential surfaces to be intersecting everywhere at right angles (flow lines and equipotential surfaces are necessarily continuous, there can be no discontinuities in them).

Let I be the total current entering **abcd** and V the voltage between **abcd** and **efgh**.

Suppose the area of the surface **abcd** is divided into m sections across each of which the current I/m flows. Let flow lines extend from the perimeter of each of these areas. These flow lines divide the conductor into tubes each tube containing a current I/m. The variation of the cross-section along the tube shows the manner in which the current density varies from section to section.

Now let n equipotential surfaces be drawn at equal intervals of V/n volts along the tubes, and the whole conductor is divided into $m \times n$ *cells*. Although the cells differ in size and shape they each have the same resistance.

The cell resistance

$$R_c = (V/n)/(I/m) \quad . \quad . \quad . \quad . \quad . \quad (14.25)$$

The conductor resistance

$$R = V/I \quad . \quad . \quad . \quad . \quad . \quad . \quad (14.26)$$

whence

$$R = R_c . (n/m) \quad . \quad . \quad . \quad . \quad . \quad (14.27)$$

$$= \text{resistance of one cell} \times \frac{\text{number of cells in series}}{\text{number of cells in parallel}}$$

14.2.3. Shape of the Cells

In general the cells have curved edges and are therefore termed *curvilinear*, but if we subdivide the cells by increasing the values of m and n, then in the limit each cell becomes a small rectangular prism.

Now resistivity has been defined as the resistance offered by a unit cube to the passage of current normally between opposite faces from which

$$R_c = \rho . l/a . \qquad \ldots \ldots \ldots \quad (14.28)$$

where l = length, and a = area of cross-section of the cell.

It follows that if we chose the ratio m/n so as to make the ratio l/a for one cell equal to unity, then for this cell

$$R_c = \rho \qquad \ldots \ldots \ldots \ldots \quad (14.29)$$

and as all the other cells have the same resistance they also will have the ratio length/area equal to unity.

14.2.4. Two-dimensional Fields

If we confine the possible divergence to two dimensions such as takes place in the case of flow in sheet material of uniform thickness, the equipotential surfaces will all be normal to the plane of the sheet and thus on the surface of the sheet *equipotential lines* and *flow lines* can be drawn. These lines must be orthogonal, and the field pattern will be determined by ensuring that this relationship exists. Fig. 14.14 represents a thin sheet of conducting material

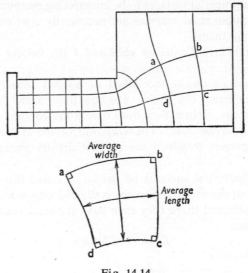

Fig. 14.14

of thickness t the width of which changes abruptly as shown. Current passes through the sheet from a block of very low resistance at one end to a similar block at the other. Current flow lines and equipotentials have been chosen so that each cell presents an area on the surface in which average width is equal to average length. These areas are squares at the left-hand end of the figure but become distorted at the centre where they are *curvilinear squares*. It will be observed that each curvilinear square has right angles at the corners and an average length equal to average width. The test of a true curvilinear square is that it is capable of subdivision into four sections each of which is a curvilinear square, further subdivision producing sections more nearly true squares

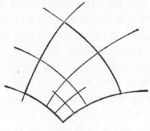

Fig. 14.15

(fig. 14.15). No matter what its size, so long as each curvilinear square $(x \times x)$ conforms to this specification, the resistance of each cell will be the same and by equation (14.28) will be equal to

$$R_c = \rho . x/tx = \rho/t \quad . \quad . \quad . \quad . \quad . \quad (14.30)$$

14.2.5. Flux Plotting

Given the flow boundaries in a particular problem, simple sketching technique enables flow lines and equipotentials to be drawn orthogonally, any errors in positioning the lines soon becoming apparent.

It is usually advisable to draw in a large number of lines and then to select those which are so spaced as to form curvilinear squares. Each square should be checked by dividers to ascertain if average width is equal to average length.

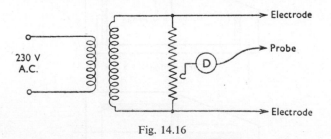

Fig. 14.16

Plots obtained in this way not only give useful indication of the direction of current-flow, but the total resistance can be estimated with reasonable accuracy from equations (14.30) and (14.28).

The plot is more easily made, and the accuracy improved, if one set of lines (the equipotentials) is obtained by an experimental method as follows.

14.2.6. Use of Electric Bath

A shallow tank is constructed, to contain water of uniform depth (about 1 cm), using insulating material and having the sides cut to the shape of the boundaries of the field. The equipotential boundaries by which current enters or leaves are made of copper strip, and an alternating p.d. of about 50 V is applied between them.   Although a frequency of 50 c/s is sufficient for many plots, higher accuracy results with frequencies of the order 1—2 kc/s due to the reduction of polarisation errors.*

A probe is arranged to dip into the water, and a potential divider is connected across the supply with a sensitive detector (vibration galvanometer or amplifier and cathode-ray tube) between the probe and the slider of the divider (fig. 14.16).   To trace an equipotential line, the divider is adjusted to the requisite voltage ratio and the position of the probe adjusted until the detector indicates zero.   If the probe is then moved in such a manner as to maintain a null reading, it will trace out the equipotential corresponding to the voltage-divider setting.   Some method of transferring the position of the probe to drawing paper on which the map is to be plotted is necessary; pantographs and various forms of parallel-motion devices have been used satisfactorily.   After plotting a series of equipotential contours with uniform voltage spacing over the complete field the flow lines are easily sketched and the curvilinear squares established.

14.2.7. Inversion of the Boundaries

The only condition determining the field is that the two families of lines must be orthogonal, consequently they may be interchanged without altering the configuration.   That is to say, the same flux plot will be obtained from a second model in which the conducting and insulating boundaries are interchanged, the flow lines in the first model becoming the equipotentials in the

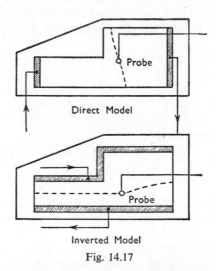

Fig. 14.17

second and vice versa.   It frequently happens that the second or inverted model is simpler to construct, or possibly one set of lines alone gives the required information in which case the model that gives these lines directly should be the one that is used (fig. 14.17).

* McDonald, "The Electrolytic Analogue in the Design of H.V. Power Transformers", *Journal I.E.E.*, **100**, Pt. II, No. 74.

14.2.8. Comparison of Flux Plots for Electric and Magnetic Fields and Current-flow Problems

A flux plot such as has been described is the solution of a certain type of geometrical problem and it relates not only to current flow but also to other

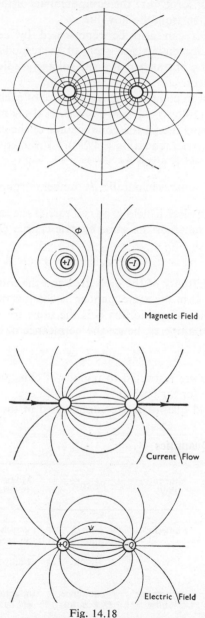

Fig. 14.18

fields involving "flux". For example, the map shown in fig. 14.18 was obtained from a tank plot of the current flow between two circular electrodes. The same type of plot is obtained for the electric field existing in a homogeneous dielectric between parallel wires (i.e. a transmission line). In this case the equipotentials again correspond to voltage but the flow lines represent electric flux.

The same plot can also represent the magnetic field due to currents flowing in opposite directions in two parallel wires. In this case the field is inverted; the magnetic "lines of force" are the equipotentials of the current plot, and the equipotentials are taken from the flow lines.

Heat-flow problems can also be represented by equivalent current-flow problems, when equipotentials are seen to correspond to isothermals, and current flow to the rate of transfer of heat, voltage gradient being the analogue of temperature gradient.

It is also of interest to compare the significance of each cell (of unit depth) in the plot. In a current-flow field each cell carries the same value of current and has the same p.d. across it, and the conductance of the cell is equal to the conductivity σ of the material (equation (14.29)). From equation (14.28) the total conductance of the field is given by

$$G = \sigma \cdot \text{(number of squares in parallel)}/\text{(number of squares in series)} \quad (14.31)$$

In the same way in an electric field each cell carries the same electric flux ψ, that is, the cross-section subtends the same electric charge Q_c. The capacitance of each cell is then

$$C_c = Q_c/V_c = \epsilon\epsilon_0 \quad . \quad . \quad . \quad . \quad . \quad . \quad (14.32)$$

where $\epsilon\epsilon_0$ is the permittivity of the dielectric, and the total capacitance between electrodes is computed in the same manner as conductance in equation (14.31).

With magnetic field, magnetic flux ϕ is the same for each cell and so is the magnetic potential in amperes, hence the permeance of each cell

$$\Lambda_c = \phi_c/I_c = \mu_0 \quad . \quad . \quad . \quad . \quad . \quad . \quad (14.32)$$

(Magnetic field plots are restricted to regions of constant permeability and are only of practical use for air paths.)

Corresponding field quantities are summarised in the following table.

14.2.9. Field Map Quantities

Field	Current flow	Electric	Magnetic (inverted)	Thermal
Total flux	I ampere	$\psi = Q$ coulomb	ϕ weber (volt-second)	P watt
Total potential difference	V volt	V volt	I ampere	θ degree C
Flux/p.d.	Conductance I/V mho	capacitance Q/V farad	Inductance ϕ/I henry	Thermal conductance P/θ watt/sec or thermal mho
Potential gradient	E volt/metre	E volt/metre	H ampere/ metre	degree C/metre

Field	Current flow	Electric	Magnetic (inverted)	Thermal
Flux density	J ampere/ metre^2	D coulomb/ metre^2	B weber/ metre^2	watt/metre^2
$\dfrac{\text{Flux density}}{\text{Potential gradient}}$	σ ampere/ volt-metre	$\epsilon\epsilon_0$ farad/metre	$\mu\mu_0$ henry/metre	g thermal mho/metre
Flux/p.d. for square cell of depth t	σt mho	$\epsilon\epsilon_0 t$ farad	$\mu\mu_0 t$ henry	gt thermal mho

14.3.   Measurement of Power in Three-phase, Three-wire Circuit

14.3.1. Two-wattmeter Method

Fig. 14.19 shows a three-phase, three-wire load connected to a three-phase supply of phase-sequence A-B-C.   Two wattmeters are connected, the first with its current coil in line A and its voltage coil between lines A and C, and the

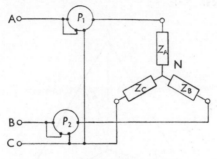

Fig. 14.19

second with its current coil in line B and its voltage coil between lines B and C. It will be shown that the sum of the two wattmeter readings is equal to the total power supplied to the load.   This is true for both balanced and unbalanced loads.

14.3.2. Balanced or Unbalanced Load

The instantaneous powers measured by:

Wattmeter No. 1

$$p_1 = v_{ac}i_{an} = (v_{an} - v_{cn})i_{an} \quad . \quad . \quad . \quad . \quad . \quad (14.33)$$

Wattmeter No. 2

$$p_2 = v_{bc}i_{bn} = (v_{bn} - v_{cn})i_{bn} \quad . \quad . \quad . \quad . \quad . \quad (14.34)$$

The total instantaneous power measured is

$$p_1 + p_2 = (v_{an} - v_{cn})i_{an} + (v_{bn} - v_{cn})i_{bn} \quad . \quad . \quad . \quad . \quad (14.35)$$
$$= v_{an}i_{an} + v_{bn}i_{bn} - v_{cn}(i_{an} + i_{bn})$$

but for a three-wire supply

$$i_a + i_b + i_c = 0 \quad \cdots \cdots \quad (14.36)$$

or

$$i_a + i_b = -i_c$$

therefore

$$p_1 + p_2 = v_{an}i_{an} + v_{bn}i_{bn} + v_{cn}i_{cn} \quad \cdots \cdot \quad (14.37)$$

$$= p_a + p_b + p_c \quad \cdots \cdots \cdot \quad (14.38)$$

which is the total instantaneous power in the three loads.

The mean values corresponding to equation (14.38) show that

$$P_1 + P_2 = P_a + P_b + P_c \quad \cdots \cdot \quad (14.39)$$

where P_1 and P_2 are the wattmeter readings and P_a, P_b and P_c are the mean powers in the loads.

14.3.3. Balanced Load only

For balanced voltage and load conditions only, it will be shown that the load power factor can be determined from the ratio of the wattmeter readings. Alternatively it is a simple matter to determine both kilowatt and reactive kilovolt-ampere values.

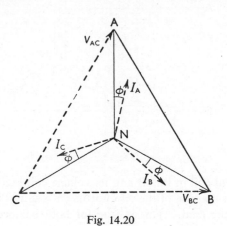

Fig. 14.20

Under balanced conditions the vector diagram shown in fig. 14.20 may be applied. If each load impedance is given by

$$Z = Z \exp j\phi \quad \cdots \cdots \cdot \quad (14.40)$$

the line currents will be as shown lagging the line-to-neutral voltages respectively by the phase angle ϕ.

The reading of the wattmeter in line A is seen to be the product of the r.m.s. voltage V_{ac}, the current I_a and the cosine of angle between these two vectors. Fig. 14.20 shows that this angle is $(\pi/6 - \phi)$, and similarly the angle between V_{bc} and I_b is $(\pi/6 + \phi)$.

Thus

$$P_1 = VI \cos (\pi/6 - \phi) \quad . \quad . \quad . \quad . \quad . \quad (14.41)$$

and

$$P_2 = VI \cos (\pi/6 + \phi) \quad . \quad . \quad . \quad . \quad . \quad (14.42)$$

where V is the r.m.s. value of the line voltage and I the r.m.s. value of line current.

Now if the ratio of the wattmeter readings

$$R = P_2/P_1 \quad . \quad . \quad . \quad . \quad . \quad . \quad . \quad . \quad . \quad . \quad . \quad . \quad (14.43)$$

we have $R = \{\cos (\pi/6 + \phi)\}/\{\cos (\pi/6 - \phi)\}$ $. \quad . \quad . \quad . \quad . \quad . \quad . \quad (14.44)$

$$= \{\cos (\pi/6) \cos \phi - \sin (\pi/6) \sin \phi\}/\{\cos (\pi/6) \cos \phi + \sin (\pi/6) \sin \phi\}$$

and $(1-R)/(1+R) = (\sin (\pi/6) \sin \phi)/(\cos (\pi/6) \cos \phi) = (1/\sqrt{3}) \tan \phi$

$$\tan \phi = \sqrt{3} . (1-R)/(1+R) \quad . \quad . \quad . \quad . \quad (14.45)$$

and the power factor

$$\cos \phi = 1/\sqrt{(1 + \tan^2 \phi)} . \quad . \quad . \quad . \quad . \quad . \quad (14.46)$$

$$= (R+1)/2\sqrt{(R^2 - R + 1)} . \quad . \quad . \quad . \quad (14.47)$$

This relationship can be plotted as a graph or alternatively used to compile a table of values which enables the power factor to be determined directly from the ratio of the wattmeter readings.

14.3.4. Negative Values of R

When $\cos \phi = 0.5$ or $\phi = \pi/3$, the value of $\cos (\pi/6 + \phi) = 0$. Thus, when the power factor is 0.5 the second wattmeter reads zero. For power factors less than 0.5, P_2 is negative, and the connections to the voltage coil of this wattmeter must be reversed to obtain a reading.

Over the complete range of power factor from zero to unity the ratio R varies from -1.0 to $+1.0$.

Table A shows the changes that take place from zero lagging power factor to zero leading power factor.

TABLE A

Power factor		Phase angle (degrees)	P_1	P_2	
Lag	0.0	90	+	−	$P_1 = -P_2$
	0.5	60	+	0	
	0.866	30	+	+	$P_1 > P_2$
	1.0	0	+	+	$P_1 = P_2$
Lead	0.866	−30	+	+	$P_1 < P_2$
	0.5	−60	0	+	
	0.0	−90	−	+	$-P_1 = P_2$

Table B gives power factor in terms of the ratio. This table may be used both for lagging and leading power factors, but, if the power factor is lagging, $R = P_2/P_1$, and, if leading, $R = P_1/P_2$, that is, the fractional value should always be used.

Current coil of wattmeter P_1 is in line A. Current coil of wattmeter P_2 is in line B. Phase sequence is A-B-C.

TABLE B

POSITIVE RATIOS

Ratio	p.f.	Ratio	p.f.	Ratio	p.f.	Ratio	p.f.	Ratio	p.f.
0	0·500	0·200	0·655	0·400	0·802	0·600	0·917	0·800	0·983
0·005	0·504	0·205	0·658	0·405	0·805	0·605	0·919	0·805	0·984
0·010	0·508	0·210	0·662	0·410	0·808	0·610	0·922	0·810	0·985
0·015	0·512	0·215	0·666	0·415	0·812	0·615	0·923	0·815	0·986
0·020	0·516	0·220	0·670	0·420	0·815	0·620	0·925	0·820	0·987
0·025	0·520	0·225	0·674	0·425	0·818	0·625	0·927	0·825	0·988
0·030	0·524	0·230	0·678	0·430	0·822	0·630	0·930	0·830	0·989
0·035	0·527	0·235	0·682	0·435	0·825	0·635	0·932	0·835	0·990
0·040	0·531	0·240	0·686	0·440	0·828	0·640	0·934	0·840	0·990
0·045	0·535	0·245	0·690	0·445	0·832	0·645	0·936	0·845	0·991
0·050	0·538	0·250	0·693	0·450	0·835	0·650	0·938	0·850	0·992
0·055	0·542	0·255	0·697	0·455	0·838	0·655	0·940	0·855	0·992
0·060	0·546	0·260	0·700	0·460	0·841	0·660	0·942	0·860	0·993
0·065	0·550	0·265	0·704	0·465	0·843	0·665	0·943	0·865	0·993
0·070	0·553	0·270	0·708	0·470	0·847	0·670	0·945	0·870	0·994
0·075	0·557	0·275	0·711	0·475	0·850	0·675	0·947	0·875	0·994
0·080	0·562	0·280	0·715	0·480	0·853	0·680	0·948	0·880	0·995
0·085	0·565	0·285	0·718	0·485	0·857	0·685	0·950	0·885	0·995
0·090	0·568	0·290	0·723	0·490	0·860	0·690	0·952	0·890	0·995
0·095	0·573	0·295	0·727	0·495	0·863	0·695	0·954	0·895	0·995
0·100	0·577	0·300	0·730	0·500	0·867	0·700	0·955	0·900	0·996
0·105	0·580	0·305	0·733	0·505	0·869	0·705	0·958	0·905	0·996
0·110	0·584	0·310	0·738	0·510	0·872	0·710	0·960	0·910	0·996
0·115	0·587	0·315	0·742	0·515	0·875	0·715	0·962	0·915	0·997
0·120	0·592	0·320	0·745	0·520	0·878	0·720	0·964	0·920	0·997
0·125	0·596	0·325	0·749	0·525	0·880	0·725	0·965	0·925	0·997
0·130	0·599	0·330	0·753	0·530	0·882	0·730	0·966	0·930	0·997
0·135	0·603	0·335	0·757	0·535	0·885	0·735	0·967	0·935	0·998
0·140	0·607	0·340	0·759	0·540	0·887	0·740	0·968	0·940	0·998
0·145	0·611	0·345	0·763	0·545	0·890	0·745	0·970	0·945	0·999
0·150	0·615	0·350	0·767	0·550	0·893	0·750	0·972	0·950	0·999
0·155	0·618	0·355	0·770	0·555	0·895	0·755	0·973	0·955	0·999
0·160	0·623	0·360	0·773	0·560	0·898	0·760	0·974	0·960	0·999
0·165	0·627	0·365	0·778	0·565	0·900	0·765	0·975	0·965	0·999
0·170	0·631	0·370	0·782	0·570	0·903	0·770	0·976	0·970	0·999
0·175	0·635	0·375	0·785	0·575	0·905	0·775	0·978	0·975	0·999
0·180	0·638	0·380	0·788	0·580	0·907	0·780	0·979	0·980	1·000
0·185	0·642	0·385	0·792	0·585	0·910	0·785	0·980	0·985	1·000
0·190	0·646	0·390	0·795	0·590	0·912	0·790	0·981	0·990	1·000
0·195	0·650	0·395	0·798	0·595	0·915	0·795	0·982	0·995	1·000
0·200	0·655	0·400	0·802	0·600	0·917	0·800	0·983	1·000	1·000

TABLE B

NEGATIVE RATIOS

Ratio	p.f.	Ratio	p.f.	Ratio	p.f.	Ratio	p.f.	Ratio	p.f.
0	0·500	0·200	0·361	0·400	0·245	0·600	0·142	0·800	0·065
0·005	0·496	0·205	0·358	0·405	0·242	0·605	0·141	0·805	0·064
0·010	0·492	0·210	0·355	0·410	0·240	0·610	0·139	0·810	0·062
0·015	0·487	0·215	0·350	0·415	0·237	0·615	0·137	0·815	0·060
0·020	0·483	0·220	0·347	0·420	0·234	0·620	0·135	0·820	0·058
0·025	0·480	0·225	0·344	0·425	0·231	0·625	0·133	0·825	0·056
0·030	0·476	0·230	0·341	0·430	0·228	0·630	0·131	0·830	0·054
0·035	0·473	0·235	0·339	0·435	0·225	0·635	0·129	0·835	0·053
0·040	0·470	0·240	0·336	0·440	0·222	0·640	0·126	0·840	0·052
0·045	0·466	0·245	0·333	0·445	0·219	0·645	0·124	0·845	0·051
0·050	0·463	0·250	0·330	0·450	0·216	0·650	0·122	0·850	0·049
0·055	0·459	0·255	0·327	0·455	0·214	0·655	0·120	0·855	0·048
0·060	0·456	0·260	0·324	0·460	0·211	0·660	0·119	0·860	0·046
0·065	0·453	0·265	0·321	0·465	0·208	0·665	0·117	0·865	0·044
0·070	0·450	0·270	0·318	0·470	0·206	0·670	0·115	0·870	0·042
0·075	0·444	0·275	0·315	0·475	0·204	0·675	0·113	0·875	0·039
0·080	0·440	0·280	0·312	0·480	0·201	0·680	0·110	0·880	0·037
0·085	0·437	0·285	0·309	0·485	0·199	0·685	0·108	0·885	0·036
0·090	0·433	0·290	0·306	0·490	0·196	0·690	0·105	0·890	0·035
0·095	0·430	0·295	0·303	0·495	0·193	0·695	0·103	0·895	0·034
0·100	0·426	0·300	0·300	0·500	0·191	0·700	0·101	0·900	0·032
0·105	0·423	0·305	0·296	0·505	0·188	0·705	0·098	0·905	0·030
0·110	0·420	0·310	0·293	0·510	0·186	0·710	0·096	0·910	0·027
0·115	0·416	0·315	0·290	0·515	0·184	0·715	0·095	0·915	0·026
0·120	0·413	0·320	0·287	0·520	0·182	0·720	0·094	0·920	0·025
0·125	0·410	0·325	0·284	0·525	0·180	0·725	0·093	0·925	0·024
0·130	0·406	0·330	0·281	0·530	0·177	0·730	0·091	0·930	0·022
0·135	0·404	0·335	0·279	0·535	0·174	0·735	0·089	0·935	0·020
0·140	0·400	0·340	0·276	0·540	0·172	0·740	0·087	0·940	0·018
0·145	0·396	0·345	0·273	0·545	0·170	0·745	0·085	0·945	0·016
0·150	0·392	0·350	0·270	0·550	0·167	0·750	0·082	0·950	0·015
0·155	0·390	0·355	0·268	0·555	0·164	0·755	0·080	0·955	0·012
0·160	0·386	0·360	0·266	0·560	0·162	0·760	0·079	0·960	0·011
0·165	0·382	0·365	0·264	0·565	0·160	0·765	0·078	0·965	0·010
0·170	0·379	0·370	0·262	0·570	0·157	0·770	0·077	0·970	0·009
0·175	0·376	0·375	0·259	0·575	0·155	0·775	0·075	0·975	0·007
0·180	0·373	0·380	0·256	0·580	0·154	0·780	0·074	0·980	0·005
0·185	0·370	0·385	0·252	0·585	0·152	0·785	0·072	0·985	0·004
0·190	0·367	0·390	0·250	0·590	0·149	0·790	0·070	0·990	0·002
0·195	0·364	0·395	0·247	0·595	0·145	0·795	0·068	0·995	0·001
0·200	0·361	0·400	0·245	0·600	0·142	0·800	0·065	1·000	0·000

14.3.5. Determination of kW and kVAr

For balanced load, the difference of the two wattmeter readings from equations (14.41) and (14.42) is

$$P_1 - P_2 = VI \cos(\pi/6 - \phi) - VI \cos(\pi/6 + \phi) \quad . \quad . \quad . \quad (14.48)$$
$$= VI \cdot 2 \sin(\pi/6) \sin\phi$$
$$= VI \sin\phi \quad . \quad . \quad . \quad . \quad . \quad . \quad . \quad . \quad (14.49)$$

Now the system power

$$P = \sqrt{3} \cdot VI \cos\phi \quad . \quad . \quad . \quad . \quad . \quad (14.50)$$

and volt-amperes reactive

$$Q = \sqrt{3} \cdot VI \sin\phi \quad . \quad . \quad . \quad . \quad . \quad (14.51)$$

Thus in terms of the wattmeter readings

$$P = P_1 + P_2 \quad . \quad . \quad . \quad . \quad . \quad . \quad (14.52)$$

and
$$Q = \sqrt{3} \cdot (P_1 - P_2) \quad . \quad . \quad . \quad . \quad . \quad (14.53)$$

14.4. Heating and Cooling

Heat is developed in all electrical machines due to the losses in the various parts, principally I^2R loss in conductors, and eddy current and hysteresis loss in iron, causing the temperature of that particular part to rise. This temperature rise continues until all the heat generated is dissipated to the surroundings by one or more of the natural methods of heat transfer, viz. conduction, convection and radiation.

Ultimately then, under steady load, each part achieves a final temperature the magnitude of which depends on the balance between the rate at which heat is developed in that part (or received by conduction from a hotter part), and the rate at which the heat can be dissipated which is determined by the effectiveness of the method of cooling. The manner in which the temperature rises depends on the following factors. Considering the case of a transformer with natural cooling let

P = power loss in a transformer on constant load (watts)—this is the total power converted to heat within the transformer,

R = power dissipated per 1°C rise of the surface of the transformer tank above the ambient.

According to Newton's law of cooling the rate of loss of energy of a hot body is proportional to the difference in temperature between that body and its surroundings. This law is approximately true for moderate temperature differences (up to 100°C) and for bodies losing heat by radiation and natural convection. This means that R is a constant dependent on the surface area of the tank, the area and disposition of the pipes and, to some extent, on the shape and type of surface.

Let A = capacity for heat of the transformer, oil and tank, that is, the energy in joules required to raise the temperature 1°C. It can be calculated from the weight of the parts and their respective specific heats.

Let θ = the temperature difference between the transformer and ambient at a time t.

Then in a short time interval dt, if the temperature θ rises by $d\theta$,

$$Pdt = \text{energy converted to heat,}$$
$$R\theta dt = \text{energy dissipated,}$$
$$A d\theta = \text{energy stored due to rise in temperature.}$$

Thus, since the total heat generated is either radiated or stored,

$$A d\theta + R\theta dt = Pdt$$

or

$$(A/R)d\theta/dt + \theta = P/R \quad . \quad . \quad . \quad . \quad . \quad (14.54)$$

which is a linear equation of the first order of the form

$$a . d\theta/dt + \theta = c \quad . \quad . \quad . \quad . \quad . \quad (14.55)$$

where $a = A/R$ and $c = P/R$.

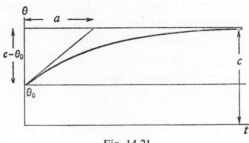

Fig. 14.21

Now if $\theta = \theta_0$ when $t = 0$, the solution is as follows.

The auxiliary equation is

$$am + 1 = 0$$

and the complementary function

$$\theta = k \exp(-t/a).$$

A particular integral is

$$\theta = c.$$

Hence the solution is

$$\theta = c + k \exp(-t/a).$$

But when $t = 0$, $\theta = \theta_0$ so that

$$\theta_0 = c + k \quad \text{or} \quad k = (\theta_0 - c).$$

Thus

$$\theta = c - (c - \theta_0) \exp(-t/a) \quad . \quad . \quad . \quad . \quad (14.56)$$

This general solution shows that the temperature rises exponentially from θ_0 to the final value $c = P/R$, which is only achieved after a long time, the rate of rise progressively diminishing. In other words, the temperature ceases to rise when all the heat is dissipated as rapidly as it is produced, i.e. when $R\theta_{max} = P$

$$\theta_{max} = P/R \quad . \quad . \quad . \quad . \quad . \quad . \quad (14.57)$$

Putting $t = 0$ in equation (14.55), the initial rate of rise is given by

$$[d\theta/dt]_{t=0} = (c-\theta_0)/a \quad . \quad . \quad . \quad . \quad (14.58)$$

and, had this rate of rise continued, the final temperature would have been attained in time

$$(c-\theta_0)/[d\theta/dt]_{t=0} = (c-\theta_0)/\{(c-\theta_0)/a\} = a = A/R \quad . \quad (14.59)$$

a is therefore known as the *time constant*, defined as the time that would have been taken to reach the final value had the initial rate of rise continued.

After time $t = a$, the actual rise is

$$\theta = c-(c-\theta_0) \exp(-1) = c-(c-\theta_0)\, 0\cdot368$$

and, when $t = 2a$,

$$\theta = c-(c-\theta_0) \exp(-2) = c-(c-\theta_0)\, 0\cdot368^2.$$

The residue diminishes to approximately one-third of its original value after each interval of time equal to the time constant (this fact enables an approximate curve to be quickly drawn) (fig. 14.21).

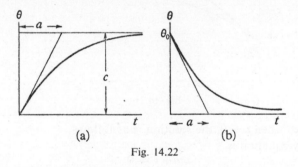

Fig. 14.22

Although the final temperature is theoretically never reached, we may assume steady-state conditions to be established when $t \simeq 4a$.

Two special cases arise shown in fig. 14.22 (a) and (b). The first applies to a transformer originally cold ($\theta_0 = 0$) with load switched on at $t = 0$.

Putting $\theta_0 = 0$, equation (14.56) reduces to

$$\theta = c\{1-\exp(-t/a)\} \quad . \quad . \quad . \quad . \quad (14.60)$$

The second case refers to a transformer originally at temperature θ_0, power being cut off at $t = 0$. The temperature falls to zero according to fig. 14.22 (b) obtained by putting $c = 0$ in equation (14.56), whence

$$\theta = \theta_0 \exp(-t/a) \quad . \quad . \quad . \quad . \quad (14.61)$$

14.5. Types of Enclosure and Ventilation

In all motors and generators heat is mainly removed by transfer to cooling air, which is drawn in and circulated within the machine usually assisted by a fan system rotating with the shaft. The paths taken by the cooling air and the effectiveness of the heat transfer vary considerably with the types of enclosure which may be classified as follows.

(a) *Open-type machines* which have no special covers giving mechanical protection to the moving parts and in which there is no restriction to natural ventilation, there being free access to the surrounding air on all sides. An open machine may have pedestal bearings supported independently of the machine frame, or end brackets containing the bearings. Air normally enters freely from both sides of the machine and due to the rotation of the rotor is drawn through radial ducts between the pockets of core laminations, the spacers acting as blades of a centrifugal fan. From the rotor surface it travels partly along the gap and partly through the ducts in the stator in the case of an a.c. machine and leaves at comparatively low speed in a simple convection stream.

(b) *Protected machines* in which all internal rotating and live parts are protected from accidental contact by suitable covers and end shields. These include *screen-protected* machines in which all ventilation openings are covered with wire mesh screens having appertures not exceeding $\frac{1}{2}$ in^2, and *drip-proof* machines where cowling is so designed as to exclude falling water or dirt.

(c) *Pipe- or duct-ventilated machines* in which the supply of ventilating air is carried to and/or from the machine in pipes.

(d) *Totally enclosed machines* so constructed that the air inside the machine has no connection with the external air, though the machine is not necessarily "air tight". These machines offer the greatest possible protection to the internal windings and rotating parts, but the cooling is considerably reduced and the rating likewise.

(e) *Totally enclosed fan-cooled machines*, i.e. totally enclosed machines with additional cooling by means of a fan driven by the machine itself blowing external air over the surface of the machine or through ducting.

(f) *Totally enclosed separately air-cooled machines*, similar to (e) but having separately driven fans.

(g) *Totally enclosed air-circuit machines*, i.e. totally enclosed machines where special provision is made for cooling the enclosed air by driving it through a cooler external to the machine.

QUESTIONS

CHAPTER 2

1. Two transformers are designed to work at the same current density and the same flux density but the linear dimensions of one are k times those of the other.

Determine their relative outputs, relative iron and copper losses and the relative heating in watts per unit area of cooling surface.

Discuss different methods of cooling for the two transformers if k is large. [L.U.]

2. Sketch the flux distribution at no load in the core of a three-phase transformer at the instants when the magnetising current in one phase is (i) zero, and (ii) a maximum, indicating the relative magnitude and directions of the fluxes in the limbs and yokes.

Determine the main dimensions of the core for a 250-kVA, 6600/415-V, 50-c/s, three-phase transformer with star-connected windings. Assume the following data: approximate voltage per turn, 9; maximum flux density, 12 500 lines per cm2; effective cross-sectional area of core/square of diameter of circumscribing circle, 0·62; window space factor, 0·27; height of window/width of window, 2; current density 250 A/cm2. [L.U.]

3. Show that the static transformer can be represented by an equivalent electric circuit and deduce the constants of this circuit.

A three-phase, core-type transformer with a star-connected primary winding is connected to a three-phase, three-wire supply having a phase sequence red, yellow, blue. The voltage to the star point from each line is 230 V and the current in each of the red and blue lines is 3·9 A and in the yellow line 2·5 A with the secondary on open circuit. A wattmeter connected to measure the power between the red line and the star point gave zero reading.

Determine the total power supplied to the transformer, stating any assumptions made.

[L.U.]

4. Determine the dimensions of the core, the number of turns and the cross-section of conductors in the primary and secondary windings for a 100-kVA, 2200/480-V, single-phase, core-type transformer to operate at a frequency of 50 c/s, assuming the following data: approximate voltage per turn, 7·5; maximum flux density, 12 000 lines/cm2; effective cross-sectional area of core/square of diameter of circumscribing circle, 0·6; height of window/width of window, 2; window space factor, 0·28; current density, 250 A/cm2. What modifications to the design of the secondary winding would be necessary to supply a three-wire system?

[L.U.]

5. Show how the performance of a transformer can be predicted from an equivalent circuit diagram.

Derive an approximate expression for the regulation rise of a transformer in terms of load current and phase angle.

A transformer has a reactance drop of 4% at full load and a copper loss of 2% at full load and unity power factor.

Plot a graph showing how the percentage regulation of the transformer varies as power factor varies from 0·1 lagging to 0·1 leading, the output voltage and current remaining constant.

[I.E.E.]

6. The voltage per turn of a transformer winding is given by $k\sqrt{}$(rated kilovolt-amperes) where k may be regarded as a constant coefficient for a particular range of transformers of similar design.

Discuss the factors affecting the value of k.

Find the number of primary and secondary turns and a suitable core area for a 750-kVA three-phase 50-c/s 3300/400-v, delta/star transformer if the value of k is taken as 0·35.

The maximum instantaneous flux density in the core is not to exceed 13 000 G (1·3 Wb/m2).

[I.E.E.]

7. Draw and explain a diagram showing the effect of the power factor of the load upon the voltage regulation of a transformer.

A 250/500-V, single-phase transformer has an iron loss of 100 W, a resistance of 0·445 Ω and a leakage reactance of 1·245 Ω, both referred to the 500-V side. Calculate the load power factor at which the voltage regulation is (a) a maximum, (b) zero.

If the full-load secondary current is 10 A, calculate (c) the minimum full-load voltage and (d) the percentage of full-load output at which the efficiency is a maximum. [C. & G.]

8. Determine the core and yoke dimensions for a 250-kVA, 50-c/s, single-phase, core-type transformer. There are 15 V/turn, the window space factor is 0·33, the current-density is 3 A/mm^2 and the maximum flux density is 11 000 lines/cm^2. The distance between the centres of the square-section core is twice the width of the core. [C. & G.]

9. The window in the core of a 2200/220-V, 15-kVA, 50-c/s, single-phase transformer has a gross available area of 340 cm^2, the space-factor being 0·35. Taking the maximum core flux-density as 10 000 lines/cm^2 and the current density in the copper as 2·1 A/mm^2, estimate the sectional area of iron in the square core section. Find also the numbers of turns in the windings and the sectional area of the conductors.

Show how all formulae used are derived. [C. & G.]

10. Calculate the core and the window-area and make an estimate of the weights of copper and iron required for a 125-kVA, 2000/400-V, 50-c/s, single-phase, shell-type transformer from the following particulars:

B_{max} = 11 000 lines/cm^2, current density = 2·2 A/mm^2, volts per turn = 11·2, window area constant 0·33. Specific gravity of copper and iron 8·9 and 7·8 respectively. The core is rectangular and the stampings are all 7 cm wide.

Sketch the core, inserting dimensions. [C. & G.]

11. Derive from first principles the output equation of a single-phase transformer. Show that the output is proportional to the fourth power of the linear dimensions; discuss the assumptions made. [C. & G.]

12. Show that the voltage per turn of a transformer may be represented by

$$E_t = K\sqrt{(\text{rated kVA})}$$

where K may be regarded as a constant coefficient for a range of transformers of similar type and proportions. Discuss the factors affecting the value of K.

Determine the number of primary and secondary turns, and a suitable core area for a 1000-kVA, 50-c/s, 11 000/3300-V, delta/star-connected transformer for which the value of K is 0·35. The maximum flux density in the core is not to exceed 1·2 Wb/m^2 (12 000 G).

Sketch a suitable arrangement of the cross-section of the core and indicate how the laminations may be securely held together. [L.U.]

13. Sketch the wave-form of the magnetising current of a single-phase transformer connected to a sinusoidal-voltage source and account for its shape. Explain the corresponding phenomena in a three-phase transformer connected:

(a) star/star, (b) delta/star, (c) star/zigzag.

Sketch the secondary phase-voltage wave-form in each case. [I.E.E.]

14. Sketch the cross-section of part of the coil stack of a large power transformer and explain the method of winding the high-voltage and low-voltage coils. Show why it is necessary to laminate the low-voltage conductors and explain the meaning of the term *transposition*, showing by means of sketches how this is accomplished. [I.E.E.]

CHAPTER 3

1. State the conditions necessary before two three-phase transformers may be connected in parallel and the conditions for their satisfactory parallel operation on load.

A single-phase, 500-kVA, 3·3-kV transformer having a resistance drop of 2% and a reactance drop of 3% at full load is connected in parallel with a 1000-kVA, 3·3-kV transformer having a resistance drop of 1% and a reactance drop of 5% at full load.

Determine, graphically or otherwise, the impedance of the two transformers and their voltage drop when the total load is 1500 kVA at 0·8 power factor lagging. Also determine the current and the kilovolt-amperes of each transformer. [L.U.]

2. Explain the principle of the regenerative (loading-back) method of testing two identical transformers. Show how to determine the rating of the auxiliary apparatus.

Draw a diagram of connections for a heating test, by the regenerative method, on two identical three-phase, star/delta transformers. Describe the procedure in connecting the transformers to the supply and controlling the load. [L.U.]

3. Draw diagrams showing the arrangement of the primary and secondary windings and their interconnections (showing polarities) for the following core-type, three-phase transformers: star/star; delta/star; star/zigzag. Give one example of the use of each of these transformers in industry. Discuss the relative advantages and disadvantages of star/star and delta/star connections for power transformers.

A three-phase, star/zigzag transformer is to be designed for a no-load secondary terminal voltage of 440 V when the primary is supplied with 11 kV at a frequency of 50 c/s. Calculate the number of turns in each coil of the primary and secondary windings if the cross-section of each core is 300 cm^2 and the maximum flux density is 12 000 lines/cm^2. [L.U.]

4. Explain, with diagrams, the principles and operation of *either* (a) the on-load tap-changing equipment of a three-phase transformer, *or* (b) a three-phase moving-coil regulator. [L.U.]

5. Explain why the line-end turns of an extra-high-voltage transformer often have extra insulation.

Determine the dimensions of the core for a 200-kVA, 3300/480-V, single-phase, core-type transformer to operate at a frequency of 50 c/s, assuming the following data: maximum flux density, 12 000 lines/cm^2; current density, 280 A/cm^2; volts per turn, 8; area factor for the three-stepped core, 0·6; height of window/width of window, 2; window space factor, 0·28. [L.U.]

6. Two single-phase tap-changing transformers—A 3000 kVA; B 2000 kVA—are to operate in parallel to supply a load having a resistance of 22 Ω and a reactance of 16 Ω. The nominal no-load voltage ratio of each transformer is 33 000/11 000 V, but the tap-changers are set incorrectly and the no-load secondary voltages, with 33 000 V on the primary, are 11 200 V on A, and 10 800 V on B. Calculate the load (in kilovolt-amperes) on transformer A, assuming the percentage equivalent voltage drops at rated load and nominal ratio to be:

Transformer A—resistance, 1%; leakage reactance, 6%.
Transformer B—resistance, 1%; leakage reactance, 5%. [L.U.]

7. Draw diagrams showing three different schemes of connections for the windings of transformers used for three-phase to three-phase transformation and state for what conditions each would be suitable.

A three-phase transformer bank with primary and secondary windings in star is connected to an 11-kV, three-phase, star-connected alternator, and the voltage between the star points of the transformer bank and the alternator is 2500 V.

Determine the maximum value of the voltage across each phase of the transformer. Explain the reasons for the voltage between the star points and show under what conditions it would be reduced to a very low value. [L.U.]

8. Discuss the relative advantages and disadvantages of the delta-star and the star-star connections for three-phase transformers. Show that a delta/star transformer cannot be connected in parallel with a star/star transformer of the same (terminal) voltage ratio.

A three-phase, 2000-kVA, 6·6/33-kV transformer has the primary winding delta-connected and the secondary winding star-connected. The resistance and leakage reactance of each phase of the primary winding are 0·5 Ω and 2·6 Ω respectively; and the corresponding values of each phase of the secondary winding are 4·3 Ω and 21·7 Ω. Calculate the secondary terminal voltage at full load when the primary is supplied at 6·6 kV. Ignore magnetising current and losses. [L.U.]

9. Draw a diagram of connections and explain the sequence of operations of an on-load tap-changer for a large transformer (no details of the operating mechanism are required). Show by diagrams how the tapped coils are arranged in relation to the other coils of the primary and secondary windings. Explain how the distribution of ampere-turns and the mechanical forces on the coils are affected when only a portion of the tapped coils are in use. [L.U.]

10. Explain the action of a single-phase moving-coil regulator.

Illustrate your answer with sketches showing a regulator with an input of 250 V and an output which is variable from 0 to 500 V. [I.E.E.]

11. Describe two types of transformer connection used to convert a three-phase supply to a two-phase supply.

Draw vector diagrams to illustrate each case and calculate the voltages of each winding section, if the line voltage on the three-phase side is 6600 V and the phase voltage on the two-phase side is 200 V.   [I.E.E.]

12. What is the purpose of insulating the core bolts of a power transformer?

Why is the failure of this insulation a serious matter?

Describe tests undertaken for the purpose of determining the components of core loss in a transformer.

Show clearly how the test results establish the individual magnitudes of these components of the total core loss at rated voltage and frequency.   [I.E.E.]

13. Two three-phase transformers operate in parallel between 33-kV and 11-kV bus-bars, the line voltages on the high-voltage side leading the corresponding voltages on the low-voltage side by 30°. The transformers are connected delta/star and star/zigzag respectively.

Draw a diagram showing the internal connections of the transformer windings and the connections to the bus-bars.

Show by means of vector diagrams that these connections will not lead to circulating currents, and calculate the voltages of each winding section.   [I.E.E.]

14. State the requirements for the satisfactory operation of a number of transformers in parallel.

A load of 1600 kW at 0·8 lagging power factor is shared by two 1000-kVA transformers having equal turn-ratios and connected in parallel on their primary and secondary sides. The full-load resistance drop is 1% and the reactive drop is 6% in one of the transformers, the corresponding values in the other transformer being 1·5% and 5%. Calculate by an exact method the power and the power factor at which each transformer is operating. [C. & G.]

15. In a 500-kVA, 11 000/2200-V transformer, a p.d. of 265 V produces rated full-load current when the low-voltage side is short-circuited, the power absorbed being 3300 W. The corresponding test values for a transformer of the same rating are 945 V and 3980 W. Calculate the greatest total load at unity power factor which can be supplied by these two transformers in parallel without either of them becoming overloaded.   [C. & G.]

16. Two high-voltage testing transformers each having 250-kV windings are connected in cascade to produce 500 kV. Explain the principle of this connection and show how the transformers are energised.

The primary winding of the first transformer is fed from an induction regulator which has a high leakage reactance. Explain why the wave-form of the output voltage of the set is likely to be peaked, and show how a harmonic shunt, tuned to 150 c/s, connected across the low-voltage winding will produce an improvement of the wave-form.   [I.E.E.]

17. Describe, with sketches, the distribution of capacitance in a transformer winding having section coils with radial ducts. Discuss the effect of this on the initial and subsequent voltage distribution along the winding if the transformer is subjected to a standard 1/50 impulse voltage between its line terminal and earth. Hence explain briefly the methods adopted to increase the impulse strength of high-voltage transformers.   [L.U.]

18. Discuss the difficulties involved in on-load tap-changing in transformers. Draw diagrams of connections, and explain the sequence of operations, of one modern form of on-load tap-changer for a large transformer. Details of the operating gear are *not* required. [L.U.]

19. Explain the principle of "back to back" testing of a pair of similar three-phase transformers.

Draw a connection diagram showing a pair of delta/star-connected, 66/3·3-kV, 750-kVA transformers together with the additional apparatus required, and describe how a heat run at full load is conducted. Estimate the approximate minimum current and voltage ratings of the test plant necessary for this test and show clearly what factors determine these values.

[I.E.E.]

CHAPTER 4

1. State and explain the conditions of symmetry for a lap winding of a multipolar d.c. machine.

The armature of a 550-kW, 500-V eight-pole d.c. generator is 120 cm in diameter and the specific electric loading is approximately 275 ampere-conductors/cm. Design a symmetrical armature winding, give particulars of the equalisers and sketch the cross-section of a slot with the insulated conductors in position, specifying the insulation.   [L.U.]

2. State the conditions of symmetry for d.c. armature windings. The armature of a 250-kW, 460-V, six-pole generator is 70 cm in diameter, and the specific electric loading at full load is approximately 275 ampere-conductors/cm. Design a symmetrical armature winding with symmetrical three-phase tappings and slip rings for use with a static balancer.   [L.U.]

3. State the conditions for electrical symmetry of armature windings for d.c. machines.

Determine suitable numbers of conductors and slots, coil-span and commutator pitch for the armature of a 400-kW, 500-V, eight-pole, d.c. generator with four circuit wave winding if the speed is 500 r.p.m. and the flux per pole $5 \cdot 1 \times 10^6$ lines.   [L.U.]

4. Deduce the relationships between the number of armature coils and the commutator pitches for simple lap and wave windings for a six-pole d.c. machine.

The diameter of the armature of a 300-kW, 460-V, six-pole d.c. generator is 100 cm. Determine the number of conductors, the number of slots and the number of commutator segments to satisfy the conditions of symmetry and to provide for tappings to three slip-rings for a static balancer. Assume provisionally a specific electric loading of 250 ampere-conductors/cm. Calculate also the cross-section of the conductors allowing a current density of 400 A/cm². Sketch the arrangement of conductors and insulation in a slot.   [L.U.]

5. Enumerate and explain the conditions which must be satisfied to obtain symmetrical armature windings for multipolar d.c. machines. Show that with multiple-circuit lap windings the several voltage polygons must be identical.

Design a suitable winding and specify the number of slots, for a 500-kW 460-V, eight-pole generator, in which the diameter of the armature is 120 cm and the specific electric loading is approximately 300 ampere-conductors/cm of periphery. The armature winding is to be arranged with tappings to three slip-rings for use with a static balancer for a three-wire system. Sketch the slot and show the arrangement of conductors.   [L.U.]

6. Derive expressions for the *pitch factor* and *spread factor* of an alternator winding.

How do these factors effect the wave-form of the output voltage of the machine? What are the advantages of employing a fractional number of slots per pole per phase? [I.E.E.]

7. Describe methods used to reduce harmonics in the terminal voltage of an alternator.

The air-gap flux distribution of an alternator contains fifth and seventh harmonics whose magnitudes are respectively 10% and 5% of the fundamental. Find the corresponding percentages of the harmonics in the terminal voltage. The machine has 105 stator slots, 14 poles and a three-phase double-layer winding with a coil pitch of 6.   [I.E.E.]

8. For what purpose are equalising connections used with d.c. armature windings? Draw a diagram of an armature winding showing the position of these connections and sketch methods by which they may be arranged on the machine.   [I.E.E.]

9. A four-pole, two-circuit armature is to develop an e.m.f. of 250 V at 550 r.p.m. with a flux of about 4 megalines. There are 171 commutator sectors and the core-disc has 57 slots. Calculate the coil and commutator pitches and make a sketch of the coils in the slots showing how they are connected to the commutator.   [C. & G.]

10. Obtain an expression for the distribution factor of the nth harmonic of the induced e.m.f. in an alternator phase winding arranged in a whole number of slots per pole per phase.

A single-phase alternator has 16 poles, 6 slots per pole (4 of which are wound), 10 conductors per slot, a slot-core length of 45 cm, a stator bore of 180 cm, a maximum gap flux-density (fundamental) of 10 000 lines/cm², and runs at 375 r.p.m. Calculate the open-circuit e.m.f. with all the conductor turns connected in series.

What are the principal harmonics in the tooth-ripple and the values of their distribution factors?   [C. & G.]

11. Determine the distribution and coil-span factors for a three-phase winding with 2 slots per pole per phase. The coil-span is 5 slot pitches. How do these factors affect the output of the machine?

If the flux wave in the gap consists of the fundamental and a 30% third harmonic, calculate the percentage increase in the r.m.s. value of the phase voltage due to this harmonic. [C. & G.]

12. Design a symmetrical winding for a 400-kW, 500-V, eight-pole d.c. generator with an armature diameter of 140 cm. The approximate value for the current in each path is 200 A and the specific electric loading is approximately 300 ampere-conductors/cm.   [C. & G.]

CHAPTER 5

1. Explain what is meant by the leakage reactance of the armature winding of an alternator.

An alternator has parallel slots, each 12 in. long, 0·6 in. wide and 3 in. deep, 0·4 in. next to the mouth of each slot being occupied by a non-magnetic wedge. The conductors occupy a space 0·3 in. wide and 2·3 in. deep. If there are 12 conductors per slot calculate the slot reactance at 50 c/s.   [L.U.]

2. Explain, with sketches, the leakage reactance associated with the armature winding of an alternator.

An alternator has parallel slots, each 0·75 in. wide and 3·5 in. deep, 0·5 in. next to the mouth of each slot being occupied by a non-magnetic wedge.

The conductors occupy a space 0·35 in. wide and 2·6 in. deep. Calculate the reactance per inch length of core due to slot leakage flux at 50 c/s.   [L.U.]

3. The armature of a d.c. machine has a diameter of 20 cm, 29 parallel slots each 0·6 cm wide and 2·5 cm. deep; the core is 15 cm long with one duct 1 cm wide, and the air-gap is 0·3 cm long. Insulation on the stampings is 10 % of the thickness.

If the maximum flux density under the pole is 9000 lines/cm2, determine the ampere-turns required to overcome the reluctance of the gap and teeth. Carter's coefficient for the slots is 0·275 and for the duct 0·39. The magnetisation curve for the iron is as follows:

Ampere-turns/cm .	.	.	18	30	65	194	630	1120
B (lines/cm2)	.	.	14 000	16 000	18 000	20 000	22 000	23 000

[L.U.]

4. Draw and explain diagrams showing the distribution of leakage flux in a core-type transformer and discuss its effect on performance.

What is the cause of eddy-current loss in the conductors and what steps are taken in large transformers to reduce this loss to a minimum?   [I.E.E.]

CHAPTER 6

1. Explain how to obtain from the circle diagram of a three-phase induction motor (a) the current and power factor for any output, (b) the maximum output and (c) the starting torque in pound-feet if normal voltage is applied.

A 400-V, three-phase, six-pole, 50 c/s induction motor gave the following test results:
No load: 400 V, 7 A, 0·15 power factor.
Short circuit: 200 V, 38 A, 0·35 power factor.
The stator is delta-connected and the resistance between any two terminals is 1·0 Ω.

Determine the output in horse-power and the torque in pound-feet when the input current is 25 A.   [L.U.]

2. Describe, with sketches, the construction of a double-cage induction motor and point out its advantages compared with a single-cage motor.

If the outer cage has an equivalent impedance of 0·5+j0·5 Ω and the inner cage an equivalent impedance of 0·1+j0·9 Ω, both at supply frequency, calculate the current in amperes and the torque in synchronous watts for the two cages at standstill and at 6% slip.

The effective standstill e.m.f. of each cage is 100 V.   [L.U.]

3. Describe briefly, with sketches, the construction and explain the action of *either* a three-phase induction regulator *or* a single-phase moving-coil regulator.

A three-phase regulator is employed on a 3300-V system to give ±10% variation of line voltage. If the primary winding is delta-connected, determine the current in this winding when the regulator is in the position for maximum boost and the load is 1000 kVA. Ignore magnetising current and losses. Draw a diagram of connections and a vector diagram.

[L.U.]

4. Deduce for a three-phase induction motor, the relationship between the input kilovolt-amperes, the specific loadings, speed and main dimensions.

Determine the approximate dimensions of the core, number of stator turns and number of stator slots for a 25-h.p., 400-V, three-phase, six-pole motor to operate at 50 c/s. Assume: specific magnetic loading, 4700 lines/cm^2; specific electric loading, 270 ampere-conductors/cm; full-load efficiency, 87%; full-load power factor, 0·88.

[L.U.]

5. Determine the main dimensions and number of slots and conductors for the stator of a 25-h.p., 400-V, three-phase, four-pole, 50 c/s induction motor. The mean flux density in the air-gap is not to exceed 4700 lines/cm^2 and the specific electric loading 280 ampere-conductors/cm. The efficiency and power factor at full load may be assumed as 85% and 0·87 respectively.

If the standstill voltage between the rotor slip rings is not to exceed 240 V, determine a suitable number of slots and conductors per slot for the rotor.

[L.U.]

6. In what important details does the design of a synchronous-induction motor differ from that of a normal induction motor? Discuss the reasons for these differences. Describe the procedure in starting a synchronous-induction motor and explain how the motor pulls into synchronism. Show how to draw the circle diagram for the motor and to determine the performance therefrom.

[L.U.]

7. The following figures refer to a three-phase, 120-h.p., 3300-V synchronous-induction motor when operating as an induction motor at normal voltage: no load, 16 A at 0·15 power factor; short circuit, 120 A at 0·25 power factor.

When running synchronously at full load the d.c. excitation is adjusted to give a leading power factor of 0·9.

Determine the reactive kilovolt-amperes at no load and the maximum horse-power as a synchronous, and as an induction, motor.

Explain, with a diagram of connections, how the power factor may be kept high over the whole range of load and point out any other advantages which arise from this arrangement.

[L.U.]

8. Compare the star-delta and transformer methods of starting three-phase squirrel-cage induction motors on the basis of (i) starting torque and starting current, (ii) adaptability to motor rating, terminal arrangements, and (iii) starting conditions. Discuss the limitations of the methods.

Calculate the ratio of transformation of a transformer-starter for a 25-h.p., 400-V, three-phase induction motor if the starting torque is to be 75% of full-load torque. Assume the slip at full load to be 3·5% and the short-circuit current at full voltage to be 6 times full-load current. Ignore the magnetising current of the transformer and of the motor. Deduce the formula for the ratio of transformation.

[L.U.]

9. Describe, with sketches, the construction of a double-cage induction motor and point out its advantages compared to a single-cage motor.

If the outer cage has an equivalent impedance of $0·6+j0·6 \, \Omega$ and the inner cage an equivalent impedance of $0·1+j0·8 \, \Omega$ both at supply frequency, calculate the current and torque in synchronous watts for the two cages at standstill and at 10% slip.

The effective standstill e.m.f. of each cage is 200 V.

[L.U.]

10. Draw a development diagram of one phase of a pole-changing stator winding for a three-phase induction motor to give either 8 or 4 poles, the winding having one coil per pair of poles per phase when connected for 8 poles. Show the external connections required for each set of poles and mark the directions of currents in the coils.

Assuming full-pitch coils and a delta connection for 8 poles, deduce an approximate expression for the ratio of the fluxes per pole for 8 and 4 poles, ignøring magnetising current and voltage drops. What other assumptions are made? [L.U.]

11. The following particulars apply to a 750-h.p., 3300-V, three-phase nduction motor with stator and rotor windings both star connected:

Stator turns per phase	210
Stator reactance per phase	$1 \cdot 65 \, \Omega$
Stator resistance per phase	$0 \cdot 30 \, \Omega$
No-load current	60 A
Rotor turns per phase	54
Rotor reactance per phase	$0 \cdot 05 \, \Omega$
Rotor resistance per phase	$0 \cdot 02 \, \Omega$
No-load power factor	$0 \cdot 10$

Draw the circle diagram to scale and determine (a) the current, power factor, efficiency and slip at full-load, and (b) the resistance to be connected in each phase of the rotor circuit to give 1·5 times full-load torque at starting if full voltage is switched on. [L.U.]

12. Explain how improved starting performance of three-phase squirrel-cage motors may be obtained by means of a double-cage rotor winding. Sketch typical slots and a speed/torque characteristic, and compare the latter with the speed/torque characteristic of a normal squirrel-cage rotor. [L.U.]

13. The impedances at standstill of the inner and outer windings of a double-cage rotor are $0 \cdot 01 + j0 \cdot 5 \, \Omega$ and $0 \cdot 05 + j0 \cdot 1 \, \Omega$, respectively.

Calculate the ratio of the torques due to the two windings (i) at starting, (ii) when running with a slip of 5%. [L.U.]

14. Deduce, for a three-phase induction motor, an expression showing the relationship between the kilovolt-ampere input (ignoring voltage drops in the windings) and the specific electric and magnetic loadings.

Apply the expression to determine the air-gap diameter and core length for a three-phase, 20 h.p., 400 V, 50-c/s, six-pole motor, assuming approximate values of the specific loadings to be 4500 lines/cm² and 250 ampere-conductors/cm. Assume the ratio (core length/pole pitch) to be 0·85; the full-load efficiency to be 88%, and the power factor at full load to be 0·88.

Determine also a suitable number of conductors per slot for the stator. [L.U.]

15. A six-pole, 400-V double-cage induction motor has a delta-connected primary winding of impedance $(1 + j2) \, \Omega$ per phase. The corresponding referred impedances of the cages are $(2 + j1)$ and $(1 + j4) \, \Omega$ per phase.

The full-load slip is 5%.

Determine the ratio of starting torque to full-load torque for direct-on-line starting. [I.E.E.]

16. The equivalent circuit of one phase of a three-phase star-connected induction motor at standstill is shown.

$V = 250$ volts, $R_0 = 100 \, \Omega$, $R_1 = 0 \cdot 1 \, \Omega$, $R_2 = 0 \cdot 2 \, \Omega$, $X_0 = 20 \, \Omega$, $X_1 = 1 \cdot 0 \, \Omega$,
$X_2 = 1 \cdot 0 \, \Omega$.

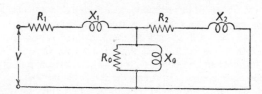

Explain the significance of each circuit element, and calculate the input current and power factor when the slip is 5%. [I.E.E.]

17. Draw the circle diagram for a 20-h.p., four-pole, three-phase, 440-V, 50-c/s cage-rotor induction motor from the following data:

Running condition	Line voltage	Line current	Wattmeter readings
	V	A	kW
Running light	440	8·7	+2·64 −1·12
Locked rotor	110	23	+2·08 −0·22

Find from the diagram for full-load output: (a) line current, (b) power factor, (c) efficiency and (d) starting torque (pound-feet).

The rotor copper loss may be assumed equal to the stator copper loss at standstill
[I.E.E.]

18. A single-phase, four-pole, 50-c/s induction motor of the capacitor-start type has the auxiliary starting winding and its series capacitor disconnected by a centrifugal switch at 1000 r.p.m.

Its speed/torque curve is given by the following data:

Speed, r.p.m.	0	200	400	600	800	1000	1100	1200	1300	1350	1400	1500
Torque, lb ft (auxiliary winding connected) .	5·0	6·4	7·5	7·7	7·6	6·5	—	—	—	—	—	—
Torque, lb ft (main winding only). . .	—	—	—	—	—	5·0	4·7	4·1	3·0	2·25	1·5	0

The moment of inertia of the motor and its load is $0·1$ lb ft/sec^2, and the load-torque is constant at $2·0$ lb ft.

Determine (a) the total time taken by the machine during starting, (b) the time during which the auxiliary winding is in circuit. [I.E.E.]

19. Explain how an equivalent circuit diagram can be set up to represent an induction motor on load.

Derive an expression for the gross mechanical torque (in pound-feet) in terms of the current in this circuit and the circuit constants at a particular value of slip. [I.E.E.]

20. Derive the torque/slip equation for a three-phase induction motor and calculate therefrom the condition for maximum torque.

A six-pole, 50-c/s, three-phase induction motor has a rotor resistance of $0·2 \, \Omega$ per phase and a maximum torque of 120 lb ft at 875 r.p.m. Calculate (a) the torque when the slip is 4% and (b) the resistance to be added to the rotor circuit to obtain 2/3 of the maximum torque at starting. State why two values of this resistance are given by the calculation. [C. & G.]

21. Draw the circle diagram for a 30-h.p., 500-V, four-pole, 50-c/s, three-phase, star-connected cage induction motor. On no-load the input at rated voltage is 1·5 kW, 8·3 A, and on short-circuit at one-fifth rated voltage the input is 1·6 kW, 32 A.

Find the full-load line current and power factor and estimate the pull-out torque in pound-feet, assuming that the rotor copper loss equals the stator copper loss. [C. & G.]

22. Draw the circle diagram for a 220-V, 50-c/s, four-pole, three-phase, star-connected induction motor from the following test results. The no-load input is 5 A and 360 W at 220 V, and the input at standstill is 1600 W and 20 A at 100 V. The copper losses are equally divided between stator and rotor.

Determine the value of the stalling torque at normal voltage. [C. & G.]

23. Show that the locus of the stator current vector for an induction motor is circular.

A three-phase, 440-V, 40-h.p. induction motor gave the following test results:

No load, 440 V, 20 A, 1250 W.

At rest, 200 V, 90 A, 10 000 W.

Find the full-load current and power factor.   [C. & G.]

24. Explain what is meant by the output-coefficient of a machine and develop an expression for the output-coefficient of a three-phase alternator.

Find the rotor core dimensions for a 25 000-kVA, two-pole, 50-c/s turbo-alternator given the peripheral speed 150 m/sec, average gap flux-density 5500 lines/cm², specific electric loading 600 ampere-conductors/cm.   [C. & G.]

25. Derive from first principles, an expression for the output coefficient of an induction motor.

Obtain the approximate core dimensions for a 25-h.p., three-phase, 50-c/s, four-pole induction motor. Take the power factor and the efficiency to be 90%, and B_{av} = 5000 lines/cm², and the specific electric loading = 240 ampere-conductors/cm.

26. Derive a formula for the total torque in kilogramme-metres developed by a three-phase induction motor.

Draw the circle diagram and obtain the full-load current and power factor for a 50-h.p., 400-V, 50-c/s, twelve-pole, three-phase, mesh-connected induction motor which gave the following test results:

	Line voltage (V)	Line current (A)	kW
No load	400	41	3·3
Standstill	80	75	3·15

[C. & G.]

27. Draw the circle diagram for a 30-h.p., four-pole, three-phase, 440-V, 50-c/s cage-rotor induction motor from the following data:

	Line voltage (V)	Line current (A)	Power (kW)
Running light . . .	440	17	3·04
Rotor locked . . .	110	46	3·72

Deduce from the diagram

(a) the line current at full load,

(b) the power factor at full load,

(c) the ratio maximum torque/full-load torque,

(d) the torque, in synchronous watts, when the stator current is 60 A.   [L.U.]

28. Draw the circle diagram for a 35-h.p., six-pole, three-phase, 400-volt, 50-c/s, induction motor, which gave the following test figures:

	Line voltage (V)	Line current (A)	Power (kW)
Light-running test . .	400	21	2·77
Locked-rotor test . .	100	43	2·42

The rotor copper loss may be assumed equal to the stator copper loss at standstill.

21—E.M.

Find from the diagram (a) the full-load current and power factor, (b) the starting torque (lb ft), (c) the maximum torque (lb ft). [I.E.E.]

29. The equivalent circuit of one phase of a three-phase induction motor at rest is shown.

$V = 200$ V, $R_0 = 100\ \Omega$, $X_0 = 25\ \Omega$, $R_1 = 0{\cdot}10\ \Omega$, $R_2 = 0{\cdot}25\ \Omega$, $X_1 = 1{\cdot}0\ \Omega$, $X_2 = 1{\cdot}0\ \Omega$

Draw and explain the equivalent circuit of the same machine operating at a slip of 5%, and calculate the input current and power factor. [I.E.E.]

30. Explain how, and in what respects, double-cage rotor windings improve the performance of induction motors. Sketch the cross-section of a typical slot and the torque/speed characteristic of such a machine.

Figures for the torque/speed curve of a cage-rotor machine designed for direct-on-line starting are given in the following table:

Speed (r.p.m.)	Torque (lb ft)
0	70
200	73
400	79
600	85
800	94
1000	100
1200	90
1400	40
1500	0

The moment of inertia of the motor and its load is equivalent to that of a mass of 50 lb at a radius of 1 ft. The load torque may be assumed constant at 30 lb ft.

Determine the time taken from the instant of closing the starting switch for the motor to reach a speed of 1400 r.p.m. [L.U.]

CHAPTER 7

1. Deduce an expression giving the relation between the specific electric and magnetic loadings and the diameter and length of the bore of a three-phase synchronous machine for a given induced power and speed.

From this expression and a suitably chosen ratio of length to diameter determine the diameter and length for a three-phase, star-connected, 1000-kVA, 11-kV, ten-pole, 600 r.p.m. alternator if the maximum flux density in the gap is 8500 lines/cm² and the specific electric loading 350 ampere-conductors/cm of periphery.

Determine also a suitable number of slots and armature conductors. [L.U.]

2. A three-phase, ten-pole, 600 r.p.m., star-connected alternator has 12 slots per pole with 8 conductors per slot, the conductors of each phase being all connected in series and the winding short chorded by two slots.

The flux per pole contains a fundamental of 9×10^6 lines, a third harmonic having an amplitude of 20% and a fifth harmonic of 10% of the fundamental.

Determine the r.m.s. values of the phase and line voltages and of the individual harmonic components. [L.U.]

3. Factory tests on a three-phase alternator of new design usually include the following: (a) open-circuit characteristic, (b) short-circuit characteristic, (c) characteristic with full-load current at zero power factor. Explain what information can be derived from these tests and how the voltage regulation of the machine may be deduced therefrom.

The following data represent the open-circuit characteristic of a 10 000 kVA, 11-kV, three-phase, star-connected alternator:

Line voltage (kV)	.	.	0	5	8	10	11	12	13
Exciting current (A)	.	.	0	38·5	65·2	89	108·5	128	154

The excitation required to give rated kilovolt-amperes at zero power factor and rated voltage is 185 A. Assuming the leakage reactance to be 15%, and ignoring resistance, determine

(i) the excitation to give full load at 0·8 power factor (lagging); (ii) the rise in voltage when this load is thrown off, the speed and excitation remaining constant. [L.U.]

4. Show how the armature reaction in a three-phase alternator can be split into two components, stating how each component is affected by the phase difference between the internal e.m.f. and the current. What is meant by synchronous reactance and how it is determined?

The results of open-circuit and short-circuit tests on a three-phase, 850-kVA, 3300-V, star-connected alternator are as follows:

Exciting amperes				50	60	70	80	90	100
Terminal volts				2560	3000	3360	3600	3800	3960
Short-circuit current amperes			190	—	—	—	—	—

The armature leakage reactance is 15% and the resistance per phase is 0·15 Ω. With the aid of a vector diagram determine the excitation required at full load, 0·8 lagging power factor. [L.U.]

5. Show by means of a vector diagram the time and space relations between the e.m.f.s, currents, fluxes and m.m.f.s in a three-phase synchronous machine.

State the assumptions made in drawing the diagram and explain how to use it to determine the field current required for any particular load conditions. [L.U.]

6. Determine, for a 500-kVA, 6600-V, twelve-pole, 500 r.p.m., three-phase alternator, suitable values for (i) the diameter at the air-gap, (ii) the core length, (iii) the number of stator conductors, (iv) the number of stator slots. Assume a star-connected stator winding, a specific magnetic loading of approximately 6000 lines/cm², and a specific electric loading of approximately 300 ampere-conductors/cm. Sketch the shape of slot and the arrangement of the conductors, and specify the insulation. [L.U.]

7. An oscillogram of the wave-form of the no-load e.m.f. of an alternator shows the presence of harmonics. Discuss their causes and the methods generally employed in the construction of machines to reduce or eliminate them.

Deduce a general expression for the winding distribution factor of the no-load e.m.f. of a three-phase alternator. Calculate the values of this factor for the fundamental and seventh harmonic in the case of the stator winding of a two-pole, three-phase turbo-alternator with 54 slots, the coil-sides having a 60° spread. [L.U.]

8. Deduce the relationship between the induced kilovolt-amperes and the specific loadings (magnetic and electric) for a three-phase alternator.

Determine for a 250-kVA, 1100-V, twelve-pole, 500-r.p.m., three-phase alternator (i) the diameter at the air-gap; (ii) the core length; (iii) the number of stator conductors, (iv) the number of stator slots; (v) the cross-section of the stator conductors, assuming the mean flux density over a pole pitch of the air-gap to be 6000 lines/cm², the approximate number of ampere conductors per centimetre of air-gap periphery to be 285, and the current density to be 350 A/cm.² [L.U.]

9. A three-phase alternator having a full-load rating of 1000 kVA at 0·8 power factor, 2200 V, 50 c/s, 300 r.p.m. has a stator diameter of 190 cm, core length 30 cm, and 180 slots. Using the information from this machine, with suitable modifications where required, determine the diameter, core length, number of slots and conductors per slot for a three-phase machine to give 2000 kVA at 0·8 power factor, 6600 V, 50 c/s, 600 r.p.m. [L.U.]

10. A three-phase, 6000-V alternator gave the following open-circuit characteristic at normal speed:

Field amperes				14	18	23	30	43
Terminal volts				4000	5000	6000	7000	8000

With the armature short-circuited and full-load current flowing the field current is 16 A, and when the machine is supplying the full-load kilovolt-amperes at zero power factor the field current is 42·5 A when the terminal voltage is 6000 V.

Determine the field current required when the machine is supplying the full load of 2000 kVA at 0·8 power factor lagging. Determine also the leakage reactance in ohms per phase and the field current required to overcome the armature reaction. Explain clearly the steps in your solution. [L.U.]

21*—E.M.

11. An 11-kV, three-phase cylindrical-rotor-type alternator has the following open-circuit characteristic at rated speed:

Line voltage (V)	.	.	.	.	7300	10 300	12 400	14 000
Field current (A)	.	.	.	.	40	60	80	100

The excitation-to produce full-load current on short circuit is 34 A, and when the machine supplies full-load output at 11 kV and zero power factor, the excitation is 106 A.
Determine:
(a) The percentage synchronous-reactance drop.
(b) The percentage leakage-reactance drop.
(c) The aramature reaction in equivalent field-amperes at full load.
Neglect the armature resistance.   [I.E.E.]

12. A 6600-V, star-connected, three-phase cylindrical-rotor-type alternator has the following open-circuit characteristics at rated speed:

Voltage (line to star point) (V)	.	1500	2600	3500	4150	4650
Field current (A) .	.	.	.	25	50	75	100	125

Full-load current on steady-state short circuit is obtained with an excitation of 87·5 A.
Assuming the resistance drop to be negligible, and the leakage reactance 20%, find the excitation to produce full-load current at rated voltage at a power factor of 0·9 lagging.
Indicate how the method would be modified if the machine had a salient-pole rotor. What additional information would be required?   [I.E.E.]

13. Describe and explain an experimental method of separating the effects of armature reaction and leakage reactance in an alternator.
Give a brief discussion of the probable errors in the prediction of the voltage regulation of an alternator by methods in which these effects are not separated.   [C. & G.]

14. Derive from first principles the output coefficient for a 1500-kVA, 2200-V, three-phase, ten-pole, 50-c/s, star-connected alternator with sinusoidal, flux-density distribution over a pole pitch. The winding has a 60° phase-spread and full-pitch coils. The specific electric loading is 300 ampere-conductors/cm of periphery and the average flux density over the pole pitch is 6000 lines/cm².
If the peripheral speed of the rotor must not exceed 100 m/sec and the ratio pole pitch/core length is to be between 0·6 and 1·0, find suitable values for the stator diameter D and the stator length L. Assume an air-gap of 0·6 cm.
Find also the approximate number of armature (stator) conductors.   [C. & G.]

15. A 6600-V, star-connected, three-phase, non-salient pole synchronous generator has the following open-circuit characteristic:

Phase voltage	.	.	2600	3500	4130	4600	5000	5500
Field current (A) .	.	100	150	200	250	300	400

Full-load current on short circuit is obtained with an excitation of 175 A. Using the ampere-turns method, determine the full-load regulation when the power factor is 0·9 lagging. The resistance drop is negligible and the reactive drop is 10 per cent on full load.
[C. & G.]

16. An 11-kV, 1000-kVA, three-phase, star-connected alternator has a resistance of 2 Ω per phase. The open-circuit curve and the characteristic with rated full-load current at zero power factor are given in the following table. Find the voltage regulation of the alternator for full-load current at a power factor of 0·8 lagging.

Field current (A) .	.	.	.	40	50	110	140	180
Line volts o.c.c. .	.	.	.	5 800	7 000	12 500	13 750	15 000
Line volts zero p.f.	.	.	.	0	1 500	8 500	10 500	12 500

[C. & G.]

17. A two-pole, 50-c/s turbo-alternator has a core length of 1·5 m. The mean flux density over the pole pitch is 5000 lines/cm², the stator ampere-conductors per centimetre 260 and the peripheral speed 100 m/sec. The average span of the stator coils is one pole pitch. Determine the output which can be obtained from the machine.   [C. & G.]

18. The following figures give the open-circuit curve of an alternator:

Percentage of normal voltage	60	80	100	120
Field current (A)	43	66	100	160

The results of the zero power-factor test with full-load current give a field current of 65 A to be equivalent to the effect of armature reaction. The leakage reactance is 10%.

Find the exciting current required for normal voltage on full load at a power factor of 0·8 lagging. [C. & G.]

19. Explain in what respects the data obtained from the open-circuit and the full-load zero-power-factor characteristics of an alternator are more useful for design purposes than the data obtained from the open-circuit and short-circuit characteristics of the machine.

The open-circuit characteristic of a 10-MVA, 6·6-kV, three-phase, star-connected alternator is given by the following data:

Exciting current (A)	0	35·5	60	82	100	118	142
Line voltage (kV)	0	3	4·8	6	6·6	7·2	7·8

and the full-load zero-power-factor characteristic is given by:

Exciting current (A)	49	92	128	156	170
Line voltage (kV)	0	3	4·8	6	6·6

Assuming the leakage reactance to be 15%, and ignoring resistance, determine the excitation required for full load, normal voltage, at a power factor of 0·8 lagging. [L.U.]

20. Explain the terms (i) *direct-axis synchronous reactance*, and (ii) *quadrature-axis synchronous reactance*, of a salient-pole alternator.

Describe tests to determine the per-unit values, x_d and x_q of these two quantities for a given machine.

If $x_d = 0.8$ per unit (i.e. 80%) and $x_q = 0.5$ per unit (i.e. 50%), draw the vector diagram corresponding to full load at a lagging power factor of 0·8, and find the open-circuit per-unit voltage with full-load excitation unchanged. Neglect resistance and saturation. [L.U.]

21. Show by means of suitable vector and space diagrams the relationships between the induced e.m.f., armature current, m.m.f. (armature and field) and flux in a three-phase alternator when operating at the following power factors: (i) unity, (ii) 0·707 lagging, (iii) 0·707 leading. State the assumptions made in drawing the diagrams. [L.U.]

22. Deduce the relationship between the generated kilovolt-amperes of a three-phase alternator and the specific loadings in terms of the internal dimensions of the stator and the speed.

Determine the dimensions of the core, number of conductors and slots for a three-phase, 250-kVA, 3300-V, 50 c/s, 750 r.p.m. star-connected alternator, assuming the mean flux density over a pole pitch to be 0·6 Wb/m^2 (6000 G), and the approximate number of ampere-conductors per centimetre of air-gap periphery to be 280. State any assumptions made. [L.U.]

23. Explain the effect of armature reaction in a salient-pole-type synchronous machine, and show how it varies with power factor.

A 6·6-kV, three-phase, salient-pole alternator has the following open-circuit characteristic at rated speed:

Line voltage (V)	4330	5580	6500	7300	7900
Field current (A)	60	80	100	120	140

At full-load current, the armature leakage reactance drop is 0·25 per unit, and the armature m.m.f. is equivalent to a field current of 50 A.

The cross-reaction coefficient is 0·5 and armature resistance may be neglected.

Determine, graphically or otherwise, the excitation when the alternator delivers the full rated current at a power factor of 0·8 (lagging) and a terminal voltage of 6·6 kV. [I.E.E.]

24. Explain the terms *direct-axis synchronous reactance, quadrature-axis synchronous reactance* of a salient-pole alternator. Upon what factors do these values depend?

An alternator has a direct-axis synchronous reactance of 0·8 per unit and a quadrature-axis synchronous reactance of 0·5 per unit.

Draw the vector diagram for full load at a lagging power factor of 0·8, and find the per-unit value of the open-circuit voltage, with full-load excitation.   Neglect resistance and saturation.

[I.E.E.]

25. Deduce an expression for the main dimensions of a three-phase induction motor in terms of the input kilovolt-amperes, the specific electric and magnetic loadings, the speed and the winding distribution factor.

Find suitable values of gap diameter and core length for a 60-h.p., 400-V, 50-c/s, three-phase, six-pole motor, assuming a specific magnetic loading of 0·48 Wb/m², a specific electric loading of 30 000-ampere-conductors/m, a full-load efficiency of 90% at a power factor of 0·88 and a winding factor of 0·9.   [I.E.E.]

26. An alternator has 72 stator slots, 10 poles and a three-phase double-layer winding with a coil pitch of 6 slots.

If the flux wave has a fifth harmonic whose magnitude is 0·1 per unit of the fundamental component, find the corresponding value of the fifth harmonic in the phase-voltage wave-form on no-load.   [I.E.E.]

CHAPTER 8

1. A three-phase, salient-pole synchronous motor is started by being switched on to the supply mains, the d.c. field circuit being connected to the exciter.

Describe the various components of the total torque and show how they vary as the machine accelerates and why, under certain conditions, the machine may only run up to about half speed.   [L.U.]

2. A three-phase, salient-pole synchronous motor is started by being switched on to the supply mains, the d.c. field circuit being connected to the exciter.

Describe the various components of the total torque and show how they vary as the machine accelerates.

Explain what happens as the machine pulls into synchronism.   [L.U.]

3. A three-phase, 3300-V synchronous motor has a star-connected stator winding with a resistance per phase of 0·15 Ω and a leakage reactance per phase of 1·2 Ω.   The open-circuit and short-circuit characteristics as an alternator when running at normal frequency are as follows:

Field current (A) .	.	.	.	.	.	25·0	37·5	50·0	62·5
Open-circuit e.m.f. (V) .	.	.	.	.	2280	3100	3600	3920
Short-circuit current (A)	.	.	.	.	250	—	—	—

Determine the excitation required to give a power factor of 0·8 (lagging) when the input is 900 kW at 3300 V.

Justify the method used in your solution.   [L.U.]

4. A three-phase, 2000-kVA, 6600-V, star-connected, salient-pole synchronous machine with 9 slots per pole and 5 conductors per slot gave the following open-circuit characteristic at normal speed:

Field amperes	.	.	.	.	13	16·7	21·4	28	40
Terminal volts	.	.	.	.	4000	5000	6000	7000	8000

The field winding has 225 turns per pole and the leakage reactance of the armature is 8% and the resistance negligible.   The winding factor for the armature is 0·96.

Determine the field current when the machine is operating as a synchronous motor with an input of 2000-kVA, 6600 V at (a) 0·8 power factor leading and (b) 0·71 power factor lagging.

State any assumptions made.   [L.U.]

5. Explain the connections and method of starting of a synchronous-induction motor.

Draw to scale the rotor m.m.f.-distribution diagram of such a machine which has 4 poles, full-pitch coils, 5 slots per pole per phase, and 8 rotor conductors per slot.   The three-phase rotor winding is star-connected, and the exciter supplies a current of 100 amperes.   All the three-phase windings are used for excitation purposes.   [I.E.E.]

6. Draw and explain the Potier diagram for a cylindrical-rotor-type alternator on load at a lagging power factor. Compare this diagram with the corresponding one for the same machine when operating as a synchronous motor on load at a leading power factor.

An 11-kV, three-phase cylindrical-rotor synchronous machine has the following open-circuit characteristic at rated speed:

Line voltage	.	.	.	.	8300	10 300	12 000	13 500	14 600
Field current (A) .	.	.	.		60	80	100	120	140

At full-load current, armature resistance drop = 2%, armature leakage reactance drop = 20% and the armature reaction is equivalent to a field current of 35 A.

Find the excitation required when the machine operates as a synchronous motor on 11-kV mains, with full rated current at a power factor of 0·6 (leading).   [I.E.E.]

7. A 440-V, 30-h.p., 50-c/s, star-connected synchronous machine has the following open-circuit characteristic:

E (phase)	.	52	108	149	192	218	238	250	259	268	276 V
I (field)	.	1	2	3	4	5	6	7	8	9	10 A

On short-circuit a field current of 4 A produces an armature current of 60 A. The resistance per phase is 0·5 Ω and at one-half full load the efficiency is 0·8. Determine for this load, and plot on the V-curve, three points corresponding to power factors of 0·9 leading, unity power factor and 0·8 lagging.   [C. & G.]

8. A three-phase synchronous motor connected to 6600-V mains has a star-connected armature with an impedance of 2·5+j15 Ω per phase. The excitation of the machine gives a generated e.m.f. of 7000 V. The iron, friction and excitation losses are 12 kW. Find the maximum horse-power output of the motor.

(A partially graphical solution will be accepted.)   [C. & G.]

9. A 2200-V, three-phase, star-connected synchronous motor has a resistance of 0·6 Ω and a synchronous reactance of 6 Ω. Find graphically or otherwise the generated e.m.f. and the angular retardation of the rotor when the input is 200 kW, (a) power-factor unity, (b) power-factor 0·8 leading.   [C. & G.]

10. Discuss the chief differences in the design of the rotors of induction and synchronous-induction motors.

A three-phase, 120-h.p., 3·3-kV synchronous-induction motor, when running light as an induction motor at normal voltage, takes a current of 16 A at 0·15 power factor. At standstill, with 550 V, the current input was 19·6 A at 0·25 power factor. If, when operating as a synchronous-induction motor, the excitation is adjusted to give a power factor of 0·9, leading, at full-load, determine (i) the maximum output (in h.p.) and (ii) the reactive kilovolt-amperes input at no load.   [L.U.]

11. What are the advantages of a synchronous-induction motor? The rotor of a four-pole synchronous-induction motor has 60 slots and a distributed three-phase winding has 8 conductors per slot. The winding is star-connected, and the exciter is connected between one slip ring and the other two which are short-circuited. If the exciter current is 100 A, sketch and describe the m.m.f. distribution due to the rotor and calculate the number of ampere-turns per pole.   [I.E.E.]

CHAPTER 9

1. Define and explain the terms—"phase swinging", "stability" and "damping winding" as applied to synchronous machines. Describe the function of the damping winding in (i) a three-phase synchronous motor, (ii) a three-phase turbo-alternator. Sketch the arrangement of the winding in each case.   [L.U.]

2. In what important details does the design of a synchronous-induction motor differ from that of a slip-ring induction motor of similar rating? Discuss the reasons for these differences.

Show how the performance curves of a synchronous-induction motor may be determined from no-load and short-circuit tests on the machine when operating as an induction motor.   [L.U.]

3. Deduce an expression for the synchronising power of an alternator.

Calculate the synchronising power in kilowatts per degree of mechanical displacement at full load for a 1000-kVA, 6600-V, 0·8-power factor, 50-c/s, eight-pole, star-connected alternator having a negligible resistance and a synchronous reactance of 60%.　　　　　[L.U.]

4. Explain the functions of the damping or pole-face winding in (i) a three-phase synchronous motor, (ii) a three-phase salient-pole alternator for direct coupling to a reciprocating engine. Sketch the arrangement of the damping winding and discuss the chief factors which determine whether the resistance of this winding should be relatively low, medium or high.

　　　　　[L.U.]

5. State under what conditions an alternator running in parallel with other machines will deviate from its true synchronous position, and explain how this deviation may be reduced.

Calculate the value of the synchronising power in kilowatts for 1 mechanical degree of displacement at full load 0·8 power factor (lagging) for a three-phase, 1000-kVA, 3300-V, 50-c/s, 500-r.p.m. machine having a synchronous reactance of 20% and negligible resistance.

　　　　　[L.U.]

6. Deduce an expression showing, for a synchronous motor, the relationship between the power output and the angular displacement between the magnetic axes of stator and rotor.

A three-phase synchronous motor, rated at 500 h.p., 3300 V, 0·9 power factor (leading), 428 r.p.m., has a star-connected stator winding. At the rated load the percentage voltage drops per phase in the stator winding due to resistance and leakage reactance are 2 and 10% respectively. When run as an alternator at 428 r.p.m., for the purpose of determining the open-circuit and short-circuit characteristics, the results were:

Field excitation (A)	.	.	.	.	.	30	40	50	60	70
Open-circuit voltage (V)		.	.	.	.	2250	2800	3250	3500	3750
Short-circuit current (A)		.	.	.	.	97	—	—	—	—

Determine (i) the excitation for rated load, (ii) the angle of displacement at rated load, assuming the core, friction and windage losses to be 20 kW.　　　　　[L.U.]

7. Explain the phenomenon of hunting when engine-driven alternators are connected to common bus-bars. What steps are taken to eliminate hunting and to ensure satisfactory parallel operation?

A 10-MVA, 10-kV, three-phase, 50-c/s, 1500-r.p.m. alternator is paralleled with others of much greater capacity. The moment of inertia of the rotor is 200 000 kg m² and the synchronous reactance of the machine is 40%.

Calculate the frequency of oscillation of the rotor.

Prove any formulae used and state any assumptions made.　　　　　[I.E.E.]

CHAPTER 10

1. The direct current per brush in a six-ring rotary converter is 100 A.

Deduce an expression for the alternating current flowing in the armature conductors.

If the efficiency is 94%, plot curves to scale of the resultant current wave in a conductor (a) at the centre of a phase and (b) next to the tapping point for both unity and 0·9 power factor.

　　　　　[L.U.]

2. A 500-kW, 550-V, four-pole, six-ring rotary converter has 15 slots per pole with 4 conductors per slot, the efficiency being 94%. Draw curves showing the m.m.f. distribution of the armature over 2 pole-pitches for both the alternating and the direct currents. Explain how values obtained from these curves would be used in determining the number of turns required on the interpoles.　　　　　[L.U.]

3. Give an account of the various methods of controlling the output voltage of a synchronous converter.

A six-ring converter has diametrical connections, the voltage on the low-voltage side of the three-phase transformer being 300 V. Calculate the reactance in each of the slip-ring leads if the output is 500 kW at 500 V and the power-factor at the transformer terminals is unity. Neglect all losses.　　　　　[C. & G.]

4. State and explain the advantages of making synchronous converters with a large number of phases.

Calculate the r.m.s. value and plot the wave-form of the current in an armature coil adjacent to a tapping in a six-ring synchronous converter delivering 400 A at 500 V.   [C. & G.]

CHAPTER 11

1. Explain, with diagrams, the process of commutation in a d.c. machine having more than two coil sides per slot.

Determine the number of turns required on the interpoles of an eight-pole generator having an output of 1000 kW at 500 V, from the following data: 96 slots; 6 conductors per slot; lap-connected armature winding; radial length of interpole gap, about 1·0 cm; mean flux density in interpole gap, 2500 lines/cm². [L.U.]

2. Explain with the aid of diagrams the electromagnetic reactions and the resulting output characteristics of *either* a variable-speed constant current dynamo, *or* a d.c. transformer (metadyne) for constant input voltage and constant output current. [L.U.]

3. Explain the principle of one type of rotating d.c. amplifier (e.g. an amplidyne) giving sketches of the magnetic and electric circuits. State the essential differences in the construction of this machine and a normal d.c. generator. Describe, giving a diagram of connections, one example of the application of a rotating amplifier in industry. [L.U.]

4. For what types of d.c. armature windings are equalising connections employed? Discuss reasons for their use and their effect on the performance of the machine. Show in a diagram of an armature winding the positions of these connections and sketch a method of accommodating them.

A 100-kW, 460-V, six-pole d.c. generator has an armature 50 cm in diameter with a wave winding, and a commutator with 244 segments. Calculate the armature ampere-turns per pole at full load and select a suitable number of slots. [L.U.]

5. A compound trolley-bus motor when run as a generator on open circuit at 1000 r.p.m. gave the following results:

Excitation (AT/pole) . . .	1800	2400	3600	4800	5400
Open-circuit e.m.f. (V) . . .	285	349	450	517	546

Calculate, for the range 50 to 200 A, the speed/torque characteristics when operating at a line voltage of 525 V as (i) a compound motor with full shunt field, (ii) a series motor. The resistances are: (armature+series field winding), 0·23 Ω; shunt winding, 160 Ω. The number of turns per pole are: series, 15; shunt, 1100. Limit your calculations to 50, 100 and 200 A.
[L.U.]

6. Explain the functions of (i) commutating poles, and (ii) compensating (or neutralising) windings in d.c. machines. For what operating conditions are compensating windings necessary in (α) a generator, (β) a motor? Draw diagrams showing the arrangements, polarities and connections of the commutating poles and compensating winding for a generator, and show how to determine the number of ampere-turns for each winding when both windings are present. [L.U.]

7. The data of the open-circuit characteristic of a compound-wound trolley-bus motor, determined by running the machine as a generator at 1000 r.p.m., are as follows:

Ampere-turns per pole . . .	1800	2400	4800	5400
Open circuit e.m.f. (V) . . .	285	349	517	546

Calculate the vehicle speed (m.p.h.) and the approximate braking tractive-effort when operating in service as a differentially-compounded generator with a rheostatic load of 3·5 Ω and an armature current of 150 A, the *separately excited* shunt-field current being 3 A.

The resistance of the armature and series-field windings is 0·15 Ω, and the number of turns per pole in the shunt and series windings is 1200 and 12 respectively. When operating in service as a compound motor at 525 V with 150 A in the armature and a total excitation of 5400 AT/pole, the speed is 10·6 m.p.h. and the tractive effort is 3100 lb. The wheels are 36 in. in diameter and the gear ratio is 9·33:1. [L.U.]

8. Deduce an expression, in terms of the dimensions of the armature core, the specific electric and magnetic loadings and the speed, for the induced power (kW) in a d.c. generator.

Determine suitable dimensions for the armature core of a 250-kW, 460-V, 500 r.p.m., six-pole, d.c. shunt generator assuming the mean flux density over the pole pitch, corresponding to the internal e.m.f. at full load, to be 6700 lines/cm² and the specific electric loading to be 280 ampere-conductors/cm. Allow 3% for voltage drop in the armature and interpole windings at full load.

Determine also a suitable number of conductors, slots and commutator segments, assuming a lap winding. Suggest a suitable diameter of the commutator, giving reasons for your choice.

[L.U.]

9. Explain, with the aid of diagrams, the process of commutation in a d.c. machine having more than two coil sides per slot.

Determine the number of turns required on each interpole of a ten-pole generator having an output of 1200 kW at 600 V from the following data: number of armature conductors, 1080; radial length of interpole gap, 1·3 cm; mean flux density in interpole gap, 2100 lines/cm².

[L.U.]

10. The characteristics, at 525 V, of a compound trolley-bus motor with full shunt field and series field are:

Armature current (A)	.	.	.	25	100	150	200
Speed (m.p.h.)	.	.	.	12·8	11·3	10·6	10·1
Tractive effort.	.	.	.	440	1950	3100	4240

Calculate (i) the speed and tractive effort as a motor, at 525 V and a current of 200 A, *with the series field only*; (ii) the speed and braking tractive effort when operating as a *differentially-compounded* generator with an armature current of 200 A, the shunt field being separately excited at 525 V and the armature loaded on a rheostat of 1·5 Ω resistance. Assume the core, friction and windage losses to remain constant for the conditions of the problem. The resistances of the windings are: armature, 0·1 Ω; series, 0·05 Ω; shunt, 175 Ω. The number of turns in each coil of the shunt and series windings is 1200 and 12 respectively. [L.U.]

11. Describe with sketches the constructional features of a cross-field generator of the meta-dyne or amplidyne type.

Explain clearly the function of the various windings and describe, giving a simplified diagram of connections, the application of this machine in a particular control scheme. [I.E.E.]

12. The open-circuit magnetisation curve of a d.c. shunt generator running at its rated speed is given by:

Field current (A) .	.	.	.	2·5	3·0	3·5	4·0	4·5	5·0	5·5
Open-circuit voltage (V).	.	.	166	188	210	230	246	260	272

Armature resistance.	0·075 Ω
Field resistance	40 Ω

Calculate the resistance of the sections of the field regulator needed to control the voltage on load in 10-V steps from 200 to 250 V

Armature current may be assumed constant at 150 A and the effects of armature reaction and brush drop may be neglected. [I.E.E.]

13. The magnetisation curve of a d.c. series motor at 1000 r.p.m. is given by:

Generated voltage .	.	.	.	150	295	402	480	530	565
Field current (A)	.	.	.	50	100	150	200	250	300

The total resistance, armature and field, is 0·2 Ω.

Plot the speed (r.p.m.)/gross-torque (lb ft) characteristic for the motor when supplied from 500-V mains.

Neglect the effects of armature reaction and brush drop. [I.E.E.]

14. Explain the function of compoles in a d.c. generator.

Describe an experimental procedure to be applied to a given machine for determining if the operation of the compoles is satisfactory.

Sketch graphs showing typical results, and indicate how these graphs show whether any adjustment is necessary. [I.E.E.]

15. A d.c. compound-wound machine has the following open-circuit magnetisation characteristics:

Percentage excitation	.	.	.	.	30	50	70	90	100	110	130
Percentage voltage at rated speed	.		.	44	65	82	95	100	104	111	

When the machine runs as a compound-wound motor the shunt ampere-turns are equivalent to 50% of the full-load excitation, and the full-load resistance drop is 5% of the applied voltage.

Deduce percentage values of speed and torque for currents of 25%, 50%, 75%, 100% and 125% of full-load current. Neglect the effects of brush drop and armature reaction. [I.E.E.]

16. A d.c. motor driving a machine tool operates on the following duty cycle:

50 h.p. for 5 sec.
50 h.p. decreasing uniformly to zero in 10 sec.
30 h.p. regenerating for 3 sec.
5 h.p. for 4 sec.

Find a suitable continuous rating for this machine.

Comment on the suitability or otherwise of a machine of normal design for this purpose.
[I.E.E.]

17. A level-compound 200-kW, 500-V generator has the following open-circuit magnetisation curve at normal speed:

Excitation (AT/pole).	.	.	.	.	.	.	6000	7000	8000	9000
Generated voltage (V)	.	.	.	.	.	.	455	510	540	555

On full load the demagnetising effect of armature reaction is 1000 AT/pole.

Find the number of series turns per pole required for level-compounding. The total armature-circuit resistance is $0 \cdot 0175 \, \Omega$. Allow a voltage drop of $1 \cdot 0$ V per brush.

If new series coils are fitted having one extra turn per pole, what will be the terminal voltage at the same full-load current as before? [I.E.E.]

18. Explain the origin of flash-over in commutator machines. Show how the distortion of the field in a loaded machine increases the possibility of its occurrence.

The armature conductors in such a machine produce 13 000 AT/pole. If the ratio of pole arc/pole pitch is $0 \cdot 7$, find the value of the ampere-turns required in a compensating winding to prevent field distortion over the whole pole arc. [C. & G.]

19. A 25-kW, four-pole, d.c. machine is designed to run at 1200 r.p.m. There are 200 ampere-conductors/cm of periphery, an average flux density over the pole pitch of 4000 lines/cm² and the length of the armature is equal to the pole pitch. Find suitable values for the length and diameter of the armature.

Deduce from first principles the output equation used. [C. & G.]

20. Deduce an expression for the output of a d.c. machine in terms of the average voltage between commutator sectors, the peripheral speed of the armature in metres per second, the ampere-conductors per centimetre of periphery, the number of pole pairs and pairs of armature circuits, and the revolutions per minute.

Taking values of 20 for the volts per sector, 50 m/sec for the peripheral speed and 500 ampere-conductors/cm, calculate the maximum output for a machine running at 1000 r.p.m.
[C. & G.]

21. A four-pole, 25-h.p., 500-V, 600-r.p.m. series-wound crane motor has an efficiency of 82%. The pole faces are square and the ratio of pole arc to pole pitch is 2/3. Assuming $B_{av} = 5500$ lines/cm² and $ac = 170$ A/cm of periphery, obtain the main dimensions of the core and particulars of a suitable armature winding. [C. & G.]

22. Give an account of the principle of the d.c. amplidyne generator.

State for what purposes the amplidyne is valuable. [C. &. G.]

23. Obtain the main dimensions of the core and particulars of a suitable armature winding for a 500-V, 25-h.p., 600-r.p.m., four-pole, d.c. series crane motor which has an efficiency of 80%. The pole faces are square and the ratio of pole arc to pole pitch is 2/3.

Take the average flux density $B = 5500$ lines/cm² and the ampere-conductors per centimetre of periphery $= 170$.

Give reasons for the type of winding chosen and prove any formula used. [C. & G.]

24. A d.c. series motor has the following open-circuit magnetisation characteristic at 800 r.p.m.:

Field current (A)	.	.	.	.	0	40	80	120	160	200
Open-circuit voltage at 8000 r.p.m. (V)				40	390	680	910	1080	1220

Armature resistance	.	.	.	.	.	0·14 Ω
Field resistance	.	.	.	.	.	0·16 Ω
Brush drop	.	.	.	.	.	.	1 V per brush.

The machine is connected to 750-V mains. Plot the speed (r.p.m.)/torque (lb-ft) characteristic of the machine if a diverter resistance of 0·16 Ω is connected across the field windings.

[I.E.E.]

25. The open-circuit magnetisation curve of a d.c. compound-wound machine is as follows:

Per-unit excitation	.	.	.	.	0·3	0·5	0·7	0·9	1·0	1·1	1·3
Per-unit voltage at rated speed	.		0·44	0·65	0·82	0·95	1·0	1·04	1·11

When the machine runs as a compound-wound motor on full load the series field contributes one-quarter of the total excitation, and the resistance drop is 0·05 per unit of the applied voltage.

Deduce the per-unit values of speed and gross torque corresponding to armature currents of 0·5, 1·0 and 1·25 per unit of full-load current.

Neglect the effects of brush drop and armature reaction. [I.E.E.]

26. Discuss the factors which must be given consideration in the design of a d.c. compound motor in which a 1:2 variation of speed at constant power output is to be obtained by variation of the shunt field.

The characteristics, at 525 V, of a compound-traction motor with full shunt and series field are:

Armature current (A)	.	.	.	.	25	100	150	200
Speed (m.p.h.)	.	.	.	.	12·8	11·3	10·6	10·1
Tractive effort (lb)	.	.	.	.	435	1950	3100	4240

Calculate the speed and tractive effort at 525 V and 200 A with the series winding only. The resistance of the windings are: armature, 0·1 Ω; series, 0·05 Ω; shunt, 350 Ω. The number of turns in each shunt coil is 1200 and in each series coil, 12. [L.U.]

27. The magnetisation curve of a level-compound wound 100-kW, 500-V generator is given below:

Ampere-turns/pole	.	.	.	.	.	6000	7000	8000	9000
E.M.F. (V)	.	.	.	.	.	455	510	540	555

The total armature circuit resistance is 0·075 Ω and the brush-drop 1 V per brush.

On full load the armature reaction has a demagnetising effect equal to 1000 AT/pole.

Determine the number of series turns per pole required for level-compounding.

If new series coils are fitted having three extra turns per pole, calculate the terminal voltage at the same value of full-load armature current, neglecting any change of resistance.

[L.U.]

28. State clearly the purpose fulfilled by (a) commutating poles, (b) compensating windings, and (c) equalising connections, in a large d.c. machine.

Draw diagrams showing the position, polarities and connections of the commutating pole and compensating windings for a motor, and show how to determine the number of ampere-turns required for each winding when both windings are used. [L.U.]

29. Distinguish between the functions of (a) commutating poles, and (b) compensating windings, in d.c. machines.

Outline a method of calculating the required flux density in the air-gap of the commutating pole.

Determine the number of turns on each commutating pole of a six-pole machine if the flux density in the air-gap of the commutating pole is 0·5 Wb/m² (5000 G) at full load, and the effective length of the air-gap is 4 mm. The full-load current is 500 A and the armature is lap wound with 540 conductors. Assume the number of ampere-turns required for the remainder of the magnetic circuit to be one-tenth that of the air-gap. [L.U.]

30. Describe, with the aid of diagrams showing the windings and magnetic fluxes, the principle of operation of a rotating amplifier depending on the action of a cross-field.

Draw a simplified diagram of a simple control system incorporating such a machine and explain the operation. [L.U.]

31. Explain the principle of operation of a rotating amplifier of the amplidyne or metadyne type. Draw simplified sketches showing the arrangements of the windings and the magnetic fields.

What advantages has this machine compared with a two-machine set comprising a conventional d.c. generator and separate exciter? [I.E.E.]

CHAPTER 12

1. Explain with a diagram of connections and a vector diagram the principle of operation of any three-phase, compensated induction motor. [L.U.]

2. Explain the principle and operation of a Schrage motor and the functions of the different windings and the brushgear.

When running at exactly synchronous speed the values of the three secondary currents are different although the three primary currents are equal.

Explain the causes of this. [L.U.]

3. A two-pole armature has its winding connected at one end to a commutator and at the other to three slip rings by tappings to points displaced from one another by 120°. There are also three brushes on the commutator displaced from one another by 120°. The armature rotates inside a laminated stator without windings.

Explain how the voltages on both sides change in magnitude, phase and frequency as the armature speed is changed from zero to above 3000 r.p.m. in both directions if balanced three-phase currents at 50 c/s are supplied to (a) the slip rings, (b) the commutator brushes.

How could such a machine be used to control the speed and power factor of an induction motor? [L.U.]

4. A two-pole armature has its winding connected to a commutator at one end and to three slip rings at the other by three tappings to points displaced from one another by 120°. There are also three brushes on the commutator displaced from one another by 120°.

Explain how the voltages on both sides change in magnitude, phase and frequency if constant currents at 50 c/s, three-phase are supplied to (a) the slip rings and (b) the commutator brushes, as the armature speed is changed from zero to about 3000 r.p.m. in both directions. The armature rotates inside a laminated stator without windings.

Explain briefly how such a machine could be used to control the speed and power factor of an induction motor. [L.U.]

5. Sketch the circuits of a Schrage motor and explain the functions of the various windings and the adjustable brushgear. Explain also the action of the motor when loaded and with the brushes set to give (i) minimum speed and (ii) maximum speed. Compare the power factors under these operating conditions, assuming constant torque, and show how improvement of the power factor could be obtained. [L.U.]

6. Explain, with diagrams, the principles of the three-phase series commutator motor and show clearly what factors determine the direction of rotation. Explain also why the motor may be unstable at low speeds. [L.U.]

7. A four-pole armature has a distributed commutator winding with symmetrical three-phase tappings brought out to slip rings. The rings are connected to a three-phase 50-c/s supply, and the armature is rotated in an unwound stator at a speed variable from standstill to 300 r.p.m.

Sketch curves showing how the magnitude and frequency of the voltage at the commutator brushgear vary with speed and give reasons for their shape.

How is this principle used in one type of a.c. polyphase commutator motor? [I.E.E.]

8. What conditions govern the voltage injected at the slip rings of an induction motor which is used (a) to vary the slip above and below synchronous speed, and (b) to improve the power factor.

Describe how both these conditions are met in one form of a.c. polyphase commutator motor. [I.E.E.]

9. Describe, with the aid of vector diagrams, the action of single- and double-wound induction regulators for use on three-phase systems. How do they differ in principle from single-phase types? How are their ratings assessed?

Explain how the double-wound regulator is used to control the speed of a variable a.c. commutator motor, and show clearly the principles involved. [I.E.E.]

10. What fundamental conditions govern the frequency and magnitude of the voltage at the brushes of a commutator winding? How are these principles used in one type of a.c. polyphase commutator motor?

Draw diagrams of connections showing brushgear and windings and explain (a) how speed is adjusted above and below synchronous speed, and (b) how power factor is improved.

[I.E.E.]

11. Give an account of the construction and action of one type of three-phase, variable-speed commutator motor. Explain fully the principle of speed regulation, and sketch and account for the shape of the efficiency, power factor and speed characteristics when the torque is varied over a wide range. [C. & G.]

12. Show that the speed of a wound-rotor induction motor can be varied by the injection of suitable voltage at the slip rings. What conditions must be fulfilled by this voltage?

Show how the same results can be obtained with some form of a.c. polyphase commutator motor, and hence describe (a) how the speed is varied, (b) how the power factor may be altered, in this type of machine. [L.U.]

13. Describe and compare the following types of a.c. polyphase commutator motor:

(a) the shunt machine,

(b) the Schrage machine.

In each case show (a) how the speed is varied above and below the synchronous speed, and (b) how the power factor may be improved. [I.E.E.]

CHAPTER 13

1. A six-anode, mercury-arc rectifier is supplied from a transformer with the secondary windings connected in double three-phase with an interphase transformer.

Draw, and explain, the shape of curves showing the wave-form of the voltage on the d.c. side, the voltage across the interphase transformer and the current in the transformer secondary on full load.

If the direct current is constant, determine the rating of the interphase transformer and of the secondary windings of the main transformer in terms of the d.c. rating. [L.U.]

2. Show that in a grid-controlled, multi-anode, mercury-arc rectifier the mean output voltage, if overlap and voltage drop are ignored, is a function of the angle by which the ignition is retarded.

Explain why impulse excitation of the grids of such a rectifier is preferred to other methods. Describe how such impulses are obtained by means of transformers and how the angle of ignition is controlled. [L.U.]

3. A six-anode, mercury-arc rectifier gives 800 V on the d.c. side on no load. It is supplied from a transformer with the secondary windings connected in double three-phase, with an interphase transformer.

If the leakage reactance of the main transformer is $0.09 \, \Omega$ per phase referred to the secondary, determine the angle of overlap and the voltage on the d.c. side when the load is 1800 A.

Deduce the expression used. [L.U.]

4. A six-anode, mercury-arc rectifier is required to give 1200 kW, 650 V on the d.c. side at full load. It is supplied from a transformer with the secondary connected in double three-phase with an interphase transformer.

If the voltage drop between transition and full load is 6% of the full-load voltage, determine the angle of overlap and the leakage reactance of the main transformer.

Deduce the expressions used. [L.U.]

5. A six-anode mercury-arc rectifier is required to give 800 kW, 650 V on the d.c. side and is supplied from a transformer with the secondary windings connected in double three-phase with an interphase transformer.

If the angle of overlap at full load is 30°, determine the leakage reactance of the main transformer and the percentage voltage variation between the transition point and full load.

Justify the various expressions used in the calculation and state any assumptions made.

[L.U.]

6. Describe, with sketches and a diagram of connections, a method of ignition and excitation for a six-anode mercury-arc rectifier.

Draw diagrams of (i) the output voltage at no load, (ii) the anode currents, of such a rectifier when the secondary windings of the transformer are connected in (α) double star without an interphase transformer, (β) double star with an interphase transformer (i.e. double three-phase).

Deduce for each case the voltage ratio at no load and the r.m.s. value of the anode currents for a given output current, ignoring overlap.

[L.U.]

7. A six-anode mercury-arc rectifier is supplied from a transformer with the secondary windings connected in double three-phase with an interphase transformer. If the direct current is constant, determine the rating of the interphase transformer and of the secondary windings of the main transformer in terms of the d.c. rating.

[L.U.]

8. Explain what is meant by "overlap" in a multi-anode mercury-arc rectifier. Show by diagrams how overlap affects the wave-form of the output voltage.

A six-anode rectifier, rated at 1000 kW, 500 V, is supplied by the ordinary six-phase transformer connection. If the leakage reactance of each section of the transformer secondary winding is 8%, determine the percentage drop in the output voltage between no load and full load, ignoring the voltage drop in the arc. The angle of overlap, α, may be determined from the relationship:

$$(1-\cos \alpha) = IX/(\sqrt{2} . E_a \sin \pi/n),$$

where I denotes the output current; X the leakage reactance of the transformer; E_a, the anode voltage (r.m.s. value); n the number of anodes.

[L.U.]

9. A three-anode mercury-arc rectifier has a transformer which is delta/zigzag connected. The output is 100 kW at 500 V, and the a.c. line voltage is 400 V.

Assuming a high-impedance load, draw diagrams showing the wave-form of:

(a) anode current,
(b) transformer-primary phase current, and
(c) transformer-primary line current.

Neglect the effects of overlap in the rectifier and of transformer losses.

[I.E.E.]

10. Draw a circuit diagram of a three-anode mercury-arc rectifier showing the excitation and ignition circuits.

The main transformer is delta/zigzag connected. Why would a delta-star transformer be unsuitable?

If the anode to neutral voltage of the transformer secondary winding is 750 V r.m.s. and the angle of overlap at full load is 30°, find the mean d.c. output voltage.

Assume a constant arc drop of 25 V and prove any formula used.

[I.E.E.]

11. Draw diagrams showing the main connections of a six-anode mercury-arc rectifier and its transformer with (a) double three-phase connections, and (b) six-phase fork connections.

Draw and explain the wave-forms of the currents in the transformer windings, and the voltage-regulation diagrams for the two cases.

When is the fork connection to be preferred to the double three-phase connection, and why?

[I.E.E.]

12. Draw a circuit diagram of a six-anode mercury-arc rectifier and its transformer connected for double three-phase working.

Sketch and compare the wave-forms of output voltage to be expected at no load, 10% load, and full load.

Explain the reason for any differences between them.

[I.E.E.]

13. Draw diagrams showing the main connections of a six-anode mercury-arc rectifier and its transformer, which is connected:

(a) double three-phase with interphase reactor, and
(b) six-phase fork (triple star).

In each case indicate the polarities of the transformer windings.

Assuming an inductive load, and ignoring overlap, sketch and explain the wave-forms of currents in the transformer primary and secondary windings in each case.   [L.U.]

14. Explain the meaning of the term *overlap* as applied to a mercury-arc rectifier. Sketch diagrams showing the related wave-forms of (a) the anode currents, and (b) the output voltage, for a three-anode rectifier if the overlap is 20°.

If the anode-to-neutral voltage of the transformer secondary winding is 1000 V r.m.s. and the angle of overlap is 20°, determine the mean output voltage.

Assume a constant arc drop of 25 V and a highly inductive load. Prove any formula used.
                                                                                        [I.E.E.]

CHAPTER 14

1. A four-pole, 400-V, d.c. shunt machine with the field coils connected in series requires 5200 AT/pole. The coils are wound with round wire having a resistivity of 2 $\mu\Omega$/cm-cube. The poles are round, 15 cm diameter, and the available winding length is 12 cm.

Determine (a) the cross-sectional area of the wire and (b) the number of turns and thickness of the field coil if the power lost is to be about 0·09 W/cm^2 of the outside surface and the two end surfaces of the coil.

The insulation on the wire increases its diameter by 0·02 cm.   [L.U.]

2. A four-pole, 460-V, d.c., shunt machine with the field coils connected in series requires 5800 AT/pole. The coils are wound with round wire having a resistivity of 2·0 $\mu\Omega$/cm-cube.

The poles are rectangular, the inside dimensions of the coil being 15 cm × 20 cm. The available winding length is 12 cm.

Determine (a) the cross-sectional area of the wire and (b) the number of turns and the thickness of the field coil if the power wasted is to be about 0·08 W/cm^2 of the outside surface and the two end surfaces of the coil.

The insulation on the wire increases its diameter by 0·02 cm.   [L.U.]

3. Explain the characteristics and running conditions of an electrical machine which determine (a) the rate of rise of temperature and (b) the final temperature.

Derive an expression showing the relation between temperature rise and time and define from it the heating time constant.   [L.U.]

4. A six-pole, 500 V, d.c., shunt machine with all the field coils connected in series requires 6000 AT/pole on the field winding, which is wound with round wire having a resistivity of 2·0 $\mu\Omega$/cm-cube. The poles are rectangular of dimensions 14 cm × 22 cm and the available winding length is 12 cm.

Determine (a) the cross-sectional area of the wire and (b) the number of turns and the thickness of the field coil if the power wasted is 0·08 W/cm^2 of the outside and two end surfaces of the coil. The insulation on the wire increases its diameter by 0·02 cm.   [L.U.]

5. A power transformer with natural cooling has a final temperature rise of 50°C on full load and a heating time-constant of 2 hours.

Find graphically or otherwise the temperature rise 6 hours after switching on if the transformer is loaded as follows:

3 hours on full load, followed by
1 hour on no load, then
2 hours on half load.

The copper loss of the transformer at half full load is equal to its iron loss.   [I.E.E.]

6. Sketch typical arrangements for the cooling of a modern turbo-alternator.

A turbo-alternator runs on test at a continuous rated load of 30 MVA at a power factor of 0·8. The following cooling-air measurements are taken:

Volume of cooling air measured at intake . . . . 30 m³/sec
Intake air temperature . . . . 15°C
Outlet air temperature . . . . 45°C
Barometer reading . . . . 750 mm Hg

Find the efficiency of the machine, taking the specific heat of air at constant pressure as 0·238, and the volume of 1 kg of air at 0°C and at a pressure of 760 mm Hg as 0·78 m³.

[I.E.E.]

7. The power loss in a transformer with natural cooling is 10 kW on full load and its rate of dissipation of heat is 0·2 kW per 1°C rise of temperature above ambient. The heat energy required to raise the temperature 1°C is 0·4 kWh.

Plot a graph showing the rise of temperature in the first six hours after switching on to full load.

Prove any formula used and state any assumptions made.

How would you expect this graph to be modified if air-blast cooling is applied? [I.E.E.]

8. An eight-pole 500-V d.c. shunt generator with all field coils connected in series requires 5000 AT/pole. The poles are of rectangular dimensions 12 cm × 20 cm and the available winding cross-section is 12 cm × 2·5 cm.

Determine (a) the cross-sectional area of the wire, (b) the number of turns, and (c) the dissipation in watts per square centimetre based on the area of the outside and two end surfaces of the coil.

A conductor of circular cross-section is to be used. The resistivity is $2 \cdot 0 \times 10^{-6}$ Ω cm and the insulation increases the diameter by 0·02 cm. Allow for a voltage drop in the field regulator of 50 V. [I.E.E.]

9. During a test on a transformer the load was kept constant and the rates of temperature rise obtained were 0·075°C per minute when the temperature rise was 19°C and 0·055°C per minute when the temperature rise was 27°C. Estimate the time-constant of the transformer and its final steady temperature rise. [C. & G.]

10. The following particulars refer to the shunt field coil for a 440-V, six-pole, d.c. generator: ampere-turns per pole 7000; depth of winding 5 cm; length of inside turn 110 cm; length of outer turn 140 cm; watts radiated per square centimetre of outside surface (excluding the ends) 0·14 W; space factor 0·625; resistivity of copper wire 2 μΩ cm.

Find (a) the diameter of wire, (b) the length of the coil, (c) the number of turns and (d) the exciting current when the p.d. across the coil is 80% of the full voltage. [C. & G.]

11. A rectangular field coil is required to produce 8000 AT when the power dissipated is 250 W, the temperature rise is 40°C and the specific heat dissipation is 0·003 W/cm²/°C from the outer surface neglecting the top and bottom of the coil. The length of a turn on the inmost layer is 68 cm and the coil is 15 cm high. The resistivity of the wire is 2 μΩ cm. Find the current density in the wire in amperes per square millimetre. [C. & G.]

12. Derive an expression from which the steady temperature rise of a winding on full load can be calculated from temperature readings obtained from a short-time run on full load.

Estimate the final temperature rise attained on full load if the rise in temperature on full load is 17°C at the end of 1 hour and 28°C after 2 hours. [C. & G.]

13. A field coil wound on a cylindrical bobbin has an inner diameter of 40 cm, an outer diameter of 48 cm and an axial length of 15 cm. If the coil is to operate at a temperature of 60°C, determine the maximum ampere-turns that can be produced. Assume a space factor of 0·75, an emissivity of 0·0033 W/cm²/°C based upon heat dissipation from the outer cylindrical surface only and an ambient temperature of 17°C. Copper wire has a resistivity of 2×10^{-6} Ω/cm-cube. [C. & G.]

14. Explain how the final steady temperature rise of electrical apparatus can be calculated from the results of a heat run of short duration.

Apply the method described to find the final steady temperature rise for a motor on full load from the following test results:

Time in hours . . .	0·25	0·5	1·0	1·5	2·0	2·5	3·0
Temperature rise in °C .	12	22	35	43	48	51	52

[C. & G.]

15. Design the main field coil for a six-pole, 60-kW, 440-V shunt motor, given the following particulars: ampere-turns per pole 4120, length of coil along pole 6 in., length of inside circular turn 30 in., resistivity of copper $0 \cdot 8$ $\mu\Omega$/in.-cube, surface dissipation $0 \cdot 7$ W/in^2 (only the external curved surface to be used), space factor $0 \cdot 5$. Insulation adds $0 \cdot 008$ in. to the diameter of the wire.   [C. & G.]

16. A transformer has a temperature rise of 20°C after 1 hour and 35°C after 2 hours continuous full load. The copper loss is $2 \cdot 5$ times the core loss. Estimate the final temperature rise in service after a consecutive loading of $1 \cdot 5$ hours at full load, $0 \cdot 5$ hour at one-half full load and 1 hour at 25% overload.   [C. & G.]

17. A rectangular copper connector, 15 yd long, is required to carry 3000 A with a power loss of $4 \cdot 5$ kW and to attain a final steady temperature rise of 40°C. The rate of heat dissipation is $0 \cdot 007$ W/cm^2/°C. Resistivity of copper $2 \cdot 0$ $\mu\Omega$-cm. Calculate the dimensions of the bar.

Find also the time constant and the time required to reach 90% of the maximum temperature rise. Copper has a specific gravity of $8 \cdot 9$ and a specific heat of $0 \cdot 1$.   [C. & G.]

18. State the advantages of the closed-air system for cooling large alternators.

In a closed-air circuit for cooling a 60-MW alternator having an efficiency of 97%, 85% of the losses are carried away by the cooling air. Calculate the weight of air required in kilograms per minute for a temperature rise in the air of 30°C when the alternator is on full load.

The specific heat of air at constant pressure is $0 \cdot 24$.   [C. & G.]

19. The power loss in a naturally cooled transformer is 20 kW on full load, and its rate of dissipation of heat is $0 \cdot 4$ kW per 1°C rise above ambient. The heat energy required to raise the temperature 1°C is $0 \cdot 8$ kWh. Find the rise of temperature (a) two hours after switching on if the current is constant over this period at half full-load value, and (b) after a further hour on full load.

At half load, the copper loss is equal to the iron loss. Prove any formula used. [I.E.E.]

20. The shunt-field spools of a ten-pole 550-V d.c. generator are connected in series. The mean length of turn is 80 cm, and the number of ampere-turns per pole is 6000. Find the area of cross-section of the conductors.

Resistivity of copper (hot) $= 2 \cdot 0 \times 10^{-6}$ Ω cm.

Allow for a voltage drop in the field regulator of 50 V. If the power loss per coil is limited to 200 W by the permissible temperature rise of the machine, and the nearest available wire gauges correspond to cross-sectional areas of $0 \cdot 01$ and $0 \cdot 02$ cm^2, how many turns of each gauge will be required?   [I.E.E.]

ANSWERS TO NUMERICAL QUESTIONS

CHAPTER 2

2. Window $33 \times 16 \cdot 5$ cm; core height 79 cm; core width 102 cm.
3. 457 W.
4. Window $39 \times 19 \cdot 5$ cm; core section 281 cm²; 294 T, 64 T; conductor sections 0·182 cm². 0·834 cm².
6. 343 T, 24 T, 0·0334 m².
7. 0·337 lag, 0·942 lead, 486 V, 150%.
8. $7 \cdot 85 \times 43$ cm; $9 \cdot 4 \times 43$ cm.
9. 54·1 cm², 1830 T, 183 T.
10. 457 cm², 310 cm², 130 kg, 360 kg.
12. 172 T, 993 T, 0·0416 m².

CHAPTER 3

1. 192 A, 633 kVA; 271 A, 896 kVA.
3. 795 T, 19 T.
5. Core section 300 cm²; height 82·5 cm, width 64·6 cm.
6. 3170 kVA.
7. 12·5 kV.
8. 32·4 kV.
14. 700 kW, 0·76 lag; 900 kW, 0·84 lag.
15. 638 kW.

CHAPTER 4

1. $S = 144$, $C = 432$, $t = 1$, $y_s = 17$, $y_{eq} = 108$, $y_{ph} = 36$.
2. Lap winding, $y_s = 14$, $Z = 720$, $C = 360$, $S = 90$.
3. $Z = 612$, $S = 102$, $y_c = 76$, coil span 39.
4. $Z = 738$, $S = 123$, $C = 369$, 0·272 cm².
5. $S = 144$, $C = 432$, $t = 1$, $y_s = 17$, $y_{eq} = 108$, $y_{ph} = 36$.
7. 0%, 0·44%.
9. $y_s = 13$, $y_c = 85$.
10. 9·38 kV.
11. 16·1%.
12. Duplex wave, $Z = 660$, $C = 330$, $U = 6$, $S = 110$. $v_c = 83$, $y_s = 13$.

CHAPTER 5

1. 0·038 Ω.
2. $2 \cdot 08 \times 10^{-5}$ Ω/in.
3. 3300 AT.

CHAPTER 6

1. 16·7 h.p.; 102 lb ft.
2. 238 A, 11·25 kW, 63·6 A, 5·82 kW.
3. 9·16 A.
4. $D_a = 25 \cdot 5$ cm, $L_c = 16 \cdot 5$ cm, 540 T, $S = 27$.
5. $D_a = 19 \cdot 25$ cm, $L_c = 19$ cm; $S_1 = 21$, $S_2 = 30$, $Z_1 = 840$, $U_2 = 10$.
7. 80·5 kVAr; 220 h.p.; 90·5 kVAr, 311 h.p.
8. 0·773:1.
9. 453 A, 39·6 kW; 185 A, 31·1 kW.
10. 1·22:1.
11. 131 A, 0·83 lag, 90%, 0·02, 0·016 Ω.
13. 1:100, 1:1·44.
14. $D_a = 28$ cm, $L_c = 12 \cdot 5$ cm, $Ut = 38$.
15. 1·36:1.
16. 58 A, 0·815 lag.
17. 28·2 A, 0·87 lag, 80%, 66·2 lb ft.
18. 4·7 sec, 2·2 sec.
20. 69·7 lb ft, 4 Ω, 0·41 Ω.
21. 32·3 A, 0·92 lag, 276 lb ft.
22. 303 lb ft.
23. 53·8 A, 0·85 lag.
24. $D_a = 96 \cdot 5$ cm, $L_c = 162 \cdot 5$ cm.
25. $D_a = 19 \cdot 5$ cm, $L_c = 19$ cm.
26. 78 A, 0·76 lag.
27. 44 A, 0·835 lag, 1·96:1, 31 kW.
28. 47·5 A, 0·8 lag; 127 lb ft, 324 lb ft.
29. 39 A, 0·85 lag.
30. 4·5 sec.

CHAPTER 7

1. $D_a = 87\cdot5$ cm, $L_c = 41\cdot25$ cm, $S = 105$, $Z = 1890$.
2. $V_1 = 2955$, $V_3 = 295$, $V_5 = 17$, $V_{an}' = 2970$, $V_{ab} = 5120$.
3. 161 A, 1900 V.　　　　　　　　　　**4.** 107 A.
6. $D_a = 94$ cm, $L_c = 37$ cm, $S = 108$, $Z = 4104$ (2 circuits in parallel).
7. 0·966, 0·141.
8. $D_a = 76$ cm, $L_c = 30$ cm, $Z = 540$, $S = 90$, $a = 0\cdot375$ cm².
9. $D_a = 144$ cm, $L_c = 45$ cm, $S = 132$, $Ut = 14$.
10. 41·5 A, 3·3 Ω, 12·5 A.　　　　　　**11.** 57%, 12·7%, 26 A.
12. 158 A.　　　　　　　　　　　　**14.** $D_a = 120$ cm, $L_c = 54$ cm, $Z = 2910$.
15. 31·9%.　　　　　　　　　　　　**16.** 21·4%.
17. 4·1 MVA.　　　　　　　　　　　**18.** 165 A.
19. 148 A.　　　　　　　　　　　　**20.** 1·6 p.u.
22. $D_a = 66\cdot3$ cm, $L_c = 26$ cm, $Z = 1344$, $S = 48$.
23. 170 A.　　　　　　　　　　　　**24.** 1·6 p.u.
25. $D_a = 31$ cm, $L_c = 26$ cm.　　　　**26.** 0·00536 p.u.

CHAPTER 8

3. 31 A.　　　　　　　　　　　　　**4.** 19·5 A, 38 A.
6. 140 A.　　　　　　　　　　　　　**7.** 11·8 A, 7·1 A, 4·8 A.
8. 206 h.p.　　　　　　　　　　　　**9.** 2·21 kV, 14·3°; 2·62 kV, 12·8°.
10. 230 h.p., 82·3 kVAr.　　　　　　　**11.** 4000 AT.

CHAPTER 9

3. 158 kW/degree.　　　　　　　　　**5.** 585 kW/degree.
6. 67·5 A, 2·85°.　　　　　　　　　　**7.** 0·2 c/s.

CHAPTER 10

3. 0·199 Ω.　　　　　　　　　　　　**4.** 4-pole lap winding, 64·6 A.

CHAPTER 11

1. 5 T.　　　　　　　　　　　　　**4.** 4410 AT, $S = 61$.
5. (i) 1045, 945, 817 r.p.m.; 162, 362, 812 lb ft.
　　(ii) 3660, 2010, 1175 r.p.m.; 49, 176, 574 lb ft.
7. 22·1 m.p.h., 1620 lb.
8. $D_a = 57\cdot5$ cm, $L_c = 19\cdot5$ cm, $Z = 1632$, $S = 68$, $C = 272$, $D_c = 40$ cm.
9. 7 T.　　　　　　　　**10.** 18 m.p.h., 2380 lb.; 24 m.p.h., 1193 lb.
12. 9·3 Ω, 2·1 Ω, 1·9 Ω, 1·5 Ω, 1·0 Ω, 0·9 Ω.
13. 52·8, 208, 424, 675, 935, 1195 lb ft; 3260, 1625, 1170, 960, 850, 780 r.p.m.
15. 141%, 122%, 110%, 100%, 93% speed; 18·5%, 42%, 70%, 100%, 133% torque.
16. 33 h.p.　　　　　　　　　　　　**17.** 3 T, 524 V.
18. 9100 AT.　　　　　　　　　　　**19.** $D_a = 27\cdot25$ cm, $L_c = 21\cdot5$ cm.
20. 1500 kW.　　　　　　　　　　　**21.** $D_a = 36\cdot2$ cm, $L_c = 18\cdot8$ cm.
23. D_a 35·25 cm, $L_c = 17$ cm, $Z = 980$, $t = 2$, $C = 245$, $S = 49$, $y_c = 122$, $y_s = 12$.
24. 2690, 1500, 1070, 840, 704 r.p.m.; 77·5, 274, 570, 956, 1410 lb ft.
25. 1·11, 1·00, 0·96; 0·46, 1·00, 1·28.　　**26.** 11·7 m.p.h., 3640 lb.
27. 7 T, 527 V.　　　　　　　　　　**29.** 11 T.

CHAPTER 13

3. 26·8°, 761 V.

5. 0·164 Ω, 7%.

10. 795 V.

4. 27%, 0·088 Ω.

8. 13·7%.

14. 1100 V.

CHAPTER 14

1. 0·0071 cm²; 3500 T, 4 cm.

4. 0·0132 cm²; 2780 T, 5·25 cm.

6. 95·7%.

9. 400 min, 49°C.

11. 1·51 A/mm².

13. 7220 AT.

15. $d = 0·045$ in., 1470 T.

17. 4·72×1·16 cm, 3·42 min, 7·93 min.

19. 12·64°C, 27·3°C.

2. 0·0087 cm²; 4000 T, 5·25 cm.

5. 22·8°C.

8. 0·0128 cm², 1360 T, 0·157 W/cm².

10. 0·195 cm, 1470 T, 4·75 A.

12. 48·2°C.

14. 53·5°C.

16. 49·8°C.

18. 3150 kg.

20. 1437 T, 63 T.

INDEX